Mammalian Cytogenetics and Related Problems in Radiobiology

Mammalian Cytogenetics

and Related Problems

in Radiobiology

*Proceedings of a symposium held at São Paulo
and Rio de Janeiro, Brazil, October 1962*

Edited by

C. PAVAN
C. CHAGAS
O. FROTA-PESSOA
L. R. CALDAS

A Pergamon Press Book

THE MACMILLAN COMPANY

NEW YORK

1964

THE MACMILLAN COMPANY
60 Fifth Avenue,
New York 11, N.Y.

This book is distributed by
THE MACMILLAN COMPANY · NEW YORK
pursuant to a special arrangement with
PERGAMON PRESS LIMITED
Oxford, England

SYMPOSIUM ON MAMMALIAN CYTOGENETICS AND RELATED PROBLEMS IN RADIOBIOLOGY

PRESIDENT

Dr. Alexander Hollaender

ORGANIZING COMMITTEE

São Paulo: C. Pavan, O. Frota-Pessoa and A. L. P. Perondini

Rio de Janeiro: C. Chagas and L. R. Caldas

SPONSORING INSTITUTIONS

National Science Foundation, U.S.A. — Program for Developmental Biology (Dr. M. N. Runner)

Division of Biology and Medicine — U. S. Atomic Energy Commission (Dr. A. Hollaender, Oak Ridge National Laboratory).

Pan American Union — Science Development Division (Dr. J. D. Perkinson)

Ministère des Affaires Etrangères de France — Direction Générale des Affaires Culturelles et Techniques (Dr. U. Basdevant)

Euratom — Biological Division (Dr. R. K. Appleyard)

Fundação de Amparo à Pesquisa do Estado de São Paulo (Prof. A. B. de Ulhôa Cintra)

Conselho Nacional de Pesquisas (Admiral O. Cunha)

Comissão Nacional de Energia Nuclear (Prof. M. Damy de Souza Santos)

Instituto de Biofísica da Universidade do Brasil (Prof. C. Chagas)

Universidade de São Paulo — Faculdade de Filosofia, Ciências e Letras (Prof. M. G. Ferri)

FOREWORD

THE development of modern biology in Latin America and the organization there of strong centers of biological research have made it desirable to set up a certain type of highly specialized biological symposium to help establish closer relations between Latin America and the rest of the scientific world. That this has been accomplished can be seen by the two symposia which have been held. The first one in Santiago de Chile in September 1961 on tissue transplantation was very successful, and the proceedings of that symposium are now available. The second, reported in this volume, was a joint conference on mammalian tissue culture and cytology held in São Paulo and Rio de Janeiro where specific topics in radiobiology closely related to tissue culture were discussed.

Such symposia can be successful only through close cooperation between scientists in different countries, and we have established a close friendship with our colleagues to the south of us in the United States as well as in the rest of the world. Like any symposium, it depends very much on the people who are in charge, and special credit should go to Drs. Crodowaldo Pavan, O. Frota-Pessoa and A. L. P. Perondini in São Paulo and Drs. C. Chagas and L. R. Caldas in Rio de Janeiro.

A list of the many agencies which supported this conference is given on page v, but special thanks should go to Dr. C. L. Dunham of the Division of Biology and Medicine of the United States Atomic Energy Commission who has encouraged us to go ahead and plan these symposia and has supported us generously. Not the least, of course, are the many scientists from all over the world who are involved in the symposium, and special thanks are also due to them. I should point out that the 1963 symposium, on the initiation of cell division and the induction of cancer, will also appear in published form. Further symposia are planned for successive years.

Biology Division, Oak Ridge National   ALEXANDER HOLLAENDER
Laboratory,* Oak Ridge, Tennessee

* Operated by Union Carbide Corporation for the United States Atomic Energy Commission.

PREFACE

SOME years ago Dr. A. Hollaender had the idea of promoting in Latin America a series of Symposia to establish close scientific contacts between Latin American scientists and their colleagues from U.S.A. and Europe. He was impressed, we presume, by the brilliant effort of several groups in Latin America in developing biological sciences in spite of the unfavourable conditions usually prevailing. One of the goals of these Symposia was to give an opportunity to our fellow scientists from the U.S.A. and Europe to appreciate the research programs under way in this part of the American continent, and to engage in a fruitful interchange with colleagues in our countries.

The Symposium on Mammalian Cytogenetics and Related Problems in Radiobiology was the second of this series. During nine days, from 22 to 30 October 1962, in São Paulo and in Rio de Janeiro, a group of eminent scientists from U.S.A., Europe and Latin America discussed important contributions to the subject in a very friendly atmosphere. This book is the summing up of the Symposium. We are very glad to state here our deepest gratitude to Dr. A. Hollaender, the true inspirer of this meeting, and to all organizations which made possible its realization. We wish also to thank all those people who came to São Paulo and Rio de Janeiro for the encouragement and help they brought to the biologists in Brazil.

C. PAVAN

C. CHAGAS

O. FROTA-PESSOA

L. R. CALDAS

ACKNOWLEDGEMENT

PUBLICATION of these proceedings was supported by the U. S. Army and U.S. Air Force Office of Aerospace Research. The Department of Defense now maintains a Science Office with Army and Air Force Elements in Rio de Janeiro as part of the U.S. Regional Science Office for Latin America. Queries relating to basic research support by the U.S. Army or U.S. Air Force should be addressed to:

U.S. Department of Defense Research Office

Caixa Postal 699

Rio de Janeiro, Brazil

CONTENTS

SELECTED TOPICS IN RADIOBIOLOGY

LIST OF PARTICIPANTS

ABREU, M. C., Instituto de Biofísica, Rio de Janeiro, Brazil.

AGUIAR, M. L. R., Instituto de Genética, Piracicaba, São Paulo, Brazil.

AKAHIRA, Y., Fac. de Filosofia de Rio Claro, São Paulo, Brazil.

ALIBERT, S., Centre d'Études Nucleaires, Commissariat à l'Energie Atomique, Paris, France.

ALMEIDA, D. F., Instituto de Biofísica, Rio de Janeiro, Brazil.

ALMEIDA, J. C. C., DE, Hospital Moncorvo Filho, Rio de Janeiro, Brazil.

AMARAL, A. D., Centro de Medicina Nuclear, São Paulo, Brazil.

AMARAL, L. A. S., Instituto Central do Cancer, São Paulo, Brazil.

ANDO, A., Instituto de Genética, Piracicaba, São Paulo, Brazil.

ANDRADE, J. D., Instituto Butantã, São Paulo, Brazil.

AZEVEDO, J. L., Instituto de Genética, Piracicaba, São Paulo, Brazil.

AZEVEDO, M., Dept. de Profilaxia da Lepra, Secretaria da Saúde, São Paulo, Brazil.

BARENDSEN, G. W., Radiobiological Institute, Rijswijk, Holland.

BARROS, R., Dept. de Biologia Geral, Univ. de São Paulo, Brazil.

BASILE, R., Dept. de Biologia Geral, Univ. de São Paulo, Brazil.

BEÇAK, M. L., Instituto Butantã, São Paulo, Brazil.

BEÇAK, W., Instituto Butantã, São Paulo, Brazil.

BEIGUELMAN, B., Dept. de Biologia Geral, Univ. de São Paulo, Brazil.

BENDER, M. A., Oak Ridge National Laboratory, Oak Ridge, Tenn., U.S.A.

BOND, V. P., Brookhaven National Laboratory, Long Island, N.Y., U.S.A.

BOTTURA, C., Fac. de Medicina de Ribeirão Prêto, São Paulo, Brazil.

BREUER, M. E., Dept. de Biologia Geral, Univ. de São Paulo, Brazil.

BUSCHINELLI, A., Fac. de Filosofia de Rio Claro, São Paulo, Brazil.

CALDAS, L. R., Instituto de Biofísica, Rio de Janeiro, Brazil.

CALDECOTT, R. S., Biology Division, U.S. Atomic Energy Commission, Washington, D. C., U.S.A.

CAMARGO, E. P., Fac. de Medicina de São Paulo, Brazil.

CARVALHO, H. C., Instituto de Biologia, Belo Horizonte, Brazil.

CASTRO, M. P., Instituto Biológico, São Paulo, Brazil.

CAVALCANTI, A. G. L., Fac. Nacional de Filosofia, Rio de Janeiro, Brazil.

CENTURO, A. J., Dept. de Genética, Instituto de Ciências Naturais, Pôrto Alegre, Brazil.

CESTARI, A. N., Dept. de Biologia Geral, Univ. de São Paulo, Brazil.

CHAGAS, C., Instituto de Biofísica, Rio de Janeiro, Brazil.

CHU, E. H. Y., Oak Ridge National Laboratory, Oak Ridge, Tenn., U.S.A.

CORDEIRO, A. R., Instituto de Ciências Naturais, Pôrto Alegre, Brazil.

CORDEIRO, H.W., Instituto de Ciências Naturais, Pôrto Alegre, Brazil.

CUNHA, A. B. DA, Dept. de Biologia Geral, Univ. de São Paulo, Brazil.

CUNHA, M. F. DA, Instituto de Biofísica, Rio de Janeiro, Brazil.

EAGLE, H., Albert Einstein College of Medicine, New York, U.S.A.

ELIAS, C. A., Instituto de Biofísica, Rio de Janeiro, Brazil.

ESTON, V. R., Centro de Medicina Nuclear, São Paulo, Brazil.

ESTRADA, R. F., Comisión Nacional de Energia Nuclear, Mexico.

FAHAD, M. A., Fac. de Filosofia de São José do Rio Prêto, São Paulo, Brazil.

FERNANDEZ, R. D., Instituto de Biologia Juan Noe, Santiago, Chile.

FRANCA, E. P., Instituto de Biofísica, Rio de Janeiro, Brazil.

FREIRE-MAIA, A., Secção de Genética, Dept. de Imigração, São Paulo, Brazil.

FREIRE-MAIA, N., Laboratório de Genética Humana, Univ. do Paraná, Curitiba, Brazil.

FROTA-PESSOA, O., Dept. de Biologia Geral, Univ. de São Paulo, Brazil.

GARAY, A. J. G., Comisión Nacional de Energia Nuclear, Mexico.

GARTLER, S. M., School of Medicine, Seattle, Washington, U.S.A.

GRADO, F. DI, Hospital das Clínicas, São Paulo, Brazil.

GUIMARÃES, A. O. C., Fac. de Higiene e Saúde Pública, São Paulo, Brazil.

HAMILTON, L. D., Sloan Kettering Institute, New York, U.S.A.

HARGREAVES, A. B., Instituto de Biofísica, Rio de Janeiro, Brazil.

HASSEN, A., Instituto de Biofísica, Rio de Janeiro, Brazil.

HAUSSMAN, R., Instituto de Microbiologia, Rio de Janeiro, Brazil.

HERCIK, F., Institute of Biophysics, Brno, Czechoslovakia.

HOLLAENDER, A., Oak Ridge National Laboratory, Oak Ridge, Tenn., U.S.A.

HUNGERFORD, D. A., The Institute for Cancer Research, Philadelphia, Pa., U.S.A.

JOLY, A. B., Dept. de Botânica, Univ. de São Paulo, Brazil.

JUNQUEIRA, L. C. U., Faculdade de Medicina, São Paulo, Brazil.

KAPLAN, H. S., Stanford University, Palo Alto, Cal., U.S.A.

KATO, S., Dept. de Biologia Geral, Univ. de São Paulo, Brazil.

KOCH-WESSER, D., Latin America Regional Science Office, Rio de Janeiro, Brazil.

KOKRON, M. I., Dept. de Botânica, Univ. de São Paulo, Brazil.

KRIEGER, H., Secção de Genética, Dept. de Imigração, São Paulo, Brazil.
LEJEUNE, J., Institut de Progénése, Paris, France.
LEON, N., Faculdade de Medicina, São Paulo, Brazil.
LIMA-DE-FARIA, A., Institute of Genetics, Lund, Sweden.
LOZZIO, C. B. DE, Facultad de Ciencias Exactas y Naturales, Buenos Aires, Argentina.
MAGALHÃES, L. E., Dept. de Biologia Geral, Univ. de São Paulo, Brazil.
MALACHOWSKA, M. I., Instituto Adolfo Lutz, São Paulo, Brazil.
MARCOVICH, H., Institut du Radium, Paris, France.
MARQUES, E. K., Instituto de Ciências Naturais, Pôrto Alegre, Brazil.
MARTINEZ, E. A. L. W., Instituto Conde Lara, São Paulo, Brazil.
MARTINS, L. F., Fac. de Farmácia e Veterinária, São Paulo, Brazil.
MERZEL, J., Escola Paulista de Medicina, São Paulo, Brazil.
MIMURA, I., Instituto de Botânica, São Paulo, Brazil.
MIRANDA, M., Instituto de Biofísica, Rio de Janeiro, Brazil.
MONTAGNINI, M. I., Dept. de Produção Animal, São Paulo, Brazil.
MORTON, N. E., Secção de Genética, Dept. de Imigração, São Paulo, Brazil.
MOSES, A., Academia Brasileira de Ciências, Rio de Janeiro, Brazil.
MOORHEAD, P. S., Wistar Institute, Philadelphia, Pa., U.S.A.
MOURÃO, C. A., Fac. de Filosofia de São José do Rio Prêto, São Paulo, Brazil.
NAPP, M., Instituto de Ciências Naturais, Pôrto Alegre, Brazil.
NAZARETH, H. R. S., Instituto Butantã, São Paulo, Brazil.
NICHOLLS, J. G., University Laboratory of Physiology, Oxford, England.
OHNO, S., City of Hope Medical Center, Duarte, Cal., U.S.A.
PAVAN, C., Dept. de Biologia Geral, Univ. de São Paulo, Brazil.
PECCININI, D., Dept. de Biologia Geral, Univ. de São Paulo, Brazil.
PEDROSO, M. L., Hospital Municipal, São Paulo, Brazil.
PERONDINI, A. L. P., Dept. de Biologia Geral, Univ. de São Paulo, Brazil.
PICARD, I., Instituto de Biofísica, Rio de Janeiro, Brazil.
PIZA, S. T., Escola Superior de Agronomia Luiz de Queiroz, Piracicaba, São Paulo, Brazil.
POLETTO, D., Univ. Mackenzie, São Paulo, Brazil.
PÓVOA, L. C., Hospital Moncorvo Filho, Rio de Janeiro, Brazil.
REGULIF, M. L., Instituto de Ciências Naturais, Pôrto Alegre, Brazil.
REY, L., Faculdade de Medicina, Univ. de São Paulo, Brazil.
ROCHA, A., Instituto de Biofísica, Rio de Janeiro, Brazil.
RODRIGUES, M. C., Instituto de Medicina Tropical, São Paulo, Brazil.
ROSENBERG, L., Dept. de Biologia Geral, Univ. de São Paulo, Brazil.
ROSENFELD, G., Instituto Butantã, São Paulo, Brazil.

ROTH, A., Instituto Adolfo Lutz, São Paulo, Brazil.

RUSSELL, L. B., Oak Ridge National Laboratory, Oak Ridge, Tenn., U.S.A.

RUSSELL, W. L., Oak Ridge National Laboratory, Oak Ridge, Tenn., U.S.A.

SAEZ, F. A. Instituto de Investigación de Ciencias Biológicas, Montevideo Uruguay.

SALDANHA, P. H., Fac. de Medicina, São Paulo, Brazil.

SALGADO, A. Q., Fac. de Filosofia de Marília, São Paulo, Brazil.

SALGADO, M. A. F., Instituto de Biofísica, Rio de Janeiro, Brazil.

SALZANO, F. M., Instituto de Ciências Naturais, Pôrto Alegre, Brazil.

SCHREIBER, G., Instituto de Biologia, Belo Horizonte, Brazil.

SETLOW, R. B., Oak Ridge National Laboratory, Oak Ridge, Tenn., U.S.A.

SHIBATA, S., Instituto Butantã, São Paulo, Brazil.

SILVA-FILHO, J. C., Fac. de Medicina, São Paulo, Brazil.

SIMÕES, L. C. G., Instituto de Biologia, Belo Horizonte, Brazil.

SLIZYNSKI, B. M., Institute of Animal Genetics, Edinburgh, Scotland.

SOARES, L. A., Escola de Veterinária, Belo Horizonte, Brazil.

SOARES, M. A., Instituto Butantã, São Paulo, Brazil.

TABORDA, A. R., Instituto Adolfo Lutz, São Paulo, Brazil.

TABORDA, L. C., Instituto Adolfo Lutz, São Paulo, Brazil.

TOLEDO-FILHO, S. A., Dept. de Biologia Geral, Univ. de São Paulo, Brazil.

TORGO, F. M. S., Instituto Oceanográfico, São Paulo, Brazil.

VALENCIA, J. I., Facultad de Ciencias Exactas y Naturales, Buenos Aires, Argentina.

VALENCIA, R. M. A., Comisión Nacional de Energia Atomica, Buenos Aires, Argentina.

VALLEJO-FREIRE, A., Instituto Butantã, São Paulo, Brazil.

VIGIER, P. C., Institut du Radium, Paris, France.

WAJCHENBERG, B. L., Hospital das Clínicas, São Paulo, Brazil.

WAJNTAL, A., Dept. de Biologia Geral, Univ. de São Paulo, Brazil.

WEILER, H. F., Latin American Regional Science Office, Rio de Janeiro, Brazil.

WELSHONS, W. J., Oak Ridge National Laboratory, Oak Ridge, Tenn., U.S.A.

YONEDA, S., Fac. de Medicina, São Paulo, Brazil.

ZAGO, D. A., Dept. de Biologia Geral, Univ. de São Paulo, Brazil.

ZELENY, V., International Atomic Energy Agency, Vienna, Austria.

ZEZZA-NETO, L., Escola de Veterinária, São Paulo, Brazil.

ZINNER, K., Centro de Medicina Nuclear, São Paulo, Brazil.

Mammalian Tissue Culture and Cytology

THE NUTRITION AND METABOLISM
OF CULTURED MAMMALIAN CELLS

H. EAGLE

Department of Cell Biology, Albert Einstein College of Medicine, New York,
U.S.A.

THE available information with respect to the nutritional requirements and metabolic activities of cultured animal cells has been presented in several recent reviews.[1-3] I propose therefore merely to recapitulate the salient features of their metabolism, emphasizing some of the differences between cultured cells and organized tissues, and to discuss possible directions of future investigation.

I. GENERAL CONSIDERATIONS

All cultured mammalian cells so far examined have proved to have basically the same requirements, summarized in Table 1. As is indicated there, a few cell lines have shown unique requirements for additional amino acids, and would appear to be blocked in one or another of the pathways of amino acid synthesis summarized in Table 2. The following points deserve particular emphasis.

1. Uniformity of metabolic activity. The nutritional requirements of cultured mammalian cells are remarkably uniform regardless of the species of origin, the particular organ, and whether the cells derive from embryonic or adult tissue. (Isolated examples of minor metabolic differences between cell strains will be discussed in following sections.) Further, no regular biochemical difference has yet been found between cells deriving from normal and malignant tissue, this despite the fact that even after years of cultivation those cells can be distinguished on reinoculation into a suitable host animal.[4]

2. Trace elements. These have not yet been shown to be required in cell culture. Since they are almost certainly necessary, they are presumably present as trace contaminants, particularly in the serum proteins present in most culture media.

3. Vitamins. Only eight vitamins have so far been shown to be required for

TABLE 1. THE MINIMUM NUTRITIONAL REQUIREMENTS OF CULTURED MAMMALIAN CELLS
(AFTER EAGLE[1])

	Generally Essential Possible Substitutes		Occasionally Essential[†]	
			Compound	Cell Line

Amino Acids	Isoleucine
	Leucine
	Lysine
	Methionine
	Phenyl-
	  alanine
	Threonine
	Tryptophan
	Valine
		α-Keto-β-methylvaleric
		α-Ketoisocaproic
		
		α-Keto-γ-methiolbutyric
		Phenylpyruvic
		
		α-Ketoisovaleric
			Asparagine	Glutamic acid-
				  adapted cells
				  at low popula-
				  tion levels
				Jensen sarcoma
				MDAB hepatoma
				Mouse leukemia
				  L5178Y
				Walker 256 car-
				  cinosarcoma

	Arginine
	(Cystine)*
	Glutamine
	Histidine
	Tyrosine
		Citrulline
		Homocystine
		Glutamic Acid
			(Glycine)*
			
			(Serine)*
				Monkey kidney
				Rabbit fibroblast
				P388 Mouse leu-
				  kemia
				All cells at low
				  population levels

Carbo- hydrate	Glucose	Mannose Fructose Galactose Ribose	(Pyruvate)*	P388 Mouse leu- kemia Detroit 98C-6B
Ionic Species	Ca^{++} Cl K^+ Mg^{++} Na^+ H_2PO_4			

Vitamins	Choline
	Folic Acid
	(Inositol)*
	Nicotinamide
	
	Panthothen-
	  ate
	Pyridoxal
	
	Riboflavin
	Thiamine
		Folic Acid
		
		Nicotinic Acid
		  DPN; TPN
		Coenzyme A
		
		Pyridoxine
		  pyridoxamine
		  pyridoxal-PO
		
		Cocarboxylase		

Protein	(Serum globulin)*			

* ( ) — dispensable under certain conditions.
† Required by only a few cell lines, or at low population densities.

TABLE 2.

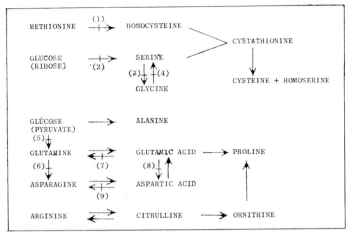

(1) TOO LITTLE PRODUCED FOR CELL SURVIVAL EXCEPT AT HIGH POPULATION DENSITIES.
(2) PARTIAL BLOCK IN RABBIT FIBROBLAST RT 6.
(3) PARTIAL BLOCK IN MONKEY KIDNEY CELLS.
(4) POSSIBLE BLOCK IN PATIENT WITH HYPERGLYCINEMIA.
(5) ALMOST COMPLETE BLOCK IN MOST CULTURED CELLS.
(6) APPARENTLY COMPLETE BLOCK IN WALKER CARCINOSARCOMA 256, JENSEN SARCOMA, MOUSE LEUKEMIA L-5178Y, AND MDAB HEPATOMA.
(7) NORMALLY LOW ACTIVITY, INADEQUATE FOR SURVIVAL OF MOST CELL LINES, UNLESS INDUCED BY HIGH CONCENTRATIONS OF GLUTAMIC ACID.
(8) POSSIBLE BLOCK IN JENSEN SARCOMA AND MOUSE LEUKEMIA L-5178Y.
(9) BLOCK, PARTIAL OR COMPLETE, IN WALKER CARCINOSARCOMA 256 AND MOUSE LEUKEMIA L-5178Y.

the indefinite growth of a wide variety of animal cells (Table 1). Although neither vitamin B12, biotin, ascorbic acid, nor any of the fat soluble vitamins have yet been shown to be required for growth, some of these may in fact be necessary and provided as trace contaminants on one or another component of the medium. The possibility may however be considered that at least some of these vitamins are required *in vivo*, not for growth, but for one or another specialized organ function; and these functions are conspicuously absent in cell culture.

4. Special amino acid requirements in cultured cells. Although eight amino acids suffice for nitrogen balance in man, all cultured mammalian cells additionally require arginine, tyrosine, histidine, cystine, and glutamine; and a fourteenth amino acid is required by a few cell strains (cf. Table 2). This apparent paradox has now been almost fully resolved.

(a) *Arginine and tyrosine.* The enzymatic apparatus necessary for the synthesis of arginine from ornithine, and of tyrosine from phenylalanine, has been demonstrated only in liver.[5,6] It is therefore not surprising that cells deriving from other tissues regularly require these two amino acids.

(b) *Histidine.* The requirement for histidine is not too surprising in view of the fact that it is required for growth or for nitrogen balance by every animal species examined except man (cf. Ref. 7); and in the latter case the possible contribution of histidine by the intestinal flora in short-term balance experiments has not been excluded.

(c) *Cystine*. The requirement for cystine and glutamine is of particular interest. Neither is necessary for nitrogen balance or for growth in any animal species yet examined; yet both are apparently rigorously essential for the survival and growth of all cultured mammalian cells. The discrepancy has proved to be more apparent than real. All cultured cells are in fact capable of synthesizing cystine from glucose and methionine, by the classical pathway involving homocysteine, serine and cystathionine as intermediates.[8] Exogenous cystine is nevertheless required because it, and the intermediates necessary for its formation, are lost by the cultured cells to the environment in amounts which exceed the biosynthetic capacity of the cell.[9] Cells growing in culture are exposed to a fluid environment exceeding by many hundredfold the volume of the cells themselves. This obviously magnifies the loss of metabolites as compared with cells in organized tissue. Under these circumstances the surprising fact is not that a compound such as cystine should be required in spite of the fact that it can be synthesized, but rather that this occurs in only a limited number of cases (cf. pp. 9–12). In point of fact, the cystine requirement by cultured cells regularly disappears if the population density is brought to a sufficiently high level, at which the medium can be "conditioned", i.e. the concentration of cystine and of the intermediates necessary for its biosynthesis brought to the necessary levels in the medium and in the cellular pool before the cells die of a cystine deficiency. In this specific case, the critical population density is a function of the intermediates which are supplied to the cell (cf. Table 5).

(d) *Glutamine*. A similar situation obtains in the case of glutamine and glutamic acid. Although glutamine can be synthesized from glutamic acid, in most cultured cells this synthethase activity is extremely limited, and glutamic acid alone does not permit growth. The conversion of glutamine to glutamic acid is however rapid, and glutamine suffices for survival and growth. However, even when cells are supplied with pre-formed glutamine, they continue to synthesize a significant proportion of their glutamic acid and glutamine residues from glucose (cf. Table 3). This suggested that, as in the case of cystine, the nutritional requirement for glutamic acid and glutamine might reflect the loss of the newly synthesized compounds to the medium. This has proved to be the case. Under the proper experimental conditions, neither glutamic acid nor glutamine are required by cultured cells for survival and growth.[10] The necessary condi-

TABLE 3. BIOSYNTHESIS OF AMINO ACIDS IN MAMMALIAN CELL CULTURES (AFTER EAGLE AND PIEZ[21])

Amino acid synthesized	% of carbon skeleton deriving from uniformly C14-labelled								% of α-NH2 deriving from N15-glutamic acid
	Glucose	Serine*	Glycine*	Ribose†	Pyruvate†	Glutamine*	Glutamic**	Arginine	
Alanine	71–101	0·4–1·4	0·2	0·8–4	85	7	7	—	80
Serine	70–111	22–102	10	63–66	1·7	2	9·9	—	75
Glycine	69–106	25–99	50	58–60	1·9		7·0	—	76
Asparagine	8–23	0·1–1·3	<0·1	0·48–12	4·7	71–87	100	—	78
Asparatic									
Glutamine	4–11	0·01–0·2	<0·1	0·31–0·63	4·1	101	84	—	83
Glutamic									
Proline	3–18	0·09–0·44	0·15	0·2–0·3	3·1	59	27	26	58

* In basal growth medium, containing glucose.
† In medium lacking glucose.
** In medium lacking glutamine.

tions are: (1) cells in which the glutamine synthase activity is at a high level, either because the cells have adaptively developed increased concentrations of glutamine synthase,[11] or because, as in the case of monkey kidney cells in primary culture, they are endowed with an initially high glutamine synthase activity,[12,13] and (2) a population density sufficiently high to limit the loss of the formed glutamic acid and glutamine. Under these conditions neither is required for survival and growth.

(e) *Specific amino acid requirements* of individual cell strains are discussed in a following section.

5. *Amino acid biosynthesis and metabolism.* Only a beginning has been made in exploring the degree to which the metabolism of cultured cells differs from that of cells in organized tissue. Most of the available data relate to the metabolism of the amino acids and protein, with little information concerning liquids and carbohydrates, or of macromolecular biosynthesis in general.

As indicated in Table 3, the nutritionally non-essential amino acids not required by the cell are synthesized by glucose, and derive their amino group from glutamic acid or glutamine, this despite the fact that the cells contain a wide spectrum of transaminases.[14] When cells are given ribose

TABLE 4. THE METABOLISM OF GLUTAMINE IN MAMMALIAN CELL CULTURE

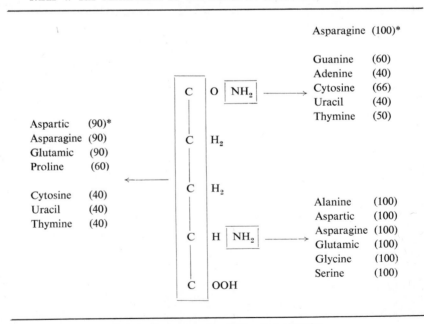

* Approximate percentage deriving from glutamine.

and pyruvate in lieu of glucose, the alanine then derives from pyruvate, and the serine and glycine from ribose, with little or no metabolic interconversion between these two groups of amino acids. This may provide an experimental approach to the mechanism of serine biosynthesis in cell cultures.

The interconversions observed to date in the biosynthesis of the non-essential amino acids have been indicated in Table 2. In contrast to the whole organism, none of the essential amino acids except glutamine is metabolized to any significant degree by cultured animal cells. They are used simply for incorporation in protein, with no evidence to date of their utilization for other biosynthetic processes. Glutamine however is actively metabolized. Its carbon skeleton serves as a source of aspartic acid, asparagine and proline, its α-amino group is the source of the α-amino group for all the nutritionally non-essential amino acids, and the amide is the unique source for the amide nitrogen of asparagine, as well as for 40–66 per cent of the purine and pyrimidine nitrogen (cf. Table 4). In these animal cell cultures, unlike micro-organisms and the intact animal, ammonia is a metabolic by-product, and is not used to any significant degree except possibly in the biosynthesis of glutamic acid (see p. 7).

II. CULTURED CELLS VS. ORGANIZED TISSUES

Cultured cells differ from the tissue of origin in three major respects: they are grown at relatively low population densities, they usually grow more rapidly, and they do not carry out the specific functions of the organ from which they were isolated.

A. The Effects of Population Density on the Metabolic Activities of Cultured Cells

Whether grown in suspension or in monolayer, cultured cells achieve maximum population densities of the order of 500,000 cells per ml, and the usual operating range is between 50,000 to 500,000 per ml. In most solid tissues, on the other hand, the population density is several hundred times greater, approximating 100,000,000 cells per ml. An important consequence of the relatively low population density in culture is a significant and sometimes fatal loss of metabolites to the environment. It is apparent that if a compound synthesized by the cell is not concentratively retained, several hundred times as much goes into the medium as remains in the cellular pool. Even if the cellular concentration at equilibrium is ten times that in surrounding fluid, the volume ratio of culture fluid cells is so large that most of the compound

TABLE 5. SUMMARY OF POPULATION DEPENDENT REQUIREMENTS BY CULTURED MAMMALIAN CELLS FOR METABOLITES WHICH THEY CAN IN FACT SYNTHESIZE (AFTER EAGLE ET AL.[9,10])

Metabolite required	Growth medium*	Cell line	Concn. permitting growth at low population densities mM	Population density in excess of which exogenous metabolite becomes unnecessary† No. cells/ml.
Cystine	0 cystine	Human‡	0·002 to 0·005	200,000 to 500,000
	0 cystine + homocystine	Human‡	0·002 to 0·005	10,000 to 60,000
	0 cystine + homocystine + serine	Human‡	0·002 to 0·005	50 to 500
Glutamine	0 glutamine + glutamic	Human (HeLa and conjunctiva cells adapted to growth in glutamic acid)	0·01 to 0·05 (varies with cell population density and glutamic acid concentration)	> 50,000 (varies with glutamic acid concentration)
Glycine	"complete"	Monkey kidney cells in primary culture		
Homocystine	0 cystine	Human‡	0·01	200,000 to 500,000
Inositol	"complete"	Human (HeLa)	0·001	200,000
		Mouse (P388)	0·1 to 1	50,000
		Detroit 98 C6B	0·1 to 1	100
Pyruvate	"complete"	Human‡	0·005 to 0·02	50 to 200
		Rabbit (RT6)	0·005	50,000
		Mouse (P388)	0·005	150,000
Serine	0 cystine + homocystine	Human‡	0·04	10,000 to 60,000

* Basal medium of Table 1, supplemented with dialyzed serum, and modified as indicated.
† Permitting growth at half of maximal rate, based on average generation time over period of 8 days.
‡ HeLa, Conjunctiva, KB, "Liver".

is perforce lost to the environment. Under these conditions, it is surprising that the minimal medium of Table 1 does in fact suffice for growth; for in such a medium a host of compounds vital to the cellular economy, intermediates in the biosynthesis of essential macromolecules, must be synthesized in amounts sufficient not only for the needs of the cell, but to "condition" the medium as well.

1. This continuing depletion manifests itself in the fact that a number of compounds actively synthesized by the cell are nevertheless rigorously required for survival. This requirement disappears at high population densities, at which the medium can be conditioned, and the concentration within the cell brought to metabolically effective levels, before the cells die of the specific deficiency. This has already been shown to underlie the requirement for *cystine* and *glutamine* by cultured cells (cf. p. 6 and Table 5). *Serine* is similarly required by every cultured cell so far examined, but

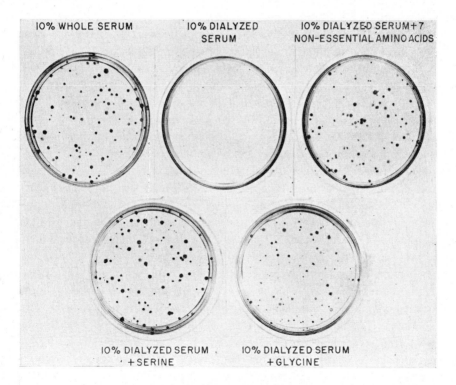

FIG. 1. Illustrating the serine requirement for the growth of small numbers of mammalian cells. HeLa cells were plated in the defined medium of Table 1 with the supplements indicated in the figure. The resulting colonies were stained after 8 days. (After Lockart and Eagle.[15])

only at extremely low population densities.[15] The minimal medium of Table 1, which suffices for the growth of ordinary inocula of, e.g., 10,000 cells per ml, does not permit the growth of single cells. Such single cells can however regularly be grown in the same minimal medium supplemented with serine (cf. Fig. 1).

2. Inositol, like glutamine, is required by almost all cultured cells despite the fact that it is synthesized by cells in significant amounts even in a medium, containing preformed inositol.[16] It is in keeping with the present discussion that in occasional experiments the inositol requirement has disappeared at sufficiently high population densities.[9]

3. A number of variant cell strains supposedly requiring either serine, glycine or pyruvate (cf. Table 5) have proved to be examples of a similar population phenomenon. These strains are capable of synthesizing limited amounts of the metabolite which they require, but it is lost to the environment in amounts which exceed their biosynthetic capacity. The requirement disappears at a sufficiently high population density.

4. *Summary of population effects in nutritional requirement.* It is apparent from the foregoing that some of the nutritional requirements of cultured cells reflect the relatively low rate at which a given metabolite is synthesized, coupled with its loss in prohibitive amounts to the medium. Thus, a compound such as serine is normally produced by most cells in such amounts that 100 cells per ml suffice to condition the medium and permit growth in the medium of Table 1. A few variant cells however apparently synthesize serine at such a reduced rate that the critical population density in a "complete" medium is increased to 50,000 per ml. Similarly, if cystine is omitted from the medium, all cells must then use serine for cystine synthesis, and higher serine concentrations become necessary for survival. The minimum population density required in order to bring the serine level in the medium and in the cellular pool to that higher concentration is then increased from approximately 100 per ml to 50,000 per ml.

Considering the fact that cells generally constitute approximately 1/1000th of the culture medium, it is indeed surprising that as few as twenty-eight defined components, supplemented with protein, usually suffice for growth. One must conclude that the hundreds of other compounds synthesized by the cell, and essential to the cellular economy, are either produced in such large excess as to compensate for that leakage, or are retained concentratively by the cell with little or no leakage to the medium.

B. Metabolic Controls

A second important respect in which cultured cells differ from most cells *in vivo* is their relatively rapid rate of growth. Even in the minimal medium of Table 1, containing only those growth factors demonstrably essential for survival, and in which the deletion of any one component results in the death of the cells, the generation time of most cultured cells is on the order of 16-24 hr; and that rate of growth is increased to only a minor degree by further supplementation. This rate of growth is approximated *in vivo* by a few tissues, such as bone marrow, intestinal mucosa and regenerating liver; but in most organs the rate of cellular turnover is of a different order of magnitude, and in liver, for example, has been estimated to be of the order of 110 days.[19]

The nature of the metabolic controls which are operative *in vivo*, and which are turned off in culture in whole or in part, remains to be determined. Enzyme repression and end product inhibition, which play so important a role as metabolic controls in micro-organisms, have not as yet been shown to play a major role in cultured mammalian cells. The repression of glutamine synthethase by glutamine is one of the few examples of enzyme repression so far reported,[11] and end product inhibition has been demonstrated only in the case of purine synthesis.[20] The possibility must therefore be considered that these control mechanisms are operative *in vivo*, but not *in vitro*.

Protein turnover does not appear to be a regulatory mechanism which would account for the differential growth rate of most cells *in vivo* and *in vitro*. The cellular proteins of cultured cells are replaced at an average rate of 1 per cent per hour,[21] approximately the same as that which has been found *in vivo*.[19] In contrast to micro-organisms, this protein turnover occurs at the same rate in both growing and resting cells.

A possible metabolic control which may differ in cultured cells and tissues, and which has not been adequately explored, is the transport of nutrilites. Amino acids are actively transported into the cell against a concentration gradient. The precise size of the pool varies with the specific amino acids and varies also with the absolute level in the environment.[22] Similarly, amino acids which are synthesized by the cell are concentratively retained to varying degrees. As previously indicated, however, the volume disparity between the cells and the medium is such that despite this concentrative retention, the amounts lost to the environment exceed by several hundred-fold those retained in the cell. Possible differences between tissues and dispersed cells in the rate of uptake of metabolites, as well as in the equilibrium ratios between the cellular pool and the environment, remain to be determined. It is pertinent to note that for each amino acid there is a relatively narrow range of intracellular concentration within which the rate of protein synthesis and cellular growth varies strikingly as a function of amino acid concentration[23] (Fig. 2). This has proved to be an effective method of controlling growth rates *in vitro*,[24] and some equally simple analogous mechanism may conceivably serve as a metabolic control *in vivo*.

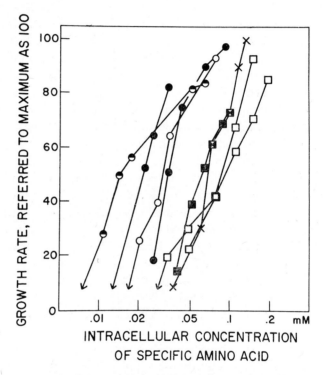

FIG. 2. The rate of cellular growth (and inferentially, protein synthesis) as a function of the intracellular concentration of amino acids. Effect of lysine concentration on growth of KB (■) and intestine (□) cell; effect of threonine concentration on growth of HeLa cell (X); and effect of valine on growth of conjunctiva (◑), KB (●) and HeLa (○) cells (cf. Fig. 1). (After Eagle, Piez and Levy.[23])

C. *Specialized Function*

One of the most disappointing aspects of cultured animal cells has been their underlying metabolic uniformity. Not only has no significant or regular difference been noted between cells deriving from normal and malignant tissue, or between embryonic and adult tissue, but more particularly, cells deriving from differentiated tissues usually do not carry out in culture the functions of the organ from which they have been derived. Thus, fibroblasts do not elaborate protein chemically identifiable as collagen; and cells deriving from liver do not hydroxylate phenylalanine or synthesize arginine. Only three clear examples have to date been reported of serially propagated animal cells which do carry out specialized functions, and it is perhaps significant that all three of these derive from malignant tissue (cf. Ref. 2).

A number of possible explanations may be considered for the failure of cultured cells to function, and these are not mutually exclusive. (a) The correct cell may not in fact have been cultured. (b) Function may require biochemical interaction between different cell types, either in the same organ or in different organs. (c) Rapid growth itself may not be consistent with sustained function. Cellular components essential to function may not be reproduced at the same rate in rapidly growing cultures as are the structural elements of the cell. There may thus be a loss by dilution of compounds essential to function, similar to the loss of the kappa factor during the rapid growth of paramecia. Alternatively, it is possible that although the total genetic and enzymatic apparatus necessary for function is duplicated in rapidly growing cells, the function can be expressed only on the cessation of rapid cellular growth. (d) In the light of the discussion in a preceding section, cellular metabolites which are essential to function and which are retained in highly cellular organized tissue, may be lost to the medium under conditions of *in vitro* growth when the cells constitute so minute a fraction of the total volume.

REFERENCES

1. EAGLE, H., Amino acid metabolism in mammalian cell cultures, *Science*, **130**, 432-437, August 1959.
2. EAGLE, H. and LEVINTOW, L., The biochemistry of cultured mammalian cells, *The Annual Review of Biochemistry*, **30**, 605-640, 1961.
3. EAGLE, H., The effect of population density of the nutritional requirements of cultured mammalian cells, and its implications with respect to specialized function, Monograph of Society of General Physiology, in press.
4. FOLEY, G. E. and HANDLER, A. H., Differentiation of "normal" and neoplastic cells maintained in tissue culture by implantation into normal hamsters, *Proc. Soc. Exper. Biol. and Med.* **94**, 661-664, 1957; Idem, "Tumorigenic" activity of tissue cell cultures, *Ann. New York Acad. Sci.* **76**, 506-512, 1958: Foley, G. E., Handler, A. H., Adams, R. A. and Craig, J. M., Assessment of potential malignancy of cultured cells: Further observations on the differentiation of "normal" and "neoplastic" cells maintained *in vitro* by heterotransplantation in Syrian hamsters.
5. UDENFRIEND, S. and COOPER, J. R., *J. Biol. Chem.* **194**, 503, 1952; Udenfriend, S., personal communication 1962.
6. JONES, M. E., ANDERSON, A. D., ANDERSON, C. and HODES, S., Citrulline synthesis

in rat tissues, *Arch. Biochem. Biophys.* **95**, 499, 1961.

7. MEISTER, A., *Biochemistry of the Amino Acids*, Academic Press, New York, 1957.
8. EAGLE, H., PIEZ, K. A., and OYAMA, V. I., The biosynthesis of cystine in human cell cultures, *J. Biol. Chem.* **236**, 1425-1428, May 1961.
9. EAGLE, H. and PIEZ, K., The population dependent requirement by cultured mammalian cells for metabolites which they can synthesize, *J. Exp. Med.* **116**, 29-43, July 1962.
10. EAGLE, J., unpublished observations.
11. DeMARS, R., The inhibition by glutamine of glutamyl transferase formation in cultures of human cells, *Biochim. Biophys. Acta*, **27**, 435-436, 1958.
12. EAGLE, H., FREEMAN, A. E., LEVY, M., The amino acid requirements of monkey kidney cells in first culture passage, *J. Exp. Med.* **107**, 543-651, May 1958.
13. DeMARS, R. and EAGLE H., cited in *Metabolic Studies with Normal and Malignant Human Cells in Culture*, The Harvey Lectures, 1958-1959, Academic Press, N.Y., 156-175, 1960.
14. BARBAN, S. and SCHULZE, H. O., Transamination reactions of mammalian cells in tissue culture, *J. Biol. Chem.* **234**, 829-831, April 1959.
15. LOCKART, R. Z., Jr. and EAGLE, H., Requirements for growth of single human cells, *Science*, **129**, 252-254, No. 3344, 30 January 1959.
16. EAGLE, H., AGRANOFF, B. W. and SNELL, E. E., The biosynthesis of meso-inositol by cultured mammalian cells, and the parabiotic growth of inositol-dependent and inositol-independent strains, *J. Biol. Chem.* **235**, 1891-1893, July 1960.
17. KROOTH, R. S. and WEINBERG, A. N., Studies on cell lines developed from the tissues of patients with galactosemia, *J. Exp. Med.* **113**, 1155, June 1961.
18. ROSEN, O. and EAGLE, H., unpublished.
19. SCHIMKE, R. T., Turnover of arginase in rat liver and mammalian tissue culture, The New York Academy of Sciences Conference on Endogenous Metabolism with Special Reference to Bacteria, New York City, 20 September 1962.
20. McFALL, E. and MAGASANIK, B., The control of purine biosynthesis in cultured mammalian cells, *J. Biol. Chem.* **235**, 2103-2108, July 1960.
21. EAGLE, H., PIEZ, K. A., FLEISHMAN, R. and OYAMA, V. I., Protein turnover in mammalian cell cultures, *J. Biol. Chem.* **234**, 592-597, March 1959.
22. EAGLE, H., and PIEZ, K. A., *Amino Acid Pools, Protein Synthesis and Protein Turnover in Human Cell Cultures*, Conference on Amino Acid Pools, Elsevier, Amsterdam, 1962.
23. EAGLE, H., PIEZ, K. A. and LEVY, M., The intracellular amino acid concentrations required for protein synthesis in cultured human cells. *J. Biol. Chem.* **236**, 2039-2042, July 1961.
24. COHEN, E. P. and EAGLE, H., A simplified chemostat for the growth of mammalian cells: Characteristics of cell growth in continuous culture, *J. Exp. Med.* **113**, 467-474, February 1961.

THE BLOOD TECHNIQUE
AND
HUMAN CHROMOSOMES

P. S. MOORHEAD

Wistar Institute of Anatomy and Biology, Philadelphia, U.S.A.

DOCTOR PAVAN has asked me to speak about the "blood technique" or the "peripheral blood culture". The culture itself might be termed more strictly "the phytohemagglutinin culture for leucocytes" since it depends upon the reaction of a specialized cell to a special substance. Our present interest in this somewhat unique system is not a concern with the nutritional factors involved nor the nature of this special property of phytohemagglutinin. Our interest is cytologic and lies in its usefulness in providing a simple method for obtaining samples of mammalian cells which are capable of division *in vitro*. I will discuss this culture system and its techniques, but I would also like to present some of our recent work which concerns the cytology of human chromosomes, much of which is derived from studies of long-term cultures of fibroblast-like cells. The cytology is the ultimate purpose of our techniques, and what I intend to present is concerned with subjects of later presentations in this symposium, especially the karyotype of man and heterochromatin.

After publication of the classic papers on the human karyotype by Tjio and Levan (1956) and by Tjio and Puck (1958) the lid was opened to Pandora's box of human anomalies — beginning with the findings by Lejeune (1959) of trisomy associated with mongolism. No one suspected the enormous variety of pathological chromosome conditions existent in man, and the blood culture method provided means which were simpler than skin biopsy techniques and required less time in cultivation. In some respects this wealth of findings in man was obtained too rapidly and without time for critical appraisal and incorporation.

This work was supported (in part) by U.S.P.H.S. Career Development Award CA-K6-18,372, Research Grant CA-04534, and Contract No. PH 43-62-157, from the National Cancer Institute.

The blood culture technique has advantages in applications to human pathologic conditions because of the ease of biopsy, the short time of culture and the simplicity of needed equipment and facilities (Moorhead, Nowell, Mellman, Battips and Hungerford, 1960).

The blood culture provides a dividing cell population which has not divided more than once or twice in culture; therefore, it is representative of interphase cells in the body. The direct processing of bone marrow has the advantage, for leukemia studies, of representing the actual dividing population of the marrow and of avoiding possible differential rates of survival in the phytohemagglutinin leucocyte culture. Sandberg and co-workers (1962) have demonstrated that some chromosomally anomalous cells of patients having acute leukemia do not survive so well in the phytohemagglutinin culture as do normal cells. However, Nowell and Hungerford (1962) have emphasized that phytohemagglutinin is, of course, not necessary for the cultivation of leukemic blood and, in fact, this information in itself is partially diagnostic.

Originally Osgood and his co-workers (1955) developed the gradient culture system during their long experience with the cultivation of leukemic and normal blood cells. Phytohemagglutinin was first employed for its known ability to agglutinate red cells, thus facilitating separation of the leucocytes. It has long been known that buffy coat cultures show some mitosis. Osgood and his group had noted mitotic figures in non-leukemic cell cultures; however, it was Nowell (1960) who pressed this point, determined that phytohemagglutinin was the essential element and sought out the cooperation of cytologists to further exploit this fact. Nowell eliminated various culture factors as the possible inducer of mitosis in these cultures and demonstrated that the brief subjection of the cells to phytohemagglutinin during the separation procedure was sufficient to induce a wave of mitosis thereafter. More recently, McIntyre and Ebaugh (1962) have eliminated other substances as possible substitutes for phytohemagglutinin: foetal calf serum, IAA, Kinetin, and estrogens.

The substance phytohemagglutinin is derived from the common bean, *Phaseola vulgaris*, and is little more than a crude extract of pulped beans which is filtered free of its coarser material and may be further filtered for sterilization, although with difficulty unless extremely diluted (Rigas and Osgood, 1955). It is a mucoprotein which does not easily permit further purification. It has been suggested that the action of phytohemagglutinin is indirect in that its removal of red cells then permits the leucocyte to proceed to a division state; however, Nowell (1960) has demonstrated the usual activity of phytohemagglutinin in agitated cultures of whole blood. Other interesting suggestions concerning its possible action on the surface of the leucocyte and on release of intracellular substances have been offered with little direct or significant information yet available.

The activity of phytohemagglutinin is not mitogenic in the sense of a release of cells already prepared for division, but its activity seems to involve the initiation of a gradual increase in morphologic types of the blast form. Only after this "de-differentiation" or conversion process, requiring 24-48 hr, do the cells proceed to divide. It has been demonstrated by Nowell (1961) that blood culture mitosis may be directly inhibited by the presence of prednisolone. At concentrations of $0·0002 = 10$ $\mu g/ml$, the mitotic index is depressed to a quarter of its control value. The interesting point in this study is that the action of prednisolone in depressing mitosis exerts its influence upon the conversion phase as does the phytohemagglutinin, although in the opposite direction.

All quantitative studies to date, particularly those of Elves and Wilkinson (1962) and MacKinney, Stohlman and Brecher (1961) indicate that the lymphocytes and possibly the monocytes originally present are the cells which are affected and that these must first convert to a state capable of division. The polymorphonuclear cells apparently do not contribute to the dividing cell population. The quantitative studies based on uptake of P32 by McIntyre and Ebaugh (1962) confirmed these findings concerning the polymorphs. For this reason Cooper and Hirschhorn (1962) advocate the use of a magnet technique for removal of the polymorphonuclear cells, removing them with a strong magnet after they have ingested iron particles. A less elaborate method is used by Osgood in which the plasma is left undisturbed, permitting attachment of polymorphs to the side of the tube; then a gentle swirling frees the desired monocytes and lymphocytes which do not adhere to glass. On the other hand, various studies (McIntyre and Ebaugh, 1962; Mellman et al., 1962) indicate that the polymorphs die off in the first 48 hr, and consistent successful cultures may be had without attention to their removal. In blood samples in which the polymorphonuclear leucocytes are unusually high in number, however, one may fail to take this into account and thereby fail to plant sufficient numbers of the mitotically competent elements.

Autoradiographic studies by MacKinney, Stohlman and Brecher (1961) as well as by Bender and Prescott (1962) have confirmed the fact that the cells undergoing eventual division after subjection to phytohemagglutinin had not been in their G2 phase as circulating leucocytes. The uptake of tritiated thymidine was seen to occur only after the in vitro conversion process. Using a quite simple modification for culture, they found that dividing cells were numerous at day 3, day 7, and even day 10, but diminished at day 14, and were absent at day 17. Cultures of buffy coat obtained by high speed centrifugation were used. (Buffy coat, serum, and some red blood cells were implanted in medium of TC199, AB serum, and phytohemagglutinin and incubated at 37°C in 5 per cent CO_2 atmosphere.) By observing the "diluting" effect of chromosomal replication, it was determined that not more than 4 successive divisions occurred. All chromatids showed labeling with tritiated thymidine in the first division, one chromatid of each chromosome was labeled at the second division, half of all chromosomes showed one labeled chromatid at the third division and at day 5 only about a quarter of all chromosomes showed labeling in one chromatid.

TECHNIQUE

The culture itself is essentially uncomplicated, consisting of these processes: separation of competent leucocytes, incubation in commercial tissue culture medium fortified with about 20 per cent autologous or heterologous serum, and the presence of phytohemagglutinin. Harvesting of cells during their mitotic peak and spreading of metaphases may be done by any of a variety of procedures developed over the last several years.

Leucocytes of various mammals have been successfully grown under the effect of phytohemagglutinin.* Nichols and Levan (1962) used 6 per cent Dextran for successful separation and growth of leucocytes from the blood of rabbit, guinea pig, rat and mouse. These workers were unable to secure mitosis in cells from the Syrian hamster. Many investigators, including these, have expressed the opinion that in the adaptation of the general technique to other animals, finding the necessary adjustment for effective cell separation is the most common difficulty. Leucocyte separation can be accomplished by light centrifugation (Nowell, 1960) by the use of Dextran or similar compounds (Nichols and Levan, 1962), by simple gravity separation (Edwards and Young, 1961), or by strong centrifugation to achieve a buffy coat (Bender and Prescott, 1962). For human blood, personal choice is wide, since few of the various factors involved are critical. After separation of leucocytes in their own plasma, they may be stored at 5°C for up to 4 days without loss of viability on subsequent culturing (Mellman, Klevit and Moorhead, 1962).

The temperature range for successful incubation of cultures has not been adequately investigated. In our lab. we have traced certain failures

* Dr Willy Beçak (Instituto Butantã, São Paulo) has recently extended the phytohemagglutinin culture to blood cells of snakes (*Amer. Nat.* **97**, 253, 1963).

to a slightly elevated temperature of 39°C, but have since learned (Nowell and Hungerford, personal communication) that 38°C produces even higher mitotic indices than usual if the culture is harvested on day 2 instead of on day 3.

Leucocyte Culture Procedure*

Commercial heparin (1000 units/ml; 0·2 ml/10 ml blood) is drawn into a 10 ml disposable syringe. As little as 2 or 3 ml of blood will provide one culture. This is sometimes the total volume obtainable from an infant in a single drawing of blood. Enough air is drawn into the syringe to unclog the needle and to provide a bubble for mixing of the blood with the heparin. The syringe is placed on end with the needle up, and the needle is bent with a sterile forceps. When the volume of cleared plasma is approximately one quarter that of the original blood volume, the plasma is extruded into a sterile tube. A second collection of smaller volume is usually made so that a total of about 4 ml plasma is obtained from 10 ml of original blood. A leucocyte count is made upon the plasma thus collected and 7–15 million leucocytes per ml may be expected. A complete medium is prepared in 100 ml lots distributed to culture vials (5 dram bottles) in 7 ml aliquots and gas tight covers are applied. This medium consists of 85 ml of TC1066 or TC199, 15 per cent calf serum, antibiotics (1000 μ penicillin and 1000 μg streptomycin per ml), and 0·5 ml of phytohemagglutinin. These culture "blanks", which lack only the leucocytes, are frozen and stored at about −15°C. To each thawed blank is added a volume of plasma which will provide approximately 10 or 12 million leucocytes per culture; this is usually about 1 ml.

The phytohemagglutinin as obtained from Difco Co. is a powder which readily goes into solution in distilled water; however, it must be sterilized by Seitz filtration with a Swinney filter attached to a small syringe. The potency of different lots varies considerably, and the manufacturers have introduced tests to insure mitotic activity. However, individual comparisons of new lots with known active lots are recommended. The type of culture vessel is unimportant as long as the approximate cell density on the bottom is of the order of 30,000 cells per mm². We have used the syringe in which the blood was originally drawn as a convenient chamber for culture. The culture should be stoppered or capped airtight and incubated at 37°C for 3 days.

* The following detailed procedure is currently in use in the laboratory of William J. Mellman and in our own.

Fixation and Spreading

On the third day colchicine is added (0·4 μg/ml or 0·05 μg Colcemide*), and after 4–6 hr the cells are suspended with a Pasteur pipette and harvested in a 12 ml conical centrifuge tube. All further steps are performed at room temperature. After centrifugation (500–800 rpm, radius 6 in. for 5 min) the medium is removed and replaced with neutral pH Hanks' balanced salt solution, and the cells suspended in this. Centrifugation is repeated and all except 0·5 ml of Hanks' BSS is removed. The cells are vigorously resuspended in this small volume of Hanks' BSS; then 4 times as much distilled water is added with mixing. After about 8 min of this hypotonic treatment, the cells are centrifuged as before, and all supernatant fluid is removed. Fixative of 3 parts methyl alcohol to 1 part glacial acetic acid is freshly mixed and added to the button of cells without stirring. This is allowed to stand for about 30 min. This initial fixation period is shortened for smaller cell buttons to avoid clumping. The fixative is then changed 3 or 4 times to rinse out remnants of the original BSS and to achieve thorough fixation. With each change the cells are suspended as completely as possible, and care is taken that the reagents are pure and fresh. For spreading metaphase cells, a drop of fixative with suspended cells is placed upon a clean wet slide and this is immediately ignited. The burning causes a rapid elimination of fixative and spreading of cells under the surface tension of the diminishing film of fixative. Effective spreading by air-drying or by flaming depends upon rapid evaporation and upon slides which are clean and free of grease. Dried slides may be stained with orcein or Giemsa and permanently mounted.

As relatively small numbers of cells are actually observed for chromosome determinations, the usual procedure of drawing 5–10 ml of blood provides more than enough leucocytes. Edwards (1962) has developed a technique for the culture of blood cells from capillary blood which is somewhat more demanding than the usual one, but permits persons relatively unskilled in venipuncture to obtain material from infants by simple finger puncture.

I am unaware of any attempts to cultivate leucocytes continuously with the aid of phytohemagglutinin. Bender and Prescott (1962) have studied the kinetics of a continuous culture up to 12 days, after which time most cells have degenerated. We have performed only preliminary experiments to determine whether there is some encouragement for such an approach. We have replanted the cells of a culture on days 3, 6, 9, 12,

---

* Courtesy CIBA Pharmaceuticals Inc., Summit, New Jersey.

and 15; dividing the cell population in *half* at each stage. The first four subdivisions were successful, but there was a noticeable drop in cell number in the fourth stage; in the fifth only a few cells remained, but some of these showed active mitosis. We feel that a more ambitious effort towards continuous cultivation of phytohemagglutinin-stimulated leucocytes might succeed. The adaptation of peripheral leucocytes to long-term continuous suspension or spinner culture might have interesting research applications as a parallel to the long-term culture of fibroblast diploid strains, especially in respect to cell markers and to possible differences of phenotypic expression *in vitro*. For example, differences such as the presence of a typical Barr body in the fibroblast and the lack of it in cultured leucocytes are of interest as would be differences concerning morphological details of the chromosomes.

Most of the studies concerning the cytology of human chromosomes in our laboratory have been conducted upon diploid and aneuploid cell strains from foetal material or skin biopsy. In collaboration with Dr. Eero Saksela of Helsinki we have recently made comparative studies of some cytologic procedures with respect to the effect on the observed appearance of secondary constrictions (Saksela and Moorhead, 1962).

In the course of observations on metaphase chromosomes from fibroblast-like cell lines in long-term culture, we noted marked secondary constrictions shortly after the introduction of the "flaming" or ignition step in our modification for spreading metaphase chromosomes. Semi-quantitative comparative studies showed that this rather drastic spreading procedure did induce a much higher incidence and a stronger appearance of these specific constrictions in chromosomes No. 1, No. 9, and No. 16 (Fig. 1).

In some cells a medium-sized metacentric, which proved to be an X chromosome, was often noted to have a different appearance, as if it were not properly fixed. Our first impression was that this indistinct chromosome might be No. 8 or No. 10, since it was usually smaller than No. 6 or the X. However, no such metacentric was ever noted in similar preparations made from male diploid cells. Male and female diploid strains were grown together in one culture vessel, harvested in two aliquots, and preparations were made according to our "ignition" method and by ordinary air-drying. The former clearly enhanced these secondary constrictions.

In other experiments a fixative of less hardening qualities, a 1:1 mixture of methyl alcohol and glacial acetic acid, was compared to the usual 3:1 mixture. This fixative of equal parts methyl and acetic acid gave even better differentiation permitting the demonstration of one, and only one, X in well over 50 per cent of the cells so treated. This fixative also exaggerated

strongly all the usually observed secondary constrictions on chromosomes
No. 1, No. 9, and No. 16, plus one on chromosome No. 4. All of these are
adjacent to the centromere. These specific regions showed a despiralized
cytologic appearance in contrast to the gap-like constrictions occasionally
observed at other loci, such as in the small arm of chromosome No. 5
and those in the long acrocentric group. Also observed was a large region
or constriction of the Y with this same indistinct or destained appearance.
In preparations made from mixed sex cultures, this was seen only in the
male cells (Fig. 1).

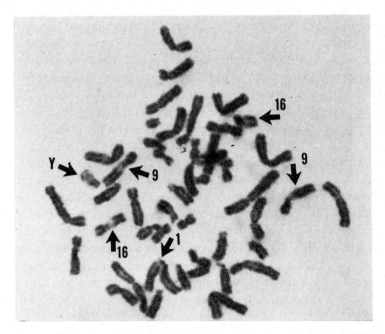

Fig. 1. Cytologically enhanced secondary constrictions on chromosomes No. 1,
No. 9, No. 16, and the Y in a metaphase from diploid human cell strain WI-26.
(From Saksela and Moorhead, 1962).

To confirm our presumption that the despiralized metacentric was actually
one of the X's, we repeated these procedures using diploid cells from the
Syrian hamster where the X is morphologically obvious. Here one entire X
appeared affected as well as only one arm of the other X. In male Syrian
hamster cells only one arm of the X was affected. These portions resembled
the indistinct X in our human material. Although we know of no autoradiographic studies on Syrian hamster cells, it is interesting that in the

Chinese hamster this is the pattern of "late-labeling" of the X's (Taylor, 1960).

We feel that these artificial means of differentiating these secondary constrictions, one X in female cells, and the Y in male cells, reflect some basic similarity of these regions. There is no question concerning the consistent location of the major secondary constrictions observed. A single negatively heteropyknotic metacentric is never seen in male cell preparations nor is more than one ever seen in female material. If the metacentric chromosome being differentiated is actually the heterochromatic X, which is known to be "late" in its DNA replication cycle, a plausible basis is laid for its differential cytologic reaction. The similarity of the cytologic appearance of the X, together with the autosomal secondary constrictions and the constrictions on the Y, suggests a similarity of allocyclic behaviour for all of these regions. However, a crucial demonstration that these regions are truly heterochromatic, that is, related to heteropyknotic regions observable at prophase, has not yet been made.*

It is of interest that these cytologic techniques have a less pronounced effect upon leucocytes from phytohemagglutinin-stimulated cultures. Whether this difference is physiologic or is only artificial is not yet known. One procedural difference present is that the fibroblast-like cultures are routinely trypsinized without warming the trypsin solution taken from the ice-box. This could possibly act as a cold-shock treatment. However, preliminary controls upon this possible factor have shown that neither the temperature nor the trypsin itself has any such effect.

Related to these studies, especially concerning the secondary constrictions of human chromosomes, is the recent finding that Simian virus 40 can induce morphological and chromosomal transformation *in vitro* of cells from human mucosa (Koprowski, Ponten, Jensen, Ravdin, Moorhead and Saksela, 1962) and from foetal kidney (Shein and Enders, 1962). This cell transformation or alteration was achieved repeatedly by exposure of the cells to SV_{40} agent at implantation. Chromosomal alterations were not discernible until after 8–12 weeks of cultivation *in vitro*. For this reason, attempts to demonstrate similar viral effects in leucocyte cultures must await the successful adaptation of such cells to long-term culture. However, since the above reports appeared, Nichols, Levan, Hall and Östergren

---

* Confirmation that the late-labeling X is differentially affected by the above cytologic technique has been obtained since this presentation, using a 5X-carrying fibroblast-like cell strain kindly supplied to us by Melvin Grumbach and A. Morishima. Four metacentrics were cytologically distinguishable, corresponding to the four "late-labeling" X's and to the four sex-chromatin bodies observed by Grumbach and Morishima (personal communication) in this cell strain.

(1962) have used the peripheral blood culture to demonstrate an *in vivo* cytologic effect of measles virus (*Rubeola*) upon human leucocytes. These workers found an increase in the frequency of visible chromosomal breaks or achromatic lesions in phytohemagglutinin-stimulated cultures of leucocytes cultured from blood taken at various periods after the onset of the measles rash. More than 50 per cent of the cells possessed visible chromosome lesions in blood taken at day 5–7 after onset of the rash, whereas control or spontaneous values are of the order of 1 per cent or less. These chromatid "breaks" or gaps (Nichols *et al.* refer to them as of the "delayed isolocus" type) are of considerable interest, since in the SV_{40} material similar lesions are common.

Four different mucosal lines and two skin-derived lines from four terminal cancer patients have been examined in our laboratory at several passage levels and all contained cells with definite chromosomal alterations. One culture from a control mucosal line was not infected until its 12th passage or subcultivation *in vitro* by exposure to culture fluid obtained from a previously transformed line derived from a different patient. Similarly, a fibroblast-like strain from the skin of a mosaic mongoloid was transformed by application of supernatant fluid from one of the other mucosal-originated lines. However, it is conceivable that a few original epithelial elements could have persisted, since this material was infected in only its 9th *in vitro* passage.

The cytology of these viral-induced changes is quite interesting. At first examination our subjective impression was that the acrocentrics were most commonly involved; that is monosomy for a small or a large acrocentric. Monosomy for a small acrocentric was reported by Shein and Enders (1962) from the work of Yerganian as most common in SV_{40}-induced transformations of human foetal kidney cells. We have not yet statistically analyzed our findings so that we can exclude a preferential involvement of the acrocentrics, but a further listing of commonly observed chromosome changes shows that various specific chromosomes are involved. Chromosomes No. 1, No. 2, Nos. 4 and 5, Nos. 13–15, Nos. 17–18, Nos. 21 and 22 have all been implicated among eight individual transformations. Within each of these, usually a particular chromosome rearrangement or missing chromosome was most common, with other changes also present. Monosomy for Nos. 21 or 22 has been observed to some extent in various transformed lines as has monosomy in the Nos. 13–15 group. In four separate *in vitro* transformations of four cell strains originated from one patient, a similar marker chromosome has been observed. This marker, a long acrocentric, is presumably the product of a break at the secondary constriction of

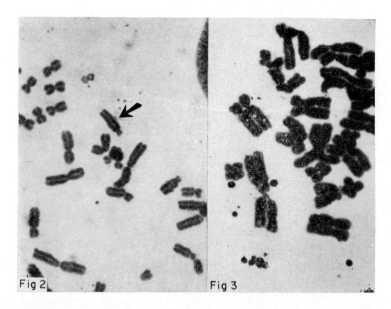

FIG. 2. Example of the long acrocentric marker presumably derived from one arm of chromosome No. 1. For comparison, note the No. 1 at lower left of field. From a metaphase of the heteroploid line W-18TRS which had been subjected to SV_{40} virus.

FIG. 3. Diplochromosomes from SV_{40} transformed line W-10TRS showing evidence of mechanical weakness at the secondary constriction of chromosome No. 1.

chromosome No. 1 (Figs. 2–3). Evidence is also present for the origin of an even longer acrocentric from chromosome No. 4 (or 5).

Most of the abnormalities observed could theoretically be derived from a postulate that the virus has indirectly interfered with processes involving the formation of secondary constrictions. Perhaps some constrictions have been affected to such an extent that they function as primary constrictions or at least may be structurally weakened so that numerous breaks occur during mitoses, leading to the creation of new chromosome types.

Our chromosomal changes were observed many weeks after the initial exposure to the virus, whereas the lesions observed by Nichols and co-workers were seen in cells taken directly from the body of the viral-infected subject. These authors (personal communication) suggest that dicentrics would not be expected to persist so long in continuous culture, due to anaphase difficulties, and that the numerous cases present in our material indicate a continuing process of structural breakage and recombination.

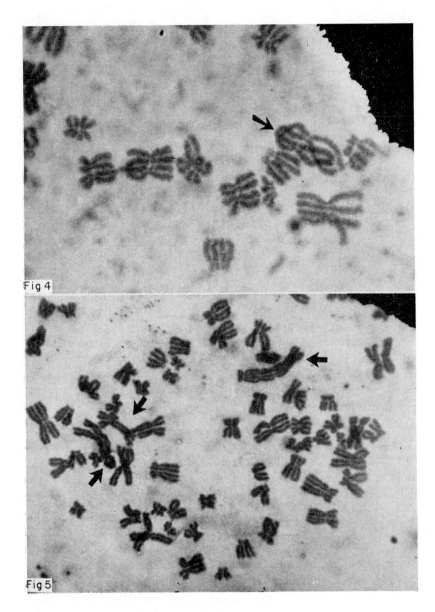

FIG. 4. Example of presumed "telomeric binding" or union of ends of sister chromosomes in a diplochromosome metaphase from SV_{40} transformed line W-1TRM. To the left is a similar case but between non-homologous chromosomes.

FIG. 5. Metaphase from W-1TRM showing two examples similar to those of Fig. 4. Note chromosome exchange involving three chromosomes.

Instances of anaphase bridges are readily observed in non-pretreated cell material from our transformed lines. A continuing process, however, could still be present since in these transformed lines virus is present and is replicating. The repeated observation of chromosomes of quite similar morphology may be explained by assuming that these represent very strong secondary constrictions induced both at known loci, such as that near the centromeres of No. 1 and No. 4, and at or near the telomeres of various chromosomes.

Further work has shown a great variety of abnormal chromosomes, but the following generalizations can be made: (1) There is a general increase in the number and degree of all types of secondary constrictions. (2) Some of these lesions or constrictions appear to be identical in locus to those normally present in uninfected material. (3) Many acentric fragments and "marker" chromosomes are interpretable as complementary products of breaks directly at these known constrictions (especially of chromosomes No. 1, Nos. 4 and 5). (4) Many apparently abnormal constrictions appear to occur at or near the ends of chromosome arms. (5) Diplochromosomes resulting from endoreduplication are increased in frequency, as would be expected from many more classic studies of abnormal cell material, and among these some show evidence of a kind of "telomeric binding" or union of the ends of chromosomes. Both homologous and non-homologous unions have been observed repeatedly.

The possible involvement of specific constrictions or lesions on the chromosomes with a virus capable of chromosomal transformation and cancer induction is encouraging in that either a site of viral action or an indirect effect of the virus is implicated. The extensive chromatid breaks, with few rearrangements, induced by measles infection may represent a much earlier stage of this viral effect and may provide us with a system suitable for the study of individual steps in the course of viral mediated tumorigenesis.

REFERENCES

BENDER, M. A. and PRESCOTT, D. M., 1962, DNA synthesis and mitosis in cultures of human peripheral leukocytes, *Exp. Cell Res.* **27**, 221–229.

COOPER, H. L. and HIRSCHHORN, K., 1962, Improvement in white cell culture including differential leukocyte separation. Symposium on Blood–Bone Marrow Tissue Culture and Cell Separation. *Blood* **20**, 101 (Abstract).

EDWARDS, J. H. and YOUNG, R. B., 1961, Chromosome analysis from small volumes of blood. *Lancet* ii, 48.

EDWARDS, J. H., 1962, Chromosome analysis from capillary blood. *Cytogenetics* **1**, 90–96.

ELVES, M. W. and WILKINSON, J. F., 1962, Effects of phytohemagglutinin on the morphology of cultured leucocytes. *Nature* **194**, 1257–1259.

FITZGERALD, P. H., 1962, The Ph₁ chromosome in uncultured leukocytes and marrow cells from human chronic granulocytic leukemia. *Exp. Cell Res.* **26**, 220–222.

KOPROWSKI, H., PONTEN, J. A., JENSEN, F., RAVDIN, R. G., MOORHEAD, P. and SAKSELA, E., 1962, Transformation of cultures of human tissue infected with simian virus SV_{40}. *J. Cell. Comp. Phys.* **59**, 281–292.

LEJEUNE, J., TURPIN, R., and GAUTIER, M., 1959, Le mongolisme, premier example d'aberration autosomique humaine. *Ann. Genet.* **2**, 41.

MACKINNEY, R. G., STOHLMAN, F. Jr. and BRECHER, G., 1961, Kinetics of leucocyte proliferation *in vitro*. *Clinical Res.* **9**, 163.

MCINTYRE, O. R. and EBAUGH, F. G. Jr., 1962, The effect of phytohemagglutinin on leukocyte cultures as measured by P incorporation in the DNA, RNA, and acid soluble fractions. *Blood* **19**, 443–453.

MELLMAN, W. J., KLEVIT, H. D. and MOORHEAD, P. S., 1962, Studies on phytohemagglutinin-stimulated leukocyte cultures. Symposium on Blood–Bone Marrow Tissue Culture and Cell Separation. *Blood* **20**, 103 (Abstract).

MOORHEAD, P. S., NOWELL, P. C., MELLMAN, W. J., BATTIPS, D. M. and HUNGERFORD, D. A., 1960, Chromosome preparations of leukocytes cultured from human peripheral blood. *Exp. Cell Res.* **20**, 613–616.

NICHOLS, W. W. and LEVAN, A., 1962, Chromosome preparations by the blood tissue culture technic in various laboratory animals. Symposium on Blood–Bone Marrow Tissue Culture and Cell Separation. *Blood* **20**, 106 (Abstract).

NICHOLS, W. W. and LEVAN, A. Personal communication.

NICHOLS, W. W., LEVAN, A., HALL, B. and OSTERGREN, G., 1962, Measles-associated chromosome breakage. Preliminary communication. *Hereditas* **48**, 367–370.

NOWELL, P. C., 1960, Phytohemagglutinin: an initiator of mitosis in cultures of normal human leukocytes. *Cancer Res.* **20** 462–466.

NOWELL, P. C., 1961, Inhibition of human leukocyte mitosis by prednisolone *in vitro*. *Cancer Res.* **21**, 1518–1521.

NOWELL, P. C. and HUNGERFORD, D. A., 1962, Chromosome studies in human leukemia. III. Acute granulocytic leukemia. *J. Nat. Cancer Inst.* **29**, 545–566.

NOWELL, P. C. and HUNGERFORD, D. A. Personal communication.

OSGOOD, E. E. and BROOKE, J. H., 1955, Continuous tissue culture of leukocytes from human leukemic bloods by applications of "gradient" principles. *Blood* **10**, 1010–1022.

RIGAS, D. A. and OSGOOD, E. E., 1955, Purification and properties of the phytohemagglutinin of *Phaseolus vulgaris*. *J. Biol. Chem.* **212**, 607–609.

SAKSELA, E. and MOORHEAD, P. S., 1962, Enhancement of secondary constrictions and the heterochromic X in human cells. *Cytogenetics* **1**, 225–244.

SANDBERG, A. A., ISHIHARA, I., CROSSWHITE, L. H. and HAUSCHKA, T. S., 1962, Chromosome dichotomy in blood and marrow of acute leukemia. *Cancer Res.* **22**, 748–56.

TJIO, J. H. and LEVAN, A., 1956, The chromosome number of man. *Hereditas* **42**, 1.

TJIO, J. H. and PUCK, T. T., 1958, Genetics of somatic mammalian cells. II. Chromosomal constitution of cells in tissue culture. *J. Exper. Med.* **108**, 259.

DNA REPLICATION IN HUMAN
CHROMOSOMES — A REVIEW

A. Lima-de-Faria

Institute of Genetics, University of Lund, Sweden

THE study of DNA replication in human chromosomes has been made possible by the merging of two fields of research which today are developing at a rapid rate. The first is the study of DNA, an essential genetic material; the second, is the study of human chromosomes, which, due to its relation to human disease, has attracted many investigators. It is thus not surprising that DNA synthesis in human chromosomes rapidly became a common point of interest for these two groups of research workers. Since we published our paper on DNA synthesis in human chromosomes (Lima-de-Faria, Reitalu and Bergman, 1961) a series of studies has appeared within the space of a year, the result of independent research at several laboratories.

THE TECHNIQUE

The technical procedure does not contain essentially new steps. It is a combination, on one hand, of the tritium autoradiography technique used for plant and animal materials and on the other hand, the squash technique and the air-dry methods used for mammalian chromosomes. However, a number of small details have been introduced and these will be mentioned briefly. Anyone interested in a description of the technical procedure is referred to Lima-de-Faria et al. (1961). The tissue cultures used have been mainly from peripheral blood (Moorhead et al., 1960), but HeLa cell cultures have also been studied.

Tritiated thymidine was added to the cultures either as a short pulse or continuously until fixation. The pulse was as short as 10 min and was administered at different times during DNA synthesis. When H³-thymidine was administered during a short period, the problem arose of removing the labelled thymidine, a difficulty solved in different ways by the various investigators. In some laboratories the labelled thymidine was not removed, but an excess of cold thymidine was added to the culture. In others, the, cells were centrifuged, washed twice with Parker 199, after which the cells were resuspended in a medium free of thymidine.

Colchicine was added before fixation. In the studies in which the H^3-thymidine was given as a short pulse and the cells were allowed to grow for several hours without tritium, the colchicine action on the chromosomes took place at a different time from the period of DNA replication studied. But in the cases where H^3-thymidine was present in the culture until fixation, colchicine and labelled thymidine were given simultaneously. In these cases one should take into consideration the effects of colchicine on DNA replication in chromosomes (review in Lima-de-Faria, 1962).

The chromosomes were stained by different methods. Among them were: (1) aceto-orcein staining, (2) the Feulgen method, (3) a combination of these two procedures, (4) Feulgen and azure B bromide, and (5) the Leishman–Giemsa stain. Human chromosomes are often stained with aceto-orcein, but this stain does not withstand well the autoradiographic procedure because of the effects of the solutions used in the development and fixation of the stripping film. The Feulgen procedure, on the other hand, resists the various steps of the autoradiographic processing; however, it has the disadvantage of removing the RNA from the chromosomes during the hydrolysis employed. As a result, the chromosomes have a less distinct appearance than in the orcein stain. Staining in aceto-orcein followed by Feulgen minimizes the disadvantages of both.

Another problem faced in this study is the inability to identify accurately the chromosomes when they are heavily labeled. Here two different approaches have been tried. In the first, the squash technique is followed by applying stripping film, and an autoradiographic image is obtained in which the number of silver grains is not too great. Information on the chromosomes and on the autoradiographic image is only obtained from this final combination (Lima-de-Faria et al., 1961; Morishima et al., 1962). In the second procedure, one uses the air-dry technique or the HeLa cell culture method. The metaphase plates are photographed first, the film applied subsequently, and after development of the film, the same metaphase plates are photographed once more. The two pictures of the same metaphase plate: one, for chromosome identification; the other for silver grain countings are then superimposed and compared (German, 1962; Gilbert et al., 1962; Stubblefield and Mueller, 1962; Bader et al., 1963).

RESULTS

The results obtained by the various groups of investigators may be summarized as follows.

(1) Experiments were carried out to determine the period of time between the end of DNA synthesis and metaphase. In pulse experiments where the cells were exposed for 20 min to H^3-thymidine it has been found that, after 3 hr and 30 min of contact with tritiated thymidine, only 17 per cent of the metaphase plates are labelled. Between 4 hr and 30 min and 5 hr and 45 min after exposure to tritium, 31–90 per cent of the metaphase plates became labelled. This is taken to mean that in human blood cells the interval between the end of DNA synthesis and metaphase is close to 5 hr under the conditions of these experiments (Lima-de-Faria *et al.*, 1961). German (1962) also found that DNA synthesis is in progress in most cells during an interval of 8–26 hr preceding metaphase and that from 4 to 8 hr before metaphase there is an abrupt decrease in the number of cells undergoing DNA synthesis. This decrease takes place mainly from the fourth to the sixth hour.

(2) Not all loci of the 46 chromosomes of the human complement are found to synthesize DNA simultaneously. In both short and long chromosomes, within each chromosome some segments are replicating at a given moment whereas others are not (Lima-de-Faria *et al.*, 1961; Morishima *et al.*, 1962; German, 1962). This conclusion was drawn by these various research groups on the basis of relative grain density.

(3) Not all the autosomes are replicating simultaneously. Two of the four chromosomes of group 21–22 replicate later than the other autosomes (Morishima *et al.*, 1962; and Gilbert *et al.*, 1962). Portions of two chromosomes in group 4–5 are also labelled later during the period of DNA synthesis (Morishima *et al.*, 1962; Gilbert *et al.*, 1962). This is also true of portions of chromosomes 9 and 13 (Gilbert *et al.*, 1962). Replicating earlier than the majority of the chromosomes of the complement are two chromosomes of the group 13–15 and two chromosomes of the group 19 and 20 (Morishima *et al.*, 1960). Bader *et al.* (1963) found this to be true for two chromosomes in group 16–18, presumably 17, and two chromosomes in group 19–20. In agreement with this result is the finding of an early replicating 17 chromosome as described by Stubblefield and Mueller (1962). Chromosome 16 shows also marked differences in the labelling of the two arms (Gilbert *et al.*, 1962). Morishima *et al.* (1962) and Bader *et al.* (1963) reached their conclusions by estimating relative grain density in different chromosomes and chromosomal segments, but Gilbert *et al.* (1962) and

Stubblefield and Mueller (1962) made a statistical analysis of their material.
Both groups arrived at essentially similar interpretations. Non-random
sequence of DNA synthesis along the length of chromosome 2 was reported
by Stubblefield and Mueller (1962). Chromosome 2 was divided into
five segments, two for the short and three for the long arm, and the number
of silver grains counted for each segment. Chromosome 2, labelled during
the initial hour of synthesis, yielded a grain distribution that was significantly different from the totally labelled chromosome 2. Segment "c",
in the long arm close to the kinetochore, synthesized initially at a relatively
slow rate while segment "e" was quite active in comparison.

(4) In the autosomes the two homologues of a chromosome pair have
been found to replicate at different periods of time. This is particularly
clear in the large chromosomes and in those chromosomes that can be
identified with accuracy, i.e. chromosomes 1, 2 and 3. In these three chromosome pairs one homologue has been found labelled in both arms whereas
the other is labelled only in one arm. The difference in the number of silver
grains in the labelled and non-labelled arm is as much as 12 silver grains
in the labelled against 0 in the non-labelled arm (Lima-de-Faria et al.,
1961). German (1962) has also found this to be true for chromosomes 1,
3 and 18. In chromosome 1, one homologue showed labelling close to the
kinetochore whereas the other had grains in the middle of the arm. In chromosome 3 he found one homologue wholly unlabelled whereas the other
homologue was labelled throughout most of its length. Chromosome 18
also had one homologue unlabelled while the other homologue showed a
heavily labelled segment. A third group of investigators (Bader et al.,
1963) have also found that the two homologues of chromosome 1 have
different labelling patterns. In one homologue of chromosome 1 DNA
synthesis occurred in the kinetochore region after duplication was completed
in the terminal part of the arm. In the other homologue the synthesis continued in the terminal region when the kinetochore segment had nearly
completed duplication. Gilbert et al. (1962) did not find an asynchrony
of replication between homologues. This may be due to the fact that their
experiments were not designed to test such heterozygosity. In order that
asynchrony be adequately studied both the duration of the H^3-thymidine
pulse used and the period of DNA synthesis studied (in this case only the
end of the period was analyzed) need to be taken into consideration.

(5) The sex chromosomes show also an asynchrony of replication of the
two homologues. In females one of the X chromosomes has been found
to synthesize at a different period of time from the other. This X chromosome
replicates later than most autosomes. Since the X is a chromosome difficult

to recognize with accuracy, a control was searched for in an XO/XX/XXX mosaic and in an individual of XO constitution. The XO individual did not show the late replicating X and in the XO/XX/XXX mosaic the late X was found in various numbers, and cells containing XXX showed either one or two late replicating X chromosomes (Morishima *et al.*, 1962; German, 1962; Gilbert *et al.*, 1962). In males the X was found to synthesize essentially at the same time as most of the autosomes (Lima-de-Faria *et al.*, 1961; Morishima *et al.*, 1962).

The results just described are based on a total of 6 males, 11 females, 2 individuals with sex anomalies, and HeLa cell cultures. The number of subjects studied is not large but there is good agreement between the findings of the different research groups.

The objection has been raised that the number of silver grains — necessarily restricted out of cytological consideration — is relatively low as to be indistinguishable from random labelling. However, in view of the general agreement of the results from different laboratories and of the statistical treatment made in specific cases this view may be questioned. Further statistical treatment of this matter is nevertheless desirable.

REPLICATION OF HETEROCHROMATIN
IN THE HUMAN MALE

Heterochromatin in the human species has been, until recently, described in somatic cells only in the human female (Barr and Bertram, 1949). In 1963 Lima-de-Faria and Reitalu reported the presence of heterochromatin in somatic cells of the human male. A male with 46 chromosomes, having a normal complement with an X and a Y, and no signs of rearrangements in the autosomes, showed in blood cells a very large block of heterochromatin. The block was found in most nuclei occupying about a quarter of the nucleus. Inspection of buccal mucosa cells revealed no heterochromatin.

The heterochromatic block found in the blood cell cultures occupied a central position in the nucleus, and it was particularly distinct in the large and medium size cell types. The incorporation of tritiated thymidine into these cells indicated that the heterochromatin synthesized DNA at a different period of time from the euchromatin, and that there was an intermediate period during which the synthesis of both chromatin types overlapped. The heterochromatic body was strongly Feulgen positive, and its number of silver grains was 2–3 times higher than that of the surrounding euchromatin (when both chromatin types were at their maximum synthesis of DNA).

The heterochromatic block at early prophase was seen to be composed of 5–6 chromosomal segments. When the nucleolus was stained in these preparations, the chromosomal elements that constitute the heterochromatic block were seen to be associated with the nucleolus but they were not a part of this organelle. The culture of the blood cells *in vitro* with phytohemagglutinin has an effect on their phenotype. There are difficulties in recognizing some of the cell types after three days of culture. It is possible that the occurrence of the heterochromatic block in the blood cell cultures may be due to the strong heterochromatinization of some of the autosomes under the new environmental conditions.

DIFFICULTIES INVOLVED IN THE STUDY OF DNA SYNTHESIS IN HUMAN CHROMOSOMES

There are several problems that make the study of DNA replication in human chromosomes quite difficult. These are: (1) the relatively large chromosome number, and (2) the difficulties in identifying with accuracy many of the chromosomes.

Humans have 46 chromosomes and this is the highest number that has so far been studied with tritium autoradiography. The analysis of the replication pattern of the 23 pairs and of the 46 chromosomes will take a very large amount of research before a coherent picture will emerge. The difficulties encountered in identifying many of the chromosomes are not easy to surmount. The finding of secondary constrictions at definite sites in the chromosomes, by using new fixatives, seems a promising line of approach (Moorhead, in this symposium). Once all the chromosomes can be identified with accuracy the study of the replication pattern will become much easier.

PERSPECTIVES FOR FUTURE RESEARCH

The number of published papers on this subject is half a dozen in one year. However, these may be considered as preliminary notes if it is taken into consideration the amount of work and the degree of refinement of technique which will be necessary before each individual chromosome and each homologue will be mapped. Following this task there are problems ahead which seem quite worthwhile investigating. The first is a study of DNA replication in cancer cells, to find out whether the replication follows the same or different patterns than those in normal cells. The second problem involves the study of different human ethnic groups to find out whether there is variability in the pattern of DNA replication as there is for example in blood group frequencies. The asynchrony of synthesis found among the different loci of the chromosomes of man may reflect genetic differentiation among chromosomes and along each chromosome.

REFERENCES

BADER, S., MILLER, O. J. and MUKHERJEE, B. B., 1963, *Exp. Cell Res.* (in press).

BARR, M. L. and BERTRAM, E. G., 1949, *Nature (London)*, **163**, 676.

GERMAN, J. L. III, *Trans. New York Acad. Sci.* Ser. II, **24**, 395, 1962.

GILBERT, C. W., MULDAL, S., LAJTHA, L. G. and ROWLEY, J., *Nature (London)*, **195**, 869, 1962.

LIMA-DE-FARIA, A., *Progress in Biophysics and Biophysical Chemistry* (Ed. by J. A. V. Butler, H. E. Huxley and R. E. Zirkle), **12**, 281, 1962.

LIMA-DE-FARIA, A. and REITALU, J., *J. Cell Biol.* **16**, 345, 1963.

LIMA-DE-FARIA, A., REITALU, J. and BERGMAN, S., *Hereditas*, **47**, 695, 1961.

MOORHEAD, P. S., NOWELL, P. C., MELLMAN, W. J., BATTIPS, D. M. and HUNGERFORD, D. A., *Exp. Cell Res.* **20**, 613, 1960.

MORISHIMA, A., GRUMBACH, M. M. and TAYLOR, J. H., *Proc. Nat. Acad. Sci.* **48**, 756, 1962.

STUBBLEFIELD, E. and MUELLER, G. C., *Cancer Res.* **22**, 1091, 1962.

Note added in proof

The study of the heterochromatin found in a human male has now been extended to 10 males and 5 females. The karyotype of these individuals does not present anomalies and they are of normal mental ability. In both males and females one can recognize the same large heterochromatic bodies surrounding the nucleoli of leukocytes cultivated *in vitro*. In cells of the oral mucosa the same heterochromatin (consisting of more discrete bodies) is seen in both sexes (Lima-de-Faria, A. and Reitalu, J., Heterochromatin in the human male, Symposium on Cytogenetics of Cells in Culture, including Radiation Studies, Pasadena, California, 1963, in press).

PROGRESS IN THE UTILIZATION OF CELL CULTURE TECHNIQUES FOR STUDIES IN MAMMALIAN AND HUMAN SOMATIC CELL GENETICS

S. M. GARTLER

Departments of Medicine and Genetics,
University of Washington, Seattle, Washington, U.S.A.

IN this paper I shall survey the progress made in attempts to utilize cell culture techniques in mammalian and human somatic cell genetic studies. There are two prime requirements for genetical analysis in any system: (1) an abundance of usable markers, or genetically controlled variations, and (2) mechanisms for genetic exchange and recombination within the system. First, I shall consider the variant cell lines that have been reported, then the studies bearing on the question of genetic exchange and recombination in mammalian cell cultures, and finally I will summarize these two areas and briefly indicate current problems and future prospects.

There are two general types of cell cultures that are being utilized in current studies. The established cell lines, such as the HeLa and L strains are characterized by the capability for continuous or permanent culture, ease of handling (comparable to microbial cell populations), general epithelial-like appearance, and aneupolidy. On the other hand, "normal" (parent tissue non-tumorous and not treated with carcinogenic or mutagenic agents) cultures are apparently not permanent, that is, they appear to have a finite life span,[1] are relatively difficult to handle, generally exhibit an extreme fibroblast-like appearance although they may occasionally be epithelial, depending on tissue of origin, and are euploid (number and karyotype as species mode). Although it is certainly possible and desirable that permanent normal diploid lines may be developed, none seem to be available at the present time.

In considering variations in cell cultures, we can begin with known mutants in the intact animal and proceed to the cell culture level, or we can

* Supported by a grant from the National Science Foundation (G14825).

start with a population of cells and through various selective and/or screening techniques look for variant lines. In the following review of variant cell culture types, I shall begin with a survey of the work that has been carried out on studies of known mutants *in vitro*.

DETECTION OF KNOWN MUTANTS IN CELL CULTURE

Three well-known human metabolic mutants, galactosemia, acatalasemia, and glucose-6-phosphate dehydrogenase deficiency, have now been studied at the cell culture level; galactosemia and acatalasemia by Krooth and collaborators,[2,3] and glucose-6-phosphate dehydrogenase (G6PD) deficiency in our laboratory.[4,5] In all studies, cultures were initiated from small biopsies (skin or marrow) from individuals with the appropriate genotypes. All cultures were of the normal, non-permanent, fibroblast type. After sufficient growth, cultures were analyzed for the presence of the known *in vivo* phenotypes. These studies showed that the known *in vivo* phenotypic differences of the various genotypes were detectable and measurable throughout the history of the cultures (see Table 1). Cultures from galactosemic individuals were not able to continue growth in the presence of large amounts of galactose, nor were they able to metabolize any galactose. Normal cultures were able to grow in the presence of galactose and to metabolize significant amounts of it, the single culture from a heterozygous individual exhibiting intermediate behavior. No catalase activity could be demonstrated in a culture from an acatalasic individual, but considerable catalase activity was found in normal and heterozygous cultures. We have studied three of the different sex linked mutants controlling G6PD at the cell culture level. These mutants *in vivo* are each characterized by a different enzyme level and in one case by an increased enzyme lability.[6,7] As can be seen (Table 1), the enzymatic characteristics of the cell cultures parallel those of the different genotypes from which they were derived. Four heterozygotes (Mediterranean type) studied could be distinguished from both normals and deficient cultures by their unique pattern of G6PD activity change with time in culture (Fig. 1), although the explanation of these enzyme activity changes is not apparent.

Another of the known *in vivo* genetic systems to be studied at the cell culture level is the human A:B:O blood group antigenic system. These antigenic specificities are present in varying amounts in many tissues and Högman[8] was able to demonstrate their presence in normal cell cultures derived from skin, utilizing mixed cell agglutination techniques. However, no more than 50 per cent of the cells in the primary cultures showed a reaction, and within

TABLE 1. KNOWN HUMAN METABOLIC MUTANTS DETECTABLE IN CELL CULTURE

Mutant	*In vivo* characteristics	Cell culture characteristics	References
Galactosemia	Deficiency galactose-1-phosphate uridyl transferase in homozygous recessive. Heterozygotes intermediate.	Known mutant cultures unable to metabolize galactose or to grow with galactose as sole carbohydrate. Normal cultures capable of normal growth and activity. Single heterozygote culture intermediate. Differences maintained throughout life of cultures. No specific enzyme studies.	2
Acatalasemia	Deficiency catalase in homozygous recessive. Heterozygotes intermediate.	Demonstrated deficiency catalase activity in single mutant culture. Heterozygote variable intermediate. Normal cultures show normal activity. Differences maintained throughout culture history.	3
Glucose-6-phosphate dehydrogenase deficiency	Negro variant RBC G6PD 15% of normal WBC G6PD. Approx. normal.	Negro mutant approximately same G6PD level as normal Negro.	4, 5, 6
	Mediterranean variant RBC G6PD 1% normal, WBC G6PD 15% normal.	Mediterranean mutant cultures G6PD about 15% normal levels.	
	Congenital non-spherocytic hemolytic anemic variant. Unstable G6PD.	Unstable G6PD activity in cultures from single congenital non-spherocytic hemolytic anemia case.	
	Heterozygotes in all cases variable.	Four Mediterranean type heterozygotes all detectable in cell culture by characteristic G6PD activity change with time in culture (Fig. 1). All differences maintained throughout culture histories.	

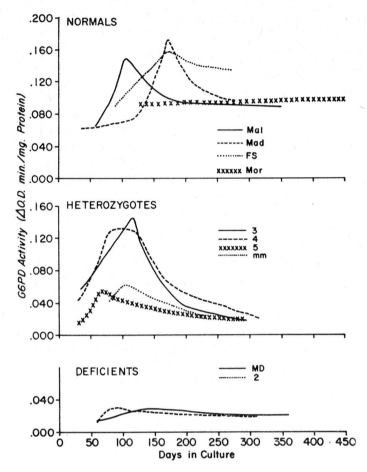

FIG. 1. Change in G6PD activity with age of cell culture for normal, heterozygote, and deficient cell cultures.

a few months of growth all of the A:B:O antigenic specificity of any particular culture had been lost. Specific antigenic reactions were detected only in epithelial-like cells, the fibroblast-like cells remaining negative at all times. Kodani[9] in a recent report has confirmed these latter observations which raises the possibility that the loss of A:B:O antigenic specificity observed by Högman could be due to the overgrowth of cultures by fibroblast cells.

In contrast to the lability of the A:B:O antigenic reactions in cell culture, Cann and Herzenberg[10] and Herzenberg[11] have shown that the specific antigenic character for three of the H-2 transplantation alleles of the mouse are maintained in established cell cultures. The antigenic characters may be detected either by hemagglutination techniques or by lysis of culture cells when mixed with specific antiserum and complement. These established cultures are apparently heteroploid and in at least one instance a culture was derived from a methyl-cholanthrene induced lymphoma. It is of special interest that the phenotype of this well-known genetic system has not been altered in this abnormal situation.

To my knowledge the reports on these five known genetic systems comprise the total reported work to date on the detection and study of known *in vivo* mutants at the cell culture level. From a general consideration of cell culture biochemistry[12,13] and from unpublished work in our laboratory, it appears that tissue restricted characters will not be detectable in cell culture with present-day cell culture materials and methods, or in other words, only cell autonomous characters with a ubiquitous distribution will be detectable. One would predict that the well-known genetic variants Von Gierke's disease (glucose-6-phosphatase deficiency) and phenylketonuria (phenylalanine hydroxylase deficiency) could not be differentiated from normals in cell culture since cultures from normal individuals would not have these enzymes. On the other hand, it is likely that orotic aciduria, and cystathionuria will be disinguishable from normals in culture.

It is possible in the case of organ-restricted characters that cultures derived from the specific tissue might exhibit the character in question (e.g. glucose-6-phosphatase might be detectable in cultures derived from liver). Several instances of cell cultures maintaining organ specific characters have been reported (hormone production in cultures derived from a pituitary tumor,[14] muscle cell formation in cultures derived from embryonic chick muscle cell,[15] maintenance of tissue specific esterase patterns in cell culture,[16] 5-hydroxytryptamine and histamine production by neoplastic mast cells in culture[17]). However, an equally impressive series of reports have appeared pointing out the general metabolic similarities between cultures of various origins[12,13] and the absence of organ-specific characters in cultures derived from the particular tissue (absence of liver specific enzymes in Chang's liver cell culture,[18] absence of human growth hormone production in cultures derived from pituitary glands,[19] and absence of various liver features in early cultures derived from liver[20]). That a general metabolic similarity exists between cultures of different origins is unquestionable. Assuming genetic equivalence of all cells of an organism, this is to be expected. It is surprising that any tissue differences remain under such leveling conditions as exist in cell culture, but there is clear evidence that in some instances they do and therefore the possibility of detecting an organ-specific character in a culture derived from the particular tissue must always be considered.

It is also possible that cultures not showing a particular character may be induced to produce the character in question under appropriate conditions. In this respect, the recent reports on the induction of alkaline phosphatase[21,22] by organic substrates in normal cell cultures and by certain steroid hormones in established cell lines may be mentioned.

USABILITY OF KNOWN DETECTABLE MUTANTS IN CELL CULTURE

It is of some interest to note which characters can, and which cannot, be detected at the cell culture level, and it seems that more intensive phenogenetic analysis at the enzymatic level might be possible with such detectable mutants. However, for the genetic applications we are considering here, detectability is a minimum requirement. More important is that the system be susceptible to selective and/or screening techniques efficient and accurate at the single cell level. Of the three metabolic mutants reviewed, only galactosemia appears to be immediately susceptible to a selective system — galactosemic cells cannot grow in the presence of large amounts of galactose. However, mixed cell experiments of normal and galactosemic cells have not been reported, so we do not know how efficient this selection system can be. The absence of primaquine sensitivity in G6PD mutant cell cultures and the leaky nature of this mutant (about 15% normal G6PD activity) appear to severely restrict obvious selective approaches to this system. Krooth et al.[3] have tried H_2O_2 as a selective agent for the acatalasemia system but have not been able to differentiate between normal and deficient cultures in this way.

Besides selective methods, it would be desirable if single cell detection or screening methods were available. We have used histochemical techniques to detect and measure G6PD in cell culture,[5,23] and can discriminate between deficient and normal cultures on a population level (Table 2). However, there is so much variability within a culture as to time and inten-

TABLE 2. PERCENTAGE OF CELLS IN A GLUCOSE-6-PHOSPHATE DEHYDROGENASE DEFICIENT (MEDITERRANEAN VARIANT) AND A NORMAL LINE STAINED AFTER A 1 HR INCUBATION

Line	Degree of Staining				
	4	3	2	1	0
Deficient	2	4	9	8	77
Normal	3	39	19	2	37

sity of staining that single cell quantitation by histochemistry does not seem practical at this time. Since in acatalasemia the enzyme deficiency is complete, histochemical methods might be thought more applicable, but unfortunately, the present histochemical procedures for catalase are not considered reliable.[24]

Aside from the problem involved in the loss of A:B:O antigenic specificity in fibroblast cell cultures, this system would not appear to be amenable to any simple selection scheme. However, screening systems utilizing mixed cell agglutination and labeled antibody techniques could be effective. The H-2 antigenic system in mouse cultures should prove very useful, since both hemagglutination techniques and lysis of cells by specific antisera can be applied as effective screening and selective methods. The specific cell lines described by Herzenberg[11] are permanent and cloneable which appears to make this system ideal. However, the heteroploid nature of these lines and the consequent possibility of mitotic instability may create some problems (see section on Development of Variant Lines in Established Cell Cultures).

With regard to the normal non-permanent cultures there are a number of technical difficulties which must be considered. The first is the problem of non-permanence. In our hands relatively rapid growth (generation time in logarithmic growth of about 30 hr) of these normal adult human euploid cultures lasts for about 7 months or even less (see Fig. 2). We have kept a

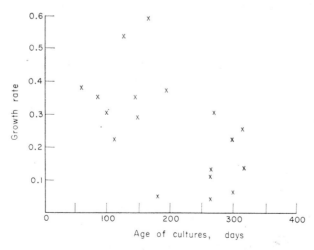

FIG. 2. Change in growth rate (relative values) with age of cell culture. Each X represents a growth rate determination on a single culture taken at a particular point in its culture history.

number of lines growing for one year and a few for as long as two years, but the rate of growth in the latter period is so slow (generation time of over 100 hr) as to make the cultures essentially non-usable for most studies. Freezing of cultures offers a partial answer[25] to this basic problem of non-permanence. However, a considerable number of cell generations may be used up in preparing a culture for freezing, and recovery often drops markedly with time in storage. If a large amount of starting tissue is available, enough early cultures may be frozen by utilizing obstetrical and surgical materials so that, in effect, a permanent culture of rapidly growing cells will be available. For most of the known mutants, only small biopsies will be available (about 10 cmm) with a fair proportion of the tissue consisting of non-dividing cells, and in these situations effective storage of cultures for long periods by freezing will be difficult. An equally important problem related to that of non-permanence is the difficulty of cloning normal cultures. Cloneability is a pre-requisite for highly effective selection and therefore of major importance. Puck and co-workers,[26] using exacting techniques, have reported considerable success cloning normal fibroblast cultures. However, even in their system, cloneability apparently drops off markedly as the cultures age.[26,27]

It is certain that the study of known mutants in cell culture will increase in the immediate future and new developments are to be expected. However, it must be admitted that as yet not even the simplest genetic study (estimation of somatic mutation rate) has been possible with these materials, one of the factors being the technical difficulties I have just mentioned and the other being that many of the detectable mutants are not easily subjectable to selective systems.

DEVELOPMENT OF VARIANT LINES IN ESTABLISHED CELL CULTURES

A number of variant lines from established cell cultures have been developed utilizing the relatively simple techniques of microbial genetics. This has involved either continuous or repeated exposure to the new environment (drug, virus, etc.) and the isolation and testing of resulting colonies for permanence of change. In Table 3 is a selected listing of such variant lines and pertinent features (these are permanent variants, in that after relaxation of selection, they still retain the variant trait). As can be seen, these variations involve resistance to purine analogues, resistance to viral infectivity, and variations regarding nutritional requirements. In a few instances, rate of appearance of variant cells have been estimated and these rates are in the usual mutation rate range. It seems clear that a considerable range of variations can be produced with the established cell lines and even more should be possible in the future as tissue culture media become better defined.

Perhaps the most thoroughly studied variants developed in established cultures are the cell lines resistant to various purine analogues. Such lines have been established with relative ease in cultures of human, mouse, and pig origin.[28-31] Where biochemical analyses have been carried out, resistance seems to be related to deficiency of a specific nucleoside pyrophosphorylase, which prevents incorporation of the analogue and also of the corresponding preformed normal purine. For example, Lieberman and Ove[30] have shown that 2,6-diaminopurine resistant lines are deficient in adenylic acid pyrophosphorylase and can no longer incorporate preformed adenine. Mercaptopurine resistant lines are deficient in inosinic acid pyrophosphorylase and cannot utilize hypoxanthine. Purine analogue resistant lines have also been used to estimate mutation rate, and in attempts at DNA mediated transformation which I shall consider later.

The permanence of change in these variant lines and the involvement of enzymatic differences suggests a genetic basis for them. However, a more convincing genetic analysis would require efficient genetic exchange and recombination mechanisms in cell culture, possibilities which are only now beginning to appear. One important aspect of these variant lines in established cell cultures is that of the possible role of chromosomal variation. It is well known that most established aneuploid cell lines exhibit a high degree of chromosomal instability,[32] and as can be seen in Table 3, whenever cytological studies have been carried out, chromosome changes have been found in derived cell lines. The basic question is whether these chromosomal changes are simply a reflection of the basic mitotic instability of established lines or are related casually to the observed phenotypic changes in the derived lines. A number of investigators[29,33,34] have contributed work in this area, but a definitive study is still lacking. Perhaps the most suggestive work is that of Harris and Ruddle[29] on cytological changes in aminopterin and[2,6] diaminopurine resistant pig cell lines. The parental established line, though diploid, has an abnormal karyotype and was derived from irradiated tissue. Both resistant lines show on the average a loss of 2 to 3 chromosomes, with fairly constant and distinct karyotypic patterns in each. Though the possibility of chromosomal rearrangement has not been excluded, the authors suggest that genetic loss is the basis of the analogue resistance in both case.

Unfortunately in none of the above cases has an adequate control been run, that is, cytological analysis of cloned unselected lines obtained at the same time as the resistant lines are being selected. Thus the role of chromo-

TABLE 3. CHARACTERISTICS OF SOME VARIANT LINES DEVELOPED FROM ESTABLISHED CELL CULTURES

Parent cell line	Phenotype of variant	Chromosomes		Rate of appearance of variant	Source
		Parent	Variant		
HeLa	Aminopterin Res 1	78	75	—	33
	Aminopterin Res 2	78	75	—	
	Aminopterin Res 3	78	76	—	
L cells	Puromycin Res	—	—	Sens $\rightarrow$ Res^1 4×10^{-6}	30, 64
	2,6DAP Res, Def AMPP	—	—	Res^1 $\rightarrow$ Res^2 1×10^{-4}	
	6MP Res, Def IMPP	—	—		
Human epidermoid carcinoma	6MP Res, Def IMPP & GMPP	—	—	—	28
Pig kidney	Aminopterin Res	37	34	—	29
	6MP Res	37	34	— x	
Detroit 98	AG Res, Permeability?	—	—	3×10^{-4}	41
	AGR Res	—	—	1×10^{-6}	
	AH Res, Def IMPP	—	—	4×10^{-6}	
HeLa	2-deoxy-d-glucose Res; fusiform morph., high alk. phosphatase	—	—	—	58
HeLa	Res poliovirus 1, fusiform morphology	78	70–76	—	57

					Ref.
HeLa	Res echovirus parental morphology	—	—	—	56
Human synovial	Res poliovirus 1, fusiform morphology	49–74	58–78	—	65
L cells	Radiation Res	64	60	—	63
Jensen sarcoma	Asparagine independent fibroblast morphology	—	—	—	62
HeLa	Glutamine requirement	—	—	—	60
L cells	Res human toxic serum spindle shaped	68	67–72 increased no. min.	—	61
Human conjunctival	Utilize xylose, ribose lactate as carbohydrate source	—	—	—	59

Res = resistant; Sens = sensitive; Def = deficient.
2,6DAP = 2,6-diaminopurine; 6MP = 6 mercaptopurine.
AMPP = adenylic acid pyrophosphorylase; GMPP = guanylic acid pyrophosporylase.
IMPP = inosinic acid pyrophosphorylase; AG = azaguanine; AH = 8 azahypoxanthine.
AGR = asaguanosine; min = minutes.

somal changes in the phenotypic expression of variant lines derived from established cell populations is far from clear; that chromosomal changes may be genetically involved is definite, and in no case has gross chromosomal change been excluded as a major genetic factor in such a variant line.

POSSIBILITIES OF GENETIC EXCHANGE AND RECOMBINATION MECHANISMS

A number of recent physical and biological studies have approached the question of the possibility of genetic exchange between cells in culture. The physical studies have essentially considered the question of DNA uptake by cells in culture.[35−40] The basic approach in these investigations was to label the donor DNA, expose host cells to the labeled DNA, and then examine DNA extracted from host cells for the presence of donor DNA. Methods for detection of donor DNA have involved radioautography, simple radioisotope counting, and separation of BUDR labeled donor DNA in a CsCl density gradient. In all cases evidence for cellular uptake of DNA as indicated by detection of label was obtained, and in one case cellular uptake of polymerized DNA was proven.[35] Incorporation of donor label into host DNA could also be shown, though it is not clear whether this incorporation involves polymerized DNA or simple precursors broken down intracellularly after initial uptake.

While cellular DNA uptake is a prerequisite for genetic exchange it is not proof that such exchange occurs. Operational evidence of a genetic exchange requires an associated phenotypic change. Several attempts at DNA mediated transformation in mammalian cell culture have been reported[9,40−43] and in one case[41,42] it appears that success has been obtained. Szybalski and workers[41,42] have reported DNA mediated transformation in an established human cell line resistant to 8-azahypoxanthine (AH). This line was derived by selection in a medium containing AH from a sensitive parental population, the basis of resistance involving a loss of inosinic acid pyrophosphorylase activity (IMPP). Upon exposure of resistant cells to parental DNA plus spermine, transformants occur with a frequency of up to 1×10^{-5}, the transformed cells having regained IMPP activity. No transformation occurred without the addition of spermine, a substance which can complex with nucleic acids and possibly protect them against degradation and/or enhance cellular uptake of macro-molecules by inducing pinocytosis.[44] There are three other features of this system which should be mentioned: (1) Reverse transformation has not been achieved (parent → mutant). (2) Another human DNA source (HeLa) is relatively ineffective at transforming

DNA; and (3) The rate of appearance of mutant cells (resistant to AH) is not increased by a variety of mutagenic agents (e.g. ultraviolet, base analogs). These latter facts warn against a simple interpretation of this transformation system (e.g. a specific infectious DNA particle could be involved), though there can be no question that a genetic exchange between cells in culture has been demonstrated.

Several DNA animal viruses are now known which can infect normal cell cultures causing morphological transformations and marked karyological changes.[45−48] Since the changes are apparently permanent and the cultures fully viable, these systems must be considered as infectious type genetic transfer mechanisms in cell culture. The viruses do not appear to induce specific chromosomal changes although there is some difference of opinion on this point.[45,46] At any rate, we must be prepared to find infectious agents which are specific for a single chromosome, and even for a very small part of one.

Another line of work demonstrating genetic transfer in cell cultures is the cell fusion studies in mouse sarcoma lines first reported by Barski, Sorieul, and Cornefert[49]. This work, which has now been verified and extended[50,51,52] involved the growing together in mixed culture of two cell lines originally derived from the same source but now differing metabolically, karyologically, and in their sarcoma inducing properties. Within a relatively short time (about two months) a new cell type was apparent in these mixed cultures. Cytological analysis indicated that the new cell type combined the chromosomal properties of the two parental types. Further studies of isolated hybrid populations (sarcoma inducing ability, etc.) confirmed their hydrid nature and gave some information on dominance: recessive relationships between the differing parental characteristics. Ephrussi[52] has reported that the hybrid cells are not stable cytologically, but yield populations which may gradually approach the parental chromosome number. If new stable types can be derived from these hybrid cells, then the above system may well be considered a mating mechanism. In a search for evidence of cell fusion in other cell lines, Ephrussi[52] has found one line related to the cultures involved in the original fusion experiments which will participate in this mating system, but has not been able to detect cell fusion in any normal cell lines as yet. Detection of hybrid cells is relatively inefficient, and it is possible that only when the hybrid cell has some growth advantage will a number sufficient for detection accumulate in the culture.

These various reports make a strong case for genetic transfer in cell cultures, at least in established cell lines. The reported mechanisms can yield some information on genetic relationships between alleles and permit the synthesis of new cell types. However, the most sensitive tool for elucidating genetic structure is recombination. At present we are in a stage in genetic cell culture work where we probably could not detect recombination even if it were occurring with some frequency. Detectable linked markers are essentially unknown in cell culture systems, and I doubt if recombination between a single marked locus and the centromere could be analyzed with present systems. As for physical evidence of the possibility of recombination, we can mention two points: (1) DNA mediated transformation in bacteria apparently involves a recombinational process[53] and if we accept the cell culture transformation report[41] as being of the bacterial type, we have the possibility of recombination in this mechanism. (2) Somatic chromosome association or pairing might also be considered as physical evidence of the possibility or recombination and at least one report has appeared on chromosome pairing in mammalian cell culture.[54] The report by Kodani[55] of maintaining spermatogenesis in rat cell culture for long periods is also important in this respect, and along the same line I might point out that we have occasionally noted what appear to be haploid cells in our current studies of bovine gonadal cell cultures (Fig. 3).

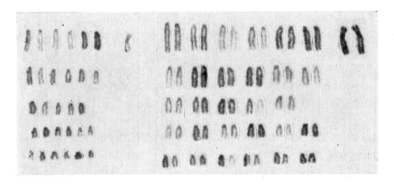

FIG. 3. Ovarian bovine karyotypes obtained from cell culture. Right: typical female karyotype; 60 chromosomes, only X's (1st row, extreme right) are metacentric. Left: karyotype of intact 30 chromosome cell with single X chromosome, possibly haploid. Right-hand print enlarged more than left-hand print.

SUMMARY

I have tried in this presentation to summarize for you the progress that has been made in the attempts to utilize cell culture techniques in the study of mammalian and human somatic cell genetics. Experimentation in this area is barely five years old. Two points stand out as positive advances in this early period: (1) abundance of variability in different lines (maintenance of known mutants *in vitro* and development of variant lines *in vitro*), and (2) mechanism of genetic transfer in cell culture: physical evidence for DNA uptake, successful DNA mediated transformation and DNA virus induced cellular transformation and fusion of cells to form functional hybrids.

Three problems stand out as important in terms of future advance: (1) finite life span and associated growth problem of normal diploid cell lines, (2) role of chromosomal variation in the phenotypic variants developed in established cell lines, and (3) the need for possible mechanism of somatic recombination.

The original impetus for work in this area was the desire to speed up genetical analysis in man. To many of us in this field, and perhaps to many in peripheral areas, it may appear that we have so far turned up more problems than we have solved. This is certainly true and was predictable. However, it seems to me that definitive progress has been made in a relatively short time and that increasing activity in the future may well bring us to a stage of productive somatic cell genetical analysis in mammalian and human cells.

REFERENCES

1. HAYFLICK, L. and MOORHEAD, P. S., 1961, *Exp. Cell Res.* **25**, 585.
2. KROOTH, R. S. and WEINBERG, A. N., 1961, *J. Exp. Med.* **113**, 1155.
3. KROOTH, R. S., HOWELL, R. R. and HAMILTON, H. B., 1962, *J. Exp. Med.* **115**, 313.
4. GARTLER, S. M., GANDINI, E. and CEPPELLINI, R., 1962, *Nature*, **193**, 602.
5. GARTLER, S. M., 1961, *Proc. 2nd Int. Conf. Human Genetics*, Rome (in press).
6. MARKS, P. A. and GROSS, R. T., 1959, *J. Clin. Invest.* **38**, 2253.
7. KIRKMAN, H. N., RILEY, H. D., Jr. and CROWELL, B. B., 1960, *Proc. Nat. Acad. Sci.* **46**, 938.
8. HÖGMAN, C. F., 1960, *Exp. Cell Res.* **21**, 137.
9. KODANI, M., 1962, *Proc. Soc. Exp. Biol. and Med.* **109**, 252.
10. CANN, H. M. and HERZENBERG, L. A., 1961, *A.M.A. J. Dis. Child.* **102**, 477.
11. HERZENBERG, L. A., 1962, *Fourth Conf. on Genetics*, Josiah Macy, Jr. Found. (in press).
12. LEVINTOW, L. and EAGLE, H., 1961, *Ann. Rev. Biochem.* **30**, 605.
13. LIEBERMAN, I. and OVE, P., 1958, *J. Biol. Chem.* **233**, 634.
14. BUONASSISI, V., SATO, G. and COHEN, A. I., 1962, *Proc. Nat. Acad. Sci.* **48**, 1184.
15. KONIGSBERG, I. R., 1961, *Proc. Nat. Acad. Sci.* **47**, 1868.
16. PAUL, J. and FOTTRELL, P., 1961, *Biochem. J.* **78**, 418.
17. SCHINDLER, R., DAY, M. and FISCHER, G. A., 1959, *Cancer Res.* **19**, 47.
18. AUERBACK, V. H. and WALKER, D. L., 1959, *Biochim. Biophys. Acta*, **31**, 268.
19. REUSSER, F., SMITH, C. G. and SMITH, C. L., 1962, *Proc. Soc. Exp. Biol. and Med.* **109**, 375.
20. SATO, G., ZAROFF, L. and MILLS, S. E., 1960, *Proc. Nat. Acad. Sci.* **46**, 963.
21. COX, R. P. and PONTECORVO, G., 1961, *Proc. Nat. Acad. Sci.* **47**, 839.
22. COX, R. P. and MACLEOD, C. M., 1962, *J. Gen. Physiol.* **45**, 439.

54   S. M. GARTLER

23. GANDINI, E., 1961, *Folia Hereditaria et Pathologica*, **10**, 61.
24. PEARSE, A. G. E., 1961, In *Histochemistry, Theoretical* and *Applied*, Little, Brown, Boston.
25. MERYMAN, H. T., 1962, *Nat. Cancer Inst. Monog.* **7**, 7.
26. PUCK, T. T., CIECIURA, S. J. and FISHER, H. W., 1957, *J. Exp. Med.* **106**, 145.
27. NORRIS, G. and HOOD, S. L., 1962, *Exp. Cell. Res.* **27**, 48.
28. BROCKMAN, R. W., KELLEY, G. G., STUTTS, P. and COPELAND, V., 1961, *Nature*, **191**, 469.
29. HARRIS, M. and RUDDLE, F. H., 1961, *J. Nat. Cancer. Inst.* **26**, 1405.
30. LIEBERMAN, I. and OVE, P., 1960, *J. Biol. Chem.* **235**, 1765.
31. SZYBALSKI, W. and SMITH, M. J., 1959, *Proc. Soc. Exp. Biol. and Med.* **101**, 662.
32. CHU, E. H. Y., 1962, *Nat. Cancer Inst. Monog.* **7**, 55.
33. VOGT, M., 1959, *Genetics*, **44**, 1257.
34. CHU, E. H. Y. and GILES, N. H., 1958, *J. Nat. Cancer Inst.* **20**, 383.
35. GARTLER, S. M., 1960, *Biochem. and Biophys. Res. Comm.* **3**, 127.
36. BORENFREUND, E., ROSENKRANZ, H. S. and BENDICH, A., 1959, In *The Kinetics of Cellular Proliferation*, F. Stohlman, ed. Grune and Stratton, New York.
37. CHORAZY, M. R., BALDWIN, H. H. and BOUTWELL, R. R., 1960, *Fed. Proc.* **19**, 307.
38. KING, D. W. and BENSCH, K. G., 1960, *Fed. Proc.* **19**, 308.
39. SIROTNAK, F. M. and HUTCHISON, D. J., 1959, *Biochim. Biophys. Acta*, **36**, 246.
40. MATHIAS, A. P. and FISCHER, G. A., 1962, *Biochem. Pharmacol.* **2**, 69.
41. SZYBALSKI, W., SZYBALSKA, E. H. and RAGNI, G., 1962, *Nat. Cancer Inst. Monog.* **7**, 75.
42. SZYBALSKI, W., 1962, *Fourth Conf. on Genetics*, Josiah Macy Jr. Found. (in press).
43. BRADLEY, T. R., ROOSA, R. A. and LAW, L. W., 1962, *Nature*, **195**, 304.
44. AMOS, H., 1961, *Biochem. and Biophys. Res. Comm.* **5**, 1.
45. SHEIN, H. M. and ENDERS, J. F., 1962, *Proc. Nat. Acad. Sci.* **48**, 1164.
46. KOPROWSKI, H., PONTEN, J. A., JENSEN, F., RAVDIN, R. G., MOORHEAD, P. and SAKSELA, E., 1962, *J. Cell. and Comp. Physiol.* **59**, 281.
47. VOGT, M. and DULBECCO, R., 1960, *Proc. Nat. Acad. Sci.* **46**, 365.
48. TEMIN, H. M. and RUBIN, H., 1958, *Virology*, **6**, 669
49. BARSKI, G., SORIEUL, S. and CORNEFERT, F., 1960, *Compt. Rend.* **17**, 1825.
50. BARSKI, G. and CORNEFERT, F., 1962, *J. Nat. Cancer. Inst.* **28**, 801.
51. SORIEUL, S. and EPHRUSSI, B., 1961, *Nature*, **190**, 653.
52. EPHRUSSI, B., 1962, *Fourth Conf. on Genetics*, Josiah Macy Jr. Found. (in press).
53. LACKS, S. and HOTCHKISS, R. D., 1960, *Biochim. Biophys. Acta*, **39**, 508.
54. WALEN, K. H. and BROWN, S. W., 1962, *Nature*, **194**, 406.
55. KODANI, M., 1962, *Records of the Genetics Society of America*, **31**, 96.
56. NAKANO, M., 1959, *Jap. J. Med-Sci. and Biol.* **12**, 79.
57. VOGT, M., 1958, In Sym. Genetic Approaches to Somatic Cell Variations. *J. Cell. and Comp. Physiol.* **52**, Supp. 1, 271.
58. BARBAN, S., 1962, *J. Biol. Chem.* **237**, 291.
59. CHANG, R. S., 1960, *J. Exp. Med.* **111**, 235.
60. DeMARS, R. and HOOPER, J. L., 1960, *J. Exp. Med.* **111**, 559.
61. FEDEROFF, S. and COOK, B., 1959, *J. Exp. Med.* **109**, 615.
62. McCOY, T. A., MAXWELL, M., IRVINE, E. and SARTORELLI, A. C., 1959, *Proc. Soc. Exp. Biol. and Med.* **100**, 862.
63. RHYNAS, P. O. W. and NEWCOMBE, H. B., 1960, *Exp. Cell. Res.* **21**, 326.
64. LIEBERMAN, I. and OVE, P., 1959, *Proc. Nat. Acad. Sci.* **45**, 867.
65. CHESSIN, L. M. and HIRSCHHORN, K., 1961, *Exp. Cell. Res.* **23**, 138.

MODIFICATION OF RADIATION EFFECTS
IN THE EHRLICH ASCITES TUMOR
BY OXYGEN OR SODIUM AZIDE*

C. B. DE LOZZIO and J. I. VALENCIA

Laboratory of Genetics, Faculty of Sciences, University of Buenos Aires, Argentina

EHRLICH ascites tumor ELD, a hyperdiploid subline with 45–46 chromosomes and 5 "marker" chromosomes, was irradiated *in vitro* with Co^{60} gamma rays (50r/sec) or with X-rays. The X-ray dose was given either concentrated (400r/min, 240 kV, 15 mA, 1 mm Al) or extended (30r/min, 145 kV, 6 mA, 1 mm Al). The oxygen concentration before and during irradiation was varied. The irradiated tumor was injected into C_3H/Ep mice, after which tumor growth curves were obtained by daily counts of the number of cells per animal. Chromosome aberrations (Fig. 2) were

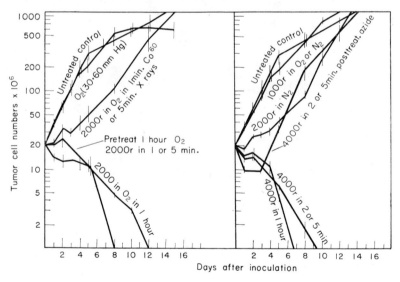

FIG. 1. Growth curves of the Ehrlich ascites tumor after irradiation with different doses and pre-treatments or post-treatments.

* This work was supported by a grant from the Argentine National Research Council.

scored in the same samples, and the cytogenetical damage was related to the inhibition of the tumor growth.

When 2000r of X-rays and the oxygen treatment were extended, so that the total time of the combined treatment was one hour, the effect depended upon the oxygen concentration. When the oxygen tension was high (30–60 mm Hg over the normal atmospheric tension) tumor growth was permanently inhibited, and all the metaphases studied presented chromosome aberrations. With anoxia or low oxygen tensions (10–20 mm Hg) the rate of tumor growth was slowed down, but there was no permanent inhibition. With anoxia, 19 per cent of the dividing cells showed no chromosome aberrations 48 hr after irradiation, while with low oxygen tensions, 6·6 per cent appeared normal at this time.

When 2000r were delivered in 5 min with X-ray or in 40 sec with Co^{60} gamma rays, and oxygen at high tensions (30–60 mm Hg) was given only during irradiation, the tumor growth was not inhibited; but when the oxy-

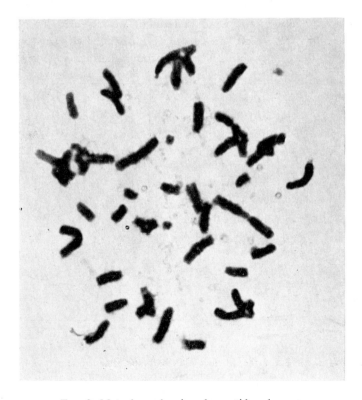

FIG. 2. Metaphase showing chromatid exchanges.

gen was given as a pre-treatment of one hour, the result was a permanent inhibition of the tumor growth. Oxygen by itself under the same conditions did not show any appreciable effect (Fig. 1).

Irradiation with 4000r always inhibited tumor growth when given in oxygen or nitrogen, in extended or concentrated treatments, but, when 4000r was delivered in 2 min from a Co^{60} gamma rays source, or in 5 min with X-rays (240 kV, 15 mA, 1 mm Al) and the sample was post-treated with 0·005 M sodium azide, the tumor cell population began to increase after the third day, reaching a total number of cells comparable to the untreated control. The animals died 15–18 days after treatment. This shows that some cells were protected from lethal damage by the sodium azide, thus allowing recovery of the tumor growth.

To determine the mechanism that modifies the lethal effect on the cell population, observed with the above pre-treatments and post-treatments, cytological studies were made, employing a lower dose (500r) of X-rays (240 kV, 15 mA, 1 mm Al) delivered in one minute. Pre-treatment during 30 min with oxygen at 30–60 mm Hg, or with 0·005 M sodium azide, increased the frequency of all types of aberrations, including chromatid exchanges. Pre-treatments with nitrogen did not produce any significant variation from the data obtained with the same dose alone. Oxygen at 30–60 mm Hg, delivered only during irradiation, increased the frequency of aberrations, but the increment was lower than that observed after pre-treatments with oxygen or azide. Sodium azide or oxygen at 30–60 mm Hg did not produce chromosomal aberrations when given without irradiation, while post-treatments with sodium azide gave results similar to pre-treatment with nitrogen (see Table 1).

These data suggest that oxygen and sodium azide given before irradiation at high dose rates might increase breakage and/or inhibit the rejoining processes, while sodium azide might protect the mechanisms of recovery when it is given as post-treatment after a high dose at high dose rates.

This increased breakage or inhibition of rejoining, produced by pre-treatments, could be due to accumulation of peroxides,[1,2] interaction with target molecules[3] or temporarily arresting mitoses at a radiosensitive stage.[3]

On the other hand the protective effect on tumor growth produced by post-treatments with sodium azide after a high dose at high dose-rate might be due to protection of some enzyme necessary for rejoining.

According to Schubert[1], respiratory inhibitors like cyanide combine with the deoxygenated form of cytochrome oxidase, increasing the intracellular levels of oxygen and allowing accumulation of peroxides. This phenomenon

TABLE 1.

Treatment	No. of cells scored	No. of aberrations per 100 cells			Aberrations per cell	Break per cell
		Chromatid and isochromatid deletion	Chromatid exchanges	Chromosome exchanges		
500r in 1 min	128	91·3	7	2·3	1	1·1
30 min pretreatment N₂ 500r	98	140	4	6·1	1·5	1·6
500r in O₂ in 1 min	110	217	21	5	2·4	2·6
30 min pretreatment O₂ 500r	100	341	44	22	4	4·8
30 min pretreatment Sodium azide 0·005 M 500	120	298	96·5	18·6	4·1	5·3
500r post-treatment Sodium azide 0·005 M	87	128	16	9·2	1·5	1·5
Sodium azide 0·005 M	46	8	—	—	0·1	0·1

might explain the increase of the damage produced by radiations that we observed with pre-treatments.

Nevertheless this author[1] considers that the complexing action of cyanide might protect oxidative enzymes from oxidation by peroxides, acting as protective agents. This could be the mechanism by which sodium azide gave protection in our case, since azide acts like cyanide on oxidative enzymes.

Modification of radiosensitivity by pre-treatments with chloramphenicol and post-treatments with cyanide or nitrogen have been found by Sobels in *Drosophila*.[4] He concluded that cyanide may produce either an increase or decrease of the mutation frequency, because two processes with contrasting effects were involved in repair of premutational damage. He first postulated that the enhancing effect of cyanide was due to accumulation of radiation produced peroxides, but afterwards he assumed that it is the result of interference with recovery mechanisms.

Wolff[2] says that cyanide and carbon monoxide increase the amount of chromosome breakage produced by radiations because they block the cytochrome system, increasing the amount of intracellular oxygen and thus of hydrogen peroxide present in the cell. But the same author[5] observed that these agents may increase genetic damage by preventing the rejoining of chromosome breaks.

Sodium azide and oxygen (in excess), may act like cyanide or carbon monoxide as respiratory inhibitors, thus increasing chromosome breakage and preventing rejoining. The mechanism of action is unknown, but it might be related to protein[6] or DNA synthesis[7] and/or oxidative phosphorylation,[8] processes which seem to be necessary for rejoining.

REFERENCES

1. SCHUBERT, J., *Rad. Res.* **14**, 499, 1961.
2. WOLFF, SH., in *Mechanisms in Radiobiology*, ed. by M. Errera, and A. Forssberg, V. I, p. 460, 1961.
3. ELDJAHEN, L. and PIHL, A. *Mechanisms in Radiobiology*, ed. by M. Errera and A. Forssberg, V. II, pp. 261–268, 1960.
4. SOBELS, F. H. and TATES, A. D., *Symposium on Recovery of Cells from Injury*, April 3–6, 1961; *J. Cell and Comp. Physiol.* **58**, Supp. 1, pp. 189–196, 1961.
5. WOLFF, S. and LUIPPOLD, H. E., *Science*, **122**, 231, 1955.
6. WOLFF, SH., *Am. Naturalist*, 94, 85, 1960.
7. TAYLOR, J. H., NANT. W. F. and TUNG, J., *Proc. Mat. Acad. Sci.* **48**, 199, 1962.
8. LEHNINGER, A. D., WADKINS, CH. L. and REMMERT LE MAR, F., In *Ciba Foundation Symposium on the Regulation of Cell Metabolism*, ed. by G.E.W. Wolstenholme and C.M. O'Connor, p. 130, Churchill, London, 1959.

EXPERIMENTAL STUDIES ON MAMMALIAN CHROMOSOME ABERRATIONS

L. B. RUSSELL

Biology Division, Oak Ridge National Laboratory,* Oak Ridge, Tennessee, U.S.A.

INFORMATION on chromosome aberrations in experimental mammals has been accumulating for decades: many important studies were carried out long before they could benefit from the recent great advances in mammalian cytology. The fields of research that have contributed to our knowledge are varied and include reproductive physiology, embryology, mutagenesis, and, of course, basic mammalian genetics.

It is hoped that a summary of this miscellaneous information on chromosomal aberrations in experimental mammals will be of interest to the members of this symposium. It should bring to their attention some potentially excellent material for cytological study. It may also help in focusing on certain genetic phenomena that could benefit dramatically from the cytological tools that have recently become available. Finally, it will suggest approaches by which experimental work could be used to elucidate some of the descriptive results from human material — results which are often tantalizing because they cannot be further tested.

Some of the material of the present paper is summarized from a recent extensive analytical review (L. B. Russell, 1962) which may be consulted for fuller discussion and detailed references. In addition, I have included results obtained since the writing of that review (most of them unpublished), particularly in the sections dealing with deletions and with X-autosome translocations. The paper is divided into two main portions. In the first, types of aberrations are discussed mainly from the points of view of mechanisms leading to them and effects on phenotype. The second section attempts to show how aberrations have been used as tools in a variety of studies in which the interest was not primarily in the aberration as such.

*Operated by Union Carbide Corporation for the United States Atomic Energy Commission.

I. TYPES OF CHROMOSOME ABERRATIONS

A. *Euploid Heteroploidy*

Euploid heteroploidy, which may be defined as the possession of exact multiples of the haploid set other than the normal 2n, has been the subject of numerous studies in reproductive physiology and embryology, particularly by Beatty, Fischberg, Austin, Braden, Edwards, Thibault, Pikó, and others (see Beatty, 1957, and L.B. Russell, 1962, for reviews). There has, to date, been no well-substantiated report of adult polyploid or haploid experimental mammals; and, in fact, no evidence of euploid heteroploid states other than the triploid exists for stages later than $3^1/_2$ days gestation. Following the use of heteroploidy-inducing agents (see below), triploids can still be found shortly after mid-gestation, both in mouse and rat; but examination of later fetal rats or newborn mice failed to show any. The reason for their non-viability is not known, although various suggestions have been made.

Abnormalities of egg maturation and fertilization observed which can potentially lead to euploid heteroploidy have been summarized diagrammatically in Fig. 1, which also shows the normal course of events (line 3, column b). Abnormalities affecting the maternally contributed chromosome complement include: expulsion of all chromosomes into first or second polar bodies (lines 1 and 2 in Fig. 1); "polar body suppression", i.e. retention in the vitellus of chromosomes that should have gone to the polar body (lines 4, 5, 6 and 7); and equal division of cytoplasm in lieu of polar body abstriction (lines 8, 9, 10, 11), an abnormality which is termed "immediate cleavage", particularly when it affects the second meiotic division. Immediate cleavage (line 8) is not too uncommon a phenomenon, and, if each of the resultant cells is fertilized by a different sperm, could lead to 2n individuals which are mosaic for paternal traits and may be hermaphrodites (if one sperm was X- and the other Y-bearing). Such a case has recently been described in humans (Gartler, Waxman and Giblett, 1962).

The most common abnormalities involving the paternally contributed chromosome complement are parthenogenesis (column a of Fig. 1) and polyspermy (illustrated for two spermatozoa in column c). It is apparently possible for three (and even more) pronuclei to come together at syngamy without resultant difficulties of division, and this may indicate that supernumerary centrosomes provided by extra spermatozoa are somehow suppressed (Austin, 1960).

The first cleavage normally follows shortly after syngamy. If cytoplasmic division at this stage should be suppressed, the resultant embryo would have ploidies double those shown for the zygotes in Fig. 1.

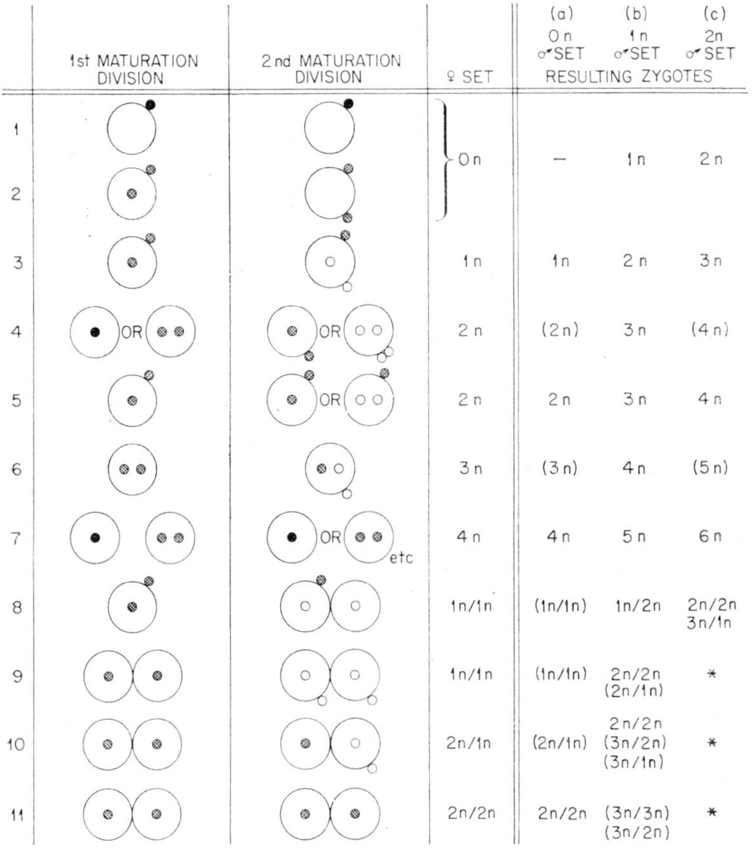

FIG. 1. Zygote ploidies resulting from combinations of various possible maternal and paternal chromosome sets (see text Section I, A). Unlikely combinations are in parentheses. (Failure of cytoplasmic division at the first cleavage would give zygote ploidies double those shown.) The designation 1n/2n, 2n/2n, etc., indicates mosaics. * = several possible but improbable types of mosaics.

Contribution from paternal chromosome sets is shown in columns (a)—(c) as follows: (a) activation without functional paternal chromosomes; (b) fertilization with 1 normal sperm; (c) dispermy. Fertilization with more than 2 spermatozoa, though possible, is not considered here.

Derivation of the maternal set of chromosomes is shown in the left portions of lines 1—11, with the normal situation represented in line 3. Shading of oocyte nuclei and polar bodies indicates number of sets: ● = 4n; ◉ = 2n; ○ = 1n. For diagrammatic purposes, the first polar body is shown on top of the vitellus, the second at the bottom. Possible division of the first polar body has been ignored.

(From L. B. Russell, 1962, Chromosome aberrations in experimental mammals. *Progress in Medical Genetics*, Ed. by A. G. Steinberg and A. G. Bearn. By permission of Grune and Stratton, publishers.)

Although, at first glance, it may appear surprising, certain abnormalities involving the maternal and the paternal complements actually appear correlated in occurrence. Most striking among these correlations is that between polyspermy and second-polar-body supression, a relation that can be explained by the normally existing interdependence between completion of the second meiotic division of the oocyte and sperm entry. Another correlation is found in the circumstance that agents that cause egg activation in the absence of sperm can also bring about suppression of the second polar body and may thus lead to diploid parthenogenesis.

Euploid heteroploids of spontaneous origin found among early mouse embryos have included ln, 3n, 4n, 6n, and mosaics of various types. Reference to the body of Fig. 1 will show that each one of these types could have had a number of different origins, particularly if suppression of the first cytoplasmic cleavage is also considered as a possible mechanism. There is some evidence that the spontaneous frequency of heteroploidy may be under some degree of genetic control, and the same is true for abnormalities of egg maturation and fertilization which presumably lead to this heteroploidy (Braden, 1957; Austin, 1960).

The frequency of abnormalities of egg maturation and fertilization can be increased by a variety of experimental treatments (for reviews, see Beatty, 1957; Austin, 1960; Russell, 1962). One of these is to delay mating until the already ovulated oocyte has aged, a procedure which causes polyspermy and second-polar-body suppression. Such delayed mating might occur "spontaneously" in nature, and could possibly be a heteroploidy-inducing factor in humans, where mating is not controlled by estrus. Cold shock as well as certain hypo- and hypertonic treatments have, in rare cases, led to diploid parthenogenesis through the combined effects of egg activation and second-polar-body suppression. More reliable in their effects are heat shock and the chemicals colchicine or colcemid, which can produce suppression of the maturation divisions, polyspermy, and cleavage suppression. The agent colcemid has, in fact, given frequencies of abnormal eggs close to 100 per cent (Edwards, 1961). Ultraviolet irradiation of spermatozoa can destroy the paternally contributed chromatin without affecting the activating function of the sperm and thus lead to gynogenetic haploids. X-rays are not as useful in this respect since the activating function of the sperm appears to be destroyed by the high doses required for chromatin destruction.

B. *Monosomy and Trisomy of Autosomes*

Autosomal trisomics have not yet been found among experimental mammals, but a number of methods have been suggested for their detection (Russell, 1962). These include cytological examination of animals bearing dominant "mutations" that produce rather generalized anomalies; the use of stocks carrying intermediate alleles in heterozygous conditions; and the use of closely linked recessive markers.

A number of different lines of evidence indicates that monosomy of autosomes is probably always lethal before birth (see dominant lethals, Section II, A). Thus, in specific-locus mutation-rate experiments (W. L. Russell, 1951; W. L. Russell, Russell, and Kelly, 1960), the two linked loci p and c (crossing-over = 14 per cent) have never mutated together. Double "mutations" of the two linked markers d and se (crossing-over = 0·16 per cent) have, indeed, occurred with considerable frequency, but recent cytological evidence (Russell and Woodiel, unpublished) has confirmed earlier indications (L. B. Russell and Russell, 1960) that these are never associated with absence of the whole chromosome bearing linkage-group II. Some of the cases of $d se$ "double mutants", including all controls, have, for reasons that cannot be discussed here, been assumed to carry two doses of the test-stock chromosome *(d se)* and none of the wild-type chromosome (Russell and Russell, 1960). Since this would imply that non-disjunction of this chromosome can occur spontaneously, the monosomic − if viable − should be found with detectable frequency. However, as already stated, none has been found, and radiation-induced $d se$'s appear to be deficient for relatively small sections of the chromosome. Further evidence for the early death of autosomal monosomics comes from experiments in which a relatively high frequency of sex-chromosome losses could be induced (see Section II, A, 3), while monosomics for any of five marked autosomes were not found among animals surviving to birth (L. B. Russell, 1961).

C. *Monosomy and Trisomy of Sex-Chromosomes*

XO mice are phenotypically normal females which are usually fertile but less viable than their XX littermates. Since their original discovery (W. L. Russell, Russell and Gower, 1959; Welshons and Russell, 1959) they have been reported by several other workers (e.g. McLaren, Cattanach and Kindred; see review, L.B. Russell, 1962). XXY mice are viable males of normal size, which copulate regularly but are sterile as the result of lack of spermatogenic elements in the testis (Russell and Chu, 1961). Such males have now been reported from several laboratories (review, L. B. Russell, 1962). In cats, the rare "tortoise shell" or "calico" males are probably XXY (Thuline and Norby, 1961). While both XO and XXY in the mouse can readily be recognized by the use of appropriate X-linked markers, it is doubtful whether XXX or XYY would be phenotypically detectable with the markers available at this time. However, such animals, if fertile, might reveal themselves by the production of XXY sons. The YO type is probably a prenatal lethal (W. L. Russell et al., 1959).

While the Y chromosome is strongly sex-determining, present data for experimental mammals do not make it necessary to assume the presence of sex-determining factors on the X. Activity of X-chromosome genes will be discussed in a later section (Section II, C, 1). The Y chromosome, in addition to carrying male-determining factors, is also responsible for production of male antigen. This was recently demonstrated by Celada and Welshons (Welshons, this symposium), using XO animals as well as the XXY male described by Russell and Chu. No other genes are known on the Y chromosome of experimental mammals.

Data on spontaneous incidence of abnormal sex-chromosome constitutions in the mouse have been summarized and analyzed (L. B. Russell, 1961). Relative frequencies, from crosses where two abnormalities being compared could be scored simultaneously, can roughly be summarized as follows:

	Absent chromosome	Extra chromosome
Y or X	+++++	+
X^M	+	0

The five "plus" symbols represent frequencies more than one order of magnitude greater than the single pluses. Since no cases of extra maternal X's are on record for experimental mammals, it must be assumed that spontaneous meiotic nondisjunction of X is extremely rare in the female. The presence of a genetic marker in the case of one XXY animal proved that nondisjunction in meiosis of the male had occurred (Russell and Chu, 1961). It should be noted that the very low frequency of XXY and relatively high frequency of XO in the mouse are the reverse of the situation found for these relative frequencies in humans. Virtually all XO mice of spontaneous origin have been the result of loss of a paternal, rather than maternal, sex-chromosome. It has been suggested (L. B. Russell, 1961) that the great bulk of cases of XO are not the result of meiotic nondisjunction or of chromosome loss during gametogenesis, but that most of them arise from events occurring between sperm penetration of the vitellus and the first cleavage.

The great preponderance of $X^M O$ over OX^P is explained by a more vulnerable state, at this time, of the paternally contributed nuclear material. It is of interest that in man, too, recent evidence points to the pronuclear stage as being sensitive to the genesis of chromosome aberrations (Lejeune, this symposium).

Since the XO-frequency is relatively high in mice, and since XO's can be easily recognized phenotypically by the use of appropriate markers, this type is a fine experimental tool. Thus, sex-chromosome anomalies have been utilized in studies of mutagenesis (see Section II, A, 3). At present, we are also using them to test for a specific type of interchromosomal effect for which some evidence exists in man (Lejeune, this symposium), namely the possibility that the presence of a translocation increases the probability of loss or nondisjunction of chromosomes not involved in the translocation.

D. *Duplications*

No cases of pure duplication have, to date, been reported for experimental mammals. There is, however, some evidence that at least one of the duplication-deficiency classes formed by segregation in translocation heterozygotes (Section I, H) may survive in a few rare cases. The only substantiated case of this is that involving an X-autosome translocation in which animals carrying a duplication for a portion of linkage-group I and possibly deficient for a small piece of X are fully viable and fertile if female, though quite inviable and small if male (Cattanach, 1961b). Two alternative explanations for this sex difference may be proposed. Either (a) the duplication is without deleterious effect, and the X-deficiency has an adverse effect only in hemizygous but not in heterozygous condition; or (b) there is no X-deficiency (as discussed later, Section I, J, the translocation may consist merely of insertion of a piece of linkage-group I into the X) and the poor condition of the males is the result of the duplication acting in each cell of the body rather than − on the assumptions of the single-active X hypothesis (see Section II, C, 1) − in only one-half, as in females.

In six X-autosome translocations studied at this laboratory (L. B. Russell and Bangham, 1959, 1960, 1961; L. B. Russell, Bangham, and Saylors, 1962; L. B. Russell, 1963), duplication-deficiency types do *not* survive, even in the female. This could presumably be due either to longer X-deficiencies, or to the possibility that the duplicated portion of autosome in our six cases is considerably more extensive than in Cattanach's case, where it may not be much longer than the 14 cross-over units between *c*- and *p*-loci.

E. *Autosomal Deficiencies*

Autosomal deficiencies in the mouse have been reported for three regions in three different linkage-groups (L. B. Russell, 1962, review); that of *waltzer* in linkage-group X; that of *belted* in linkage-group VI; and that of *dilute short-ear* in linkage-group II. Deficiencies in the last named of these regions have been subjected to thorough study.

The closely linked *d* and *se* markers (cross-over frequency = 0·16 per cent) were from the start included in specific-locus mutation-rate experiments (W. L. Russell, 1951) in the hope of detecting deficiencies if they occurred. Over the years, 25 *d se* "double-mutants" have occurred at Oak Ridge and four at Harwell. Relative to single *d* or *se* mutants, double mutants are relatively frequent in irradiated oocytes and postspermatogonial stages, but quite rare from irradiated spermatogonia. Of the 25 Oak Ridge cases, 21 have now been extensively analyzed (Russell and Russell, 1960, and unpublished).

With the exception of 6 cases, which are presumably homozygous for the test-stock linkage-group II and which have already been discussed (Section I, B), the double-mutants are apparently the result of deficiencies in linkage-group II. All of these act recessive with respect to the coat color and ear phenotypes; but, in the case of several, the heterozygotes are smaller than normal. All are prenatally lethal in the homozygous state, in all possible combinations with each other, and in combination with prenatally lethal *d*- or *se*-locus mutations. Preliminary embryological analysis by Miss Hunsicker of our laboratory (unpublished) indicates that the death of homozygotes, at least in some of the stocks, occurs prior to the time of implantation. There are some indications that some of the *d se* deficiencies may have a semi-lethal effect on gametes.

Mitotic metaphase preparations for eight of the *d se*-deficiencies have been studied by Mrs. Woodiel of our laboratory (unpublished). None of these, so far, shows any obviously shortened chromosomes; but ideograms are now being prepared in order to determine whether the deficiencies would be cytologically detectable on more refined analysis.

F. *Sex-linked Deficiencies*

In experiments on induction of sex-chromosome anomalies (L. B. Russell and Saylors, 1963), which will be discussed in more detail below (Section II, A, 3), presumed XO animals are first detected phenotypically by the use of sex-linked markers. Of 34 presumed XO's found in experiments involving irradiation of a variety of spermatogenic stages, 23 were analyzed cytologically. Of these, 18 had the expected 39 chromosomes. Five, however, had 40 chromosomes; and in at least two of these five, one of the 40-chromosomes was markedly shortened (see Fig. 2) (Woodiel, unpublished). It is

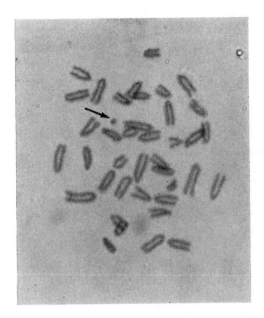

FIG. 2. Mitotic metaphase in a female mouse deficient for portion of the X chromosome as a result of paternal irradiation (L. B. Russell and Saylors, 1963). The centric fragment indicated by the arrow is presumed to be the deficient X.

suggested that these represent cases of X chromosomes in which the region bearing the marker loci has been deleted. If we are successful in establishing lines from these animals, they will be useful for a great variety of investigations.

G. *Intra-chromosomal Rearrangements*

Although several investigations have suggested possible cytological or genetic evidence for inversions, not a single well-substantiated case of an inversion exists in any experimental mammal. The only situation possibly suggestive of the presence of intra-chromosomal rearrangements involves the T-locus mutations in the mouse. These have been intensively studied by Dunn, Bennett, Gluecksohn-Waelsch, and their co-workers, and recently also by Lyon and Phillips. There is, however, also the possibility that some mutants at this locus represent deleted sections of chromosome rather than inversions. The whole problem of mutation and recombination in the T-region has recently been extensively discussed by Dunn, Bennett and Beasley (1962).

At this complex locus there are known a large number of recessive mutations, t^0, t^1, t^2, . . ., etc., collectively named t^n, as well as the dominant mutation T. The phenotypic effects of the various compounds may be summarized as follows:

$T/+$ = short-tailed
T/T = lethal prenatally
T/t^n = tailless
$+/t^n$ = normal
t^n/t^n = either prenatally lethal, or viable and normal-tailed, though frequently male-sterile.
t^n/t^x = normal-tailed, though frequently male-sterile (where t^n and t^x are different, t-locus mutations).

Dunn has assumed that the complex T-locus is a functional unit which, so far, has revealed its diversification only by complementarity. The t "alleles" differ in many properties: in whether or not they are homozygous viable; if lethal, in the manner in which they affect the embryo; if viable, in the relative fertility of the homozygous male and in the combinations (with other t's) which give male sterility; in the transmission ratios from heterozygous males (presumably affected by t^n acting in the male gamete); and in the degree with which they interfere with recombination in the vicinity of the T-locus (most of the lethal alleles suppress recombination, most of viable ones do not). The t alleles have, in fact, only one property in common — that of producing taillessness in combination with T.

One of the interesting features of mutation to new t alleles is that they have never been observed to occur in either $T/+$ or $+/+$ animals but only in animals already carrying a t allele (i.e. T/t^n or $+/t^n$), where the mutation rate is very high (in the order of 0·2 per cent). Grüneberg's (1952) suggestion, that newly arising t factors, rather than being point mutations, result from crossing-over in an aberrant chromosome region, seems to be supported (though not proved) by results both of Lyon (1960) and of Dunn et al. (1962). In both sets of experiments, animals heterozygous for t^n (almost in all cases a cross-over inhibiting allele) and carrying, in the opposite chromosome, T or + and the linked marker tf, produced gametes of the type t^x tf, where t^x was a new allele, usually viable. While this may be strongly suggestive that t^x alleles originate from exceptional recombination in the region between the T and tf loci, it cannot be taken as proof. Since the possibility exists that the cross-over inhibiting t^n alleles (which are presumably aberrations) in some way induce "mutations" in the homologous chromosome, it will be important to find markers on the other side of T from tf in order to obtain definitive evidence for or against the cross-over hypothesis of t mutations. It would also appear of interest to look for the complementary cross-over classes.

Dunn believes that the t lethals are a series of spatially separated inversions or deficiencies situated between T and tf and that only the "locus" for interaction effect (i.e. production of taillessness in combination with T) lies opposite T. When a recombination occurs within the aberrant region, it is thought to produce arrangements differing from the parental one in their effects on such properties as lethality, recombination suppression and male transmission ratio. Changes to viable, nonsuppressor alleles would involve recombination between the "interaction locus" and aberrant segments (Dunn *et al.*, 1962).

H. *Translocations: Degrees of Sterility*

Translocations in the mouse were first demonstrated by Snell in radiation studies carried out in the 1930's (W. L. Russell, 1954, review). Snell showed that, parallel to the situation in other organisms investigated earlier, translocation heterozygotes were "semi-sterile" as a result of some of their progeny dying *in utero*. This inviable progeny presumably results from the unbalanced gametes produced by the translocation bearer. The translocation hypothesis for heritable semi-sterility was confirmed by linkage data obtained by Snell (1946) and cytological data obtained by Koller (1944).

The types of unbalanced gametes formed and their frequency can vary in different translocations according to proportion of the chromosome involved in the exchange and according to centromere position. These parameters determine the relative frequencies of chiasmata in various locations — some of which can lead to more than, or fewer than, 50 per cent balanced gametes — as well as the incidence of nondisjunction. Koller (1944) and Slizynski (1957b) have considered these problems and have found fairly good correspondence between "fertility" theoretically calculated on cytological grounds, and actual "fertility" found in breeding experiments. (For a more detailed discussion of this rather complex problem, see the recent review—L. B. Russell, 1962.)

W. L. Russell (1954) prefers the phrase "partially sterile" to "semi-sterile" since it avoids any implication as to degree of littersize reduction. Several translocation lines with "fertility" significantly greater or smaller than 50 per cent have actually been found (Snell, 1946; Carter, Lyon and Phillips,

1955). The segregational explanations could account for either of these types. In addition, greater than 50 per cent "fertility" can result from survival of one class of unbalanced segregants, as discussed earlier (Section I, D).

One mouse result of interest in connection with recent findings in man is that female translocation heterozygotes appear to produce relatively more aneuploid gametes at segregation than do males, as indicated by their slightly lower "fertility" in most stocks (Snell, 1946; Carter *et al.*, 1955). In humans, a difference in the same direction, but of a more marked degree, has recently been noted in the progeny of male and female carriers of translocations that produce a viable class of unbalanced segregants, recognizable by their phenotype (Down's syndrome). As in the mouse, different types of segregation in the two sexes seems to be the most plausible mechanism. Originally (Hamerton, Cowie, Gianelli, and Polani, 1961), it also appeared necessary to explain a scarcity of normal progeny by assuming selective fertilization, such as is found for t alleles and possibly *d se*-deficiencies in the mouse (Section I, G and E). This scarcity of the normal class seems, however, to have disappeared in later data (Lejeune, this symposium).

One phenomenon awaiting solution is the occurrence, in some translocation lines, of a fairly high proportion of animals which are completely sterile, rather than partially sterile, and which are, by their genetic markers, diagnosed as carrying the translocation. It is not impossible that these represent an unbalanced class of segregants.

Another type of sterility that also has not yet been as fully investigated as it deserves to be is that occurring in a relatively high proportion of sons of males treated with X-rays or chemical mutagens (W. L. Russell, 1954; Cattanach, 1959). Most of these sterile sons are characterized by absence of spermatozoa, with the interruption in spermatogenesis frequently occurring at the maturation divisions. A somewhat similar situation exists in males heterozygous for any one of six independent X-autosome translocations studied by us (L. B. Russell and Bangham, 1959, 1960, 1961; Russell, Bangham, and Saylors, 1963). However, since, in the mutagen experiments under consideration, the sterile animals are *sons* of postreductionally treated *males*, they would not be expected to carry translocations involving the X chromosome. There are some indications that multiple complex translocations may occasionally interfere with formation of normal spermatozoa (Slizynski, 1957a). However, among those sterile sons of treated males in which meiotic metaphases can be cytologically analyzed, hardly any show evidences of the presence of translocations (Cattanach,

1959). Whether or not certain types of translocations are present in males whose spermatogenesis is interrupted *prior to* meiotic metaphase could, perhaps, in the future be determined in meiotic prophase, or, if the translocations are unequal, in mitotic metaphase.

Translocations have been widely used as tools in cytogenetic investigations and also, to some extent, in studies of mutagenesis. In this connection they will be discussed in Section II.

J. *Position Effects: Sex-linked Translocations*

Circumstantial evidence of various kinds indicates that position effects from purely autosomal translocations are probably relatively rare in the mouse (L. B. Russell, 1962). Variegated-type position effects, previously known only in *Drosophila* and *Oenothera*, were first described by us for the mouse in 1959 (L. B. Russell and Bangham). To date, seven independent cases have been discovered, six of them by us (Russell and Bangham, 1959, 1960, 1961; Russell, Bangham and Saylors, 1962; Russell, 1963), and one by Cattanach (1961b). All of them are the result of X-autosome translocations (Fig. 3). That the X is one of the chromosomes involved in the translocation is shown by the mode of inheritance of the effect, and, in two cases, by linkage studies with sex-linked markers. We have also shown, by a series of crosses, that variegation is the result of the rearranged position of the variegating autosomal gene, rather than being caused either by structural heterozygosity or by any change in the wild-type allele.

Figure 4 summarizes the types of animals produced in X-autosome translocation stocks. The figure also shows at a glance the difference in behaviour between the six independent Oak Ridge translocations studied by Russell and co-workers (indicated on the figure by R) and the translocation studied by Cattanach (indicated by C).

Translocation heterozygotes, carrying the recessive marker on the standard autosome (line 1 of Fig. 4) are variegated if they are females. In males, however, the wild-type allele behaves fully dominant, as if it were in its normal position. The sexes also differ in that while females show the typical partial sterility, the males of all six of Russell's stocks are completely sterile as the result of degeneration of primary spermatocytes in pachytene. It has been suggested (L. B. Russell, 1962) that this sterility could, perhaps, be due to some upset in the timing of synapsis or subsequent events. The X-Y bivalent normally does not behave synchronously with the autosomal bivalents; and the translocated chromosome, in having affinity both to the Y and to an autosome, may, perhaps, upset various relations of meiosis. It is notable that a very high proportion of T(X;A)'s in *Drosophila* have

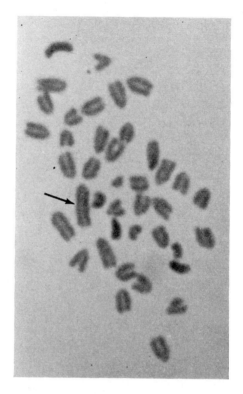

Fig. 3. Mitotic metaphase in a female mouse heterozygous for the X; 1 translocation designated R4 in Fig. 5. As is the case for all of our T(X;A)'s, the translocation is quite unequal. One of the translocated chromosomes is very long (see arrow); the other is probably one of the medium length chromosomes.

likewise been found to be male-sterile (Schultz, 1947). The one sex-linked translocation in the mouse that is not completely male-sterile is that reported by Cattanach, which probably represents insertion of a small autosomal piece into X (see below), possibly without reciprocal translocation of an X portion into autosome. If a piece of X has been transposed, it is probably very small.

In all six of Russell's translocations, crossing over between the rearrangement point and one, two, or three variegating loci has been observed (right-hand portion of Fig. 4) and is, in certain cases, quite frequent. This recombination has made possible a number of analyses, most important among which is that concerning the relation between the position of break point and variegation of locus. This will be discussed in a subsequent section (Section II, C, 1). Cattanach has not observed any crossing over with autosomal loci.

NON-RECOMBINANT		CROSSOVER (BETWEEN BREAK AND m-LOCUS)	
1 VARIEG. PART. ST. (R)(C)	WILD TYPE (R)(C) STERILE (R) POORLY FERT. (C)	RECESS.* PART. ST. (R)	RECESS. STERILE (R)
2 RECESS. FERT. (R)(C)	RECESS. FERT. (R)(C)	WILD TYPE FERT. (R)	WILD TYPE FERT. (R)
3 LETHAL (R) VARIEG. FERT. (C)	LETHAL (R) WILD TYPE, FERT. POORLY VIAB. (C)		
4 LETHAL (R)(C)	LETHAL (R)(C)		

FIG. 4. X-autosome translocation: as presumed chromosomal basis for varie-gated-type position effect in the mouse (see text, section I, J). Action of an auto-somal gene transposed to the vicinity of an inactivating portion of X chromosome is suppressed, thus allowing the recessive marker (on the intact autosome) to express itself in scattered regions of the body (= variegation). This effect occurs only when two X's are present. (Modified from L. B. Russell, 1962. By permission of Grune and Stratton.)

.... X chromosome
··. Y chromosome
——— autosome
m = recessive marker.
R = results of L. B. Russell, Bangham, and Saylors on six independent radiation-induced and spontaneous X-autosome translocations.
C = results of Cattanach on a TEM-induced translocation.

* Where m is an amorph (e.g. c, b), this type is of m/m phenotype; but where m is not an amorph (e.g. c^{ch}, p), this type shows variegation on an m/m background.

Another difference in results concerns the fate of unbalanced segregants. In Russell's six cases, both of the main classes of unbalanced segregants die prenatally. One of the two classes, however, survives in Cattanach's translocation, namely, the type bearing the autosomal duplication and probably a deficiency for part of the X (Section I, D).

Cytologically, all of the T(X;A)'s in the mouse have been studied in mitotic divisions. In mitotic metaphase, at least one, and in some cases both, of the translocated chromosomes can be recognized in Russell's translocations (Fig. 3). In Cattanach's translocation, one of the X's at prophase is seen to be somewhat lengthened (Ohno, this symposium). Various of the genetic findings with Cattanach's translocation, as mentioned, indicated that only relatively small pieces of the chromosomes were exchanged. If only a single break were assumed for linkage group I, however, the piece of autosome involved would have to be a rather long one. For this reason it seemed probable that the translocation was not a simple reciprocal one (L. B. Russell, 1962). Cytological investigations now indicate that there is indeed a piece of linkage-group I inserted in the X (Ohno, this symposium).

X-autosome translocations have had a large part in developing theories about the activity of the mammalian X chromosome. They will be discussed again in this connection (Section II, C, 1).

II. THE USE OF CHROMOSOME ABERRATIONS AS TOOLS IN OTHER INVESTIGATIONS

A. *Studies in Mutagenesis*

Chromosome aberrations of various types have been extensively used in studies on mutagenesis, where they provide an index of chromosome breakage. Many of these studies are comparative: comparisons of doses, of conditions of treatment, and of germ-cell stages treated, all have been made. Others involve the testing of new agents for mutagenecity. Among the aberrations most frequently used are dominant lethals, translocations, deletions, and, more recently, sex-chromosome losses. Attempts have also been made to induce nondisjunction (L. B. Russell and Saylors, 1963).

Dominant lethals have not been considered as a separate category in Section I because they are probably a composite class that cannot be studied genetically and has not been studied cytologically. Information on this group of aberrations will be briefly reviewed here before mutagenic studies are discussed.

1. *Dominant lethals.* The class of "dominant lethals" probably includes a variety of aberrations which cause early embryonic death of first-generation offspring of the treated animal. A high percentage of these deaths are probably the result of chromosome loss. Thus, breakage of single chromosomes in parental germ cells is assumed, in most cases, to result in elimination of these chromosomes during cleavage divisions by formation of bridges and fragments. The same is true of asymmetrical exchanges. The eliminated chromatin forms "sub-nuclei" which can be seen in early blastomeres. Already in the 1930's such sub-nuclei were shown by Hertwig and Brenneke to occur following irradiation of various male germ-cell stages (W. L. Russell, 1954, review); more recently, following irradiation of oocytes, they have been found by us with almost sufficient frequency to account for the deficit in the number of viable offspring (L. B. Russell and Russell, 1954, 1956). Evidence that monosomy for any one or more autosomes would probably act as a dominant lethal has been discussed (Section I, B).

As already shown in the pioneer studies of the 1930's (W. L. Russell, 1954, review) and fully confirmed in more recent experiments (L. B. Russell, 1962, review), death from dominant lethals occurs no later than shortly following implantation of the embryo into the uterus, and the actual time span over which the deaths are distributed may be very short. A number of separate investigations have indicated that the proportion of embryos dying before implantation and not eliciting a deciduomatal reaction increases with dose (W. L. Russell *et al.*, 1954; Bateman, 1958, etc.). These results are in keeping with Lea's (1947) suggestion that the length of survival of the embryo is inversely related to the number of chromosome breaks induced in the parental germ-cell. Bateman (1958) found the data to fit the assumption that all single-break embryos as well as one-quarter of the multi-break embryos are capable of forming deciduomata.

The many factors which contribute to the complexities of dominant lethal experiments in the mammalian (viviparous) female have been critically examined in various experiments (L. B. Russell, 1962, review). One complication that had not been suspected prior to the start of that work was the induction by radiation of superovulation. We were, however, able to show that there was no interference with normal fertilization and cleavage even among superovulated eggs; and that most, if not all, of the death of embryos following irradiation could be accounted for by chromosome aberrations presumably resulting from breaks induced in primary oocytes (L. B. Russell and Russell, 1954, 1956; L. B. Russell, 1962).

2. *Tests of mutagenic agents and comparison of conditions of mutagenesis.*

Most of the early studies made to measure induced chromosome-breakage frequencies in mammalian germ cells were carried out with acute X-irradiation in air. Both dominant lethals and translocations were utilized as indices of breakage (W. L. Russell, 1954, review). More recently, various investigators have carried out a number of comparisons of different types and conditions of irradiation, using primarily dominant lethals (L. B. Russell 1962, review). Thus, the effect of lowering environmental oxygen tension during acute X-irradiation, both of spermatozoa and oocytes, has been investigated; the effect of varying dose rate of radiation in postspermatogonial germ-cells has been studied; several different types of radiation—neutrons, gamma, ultraviolet—have been compared with X-rays, and, among neutrons, different radiation qualities have been tested. Recently, the genetic effects of tritiated thymidine (Bateman and Chandley, 1962) and of radioactive strontium (Lüning, 1963) have been explored by means of dominant lethal studies. Among chemicals tested for the induction of chromosome-breakage in germ-cells, are trypaflavine, toluidine blue, nitrogen mustard, and TEM. The first two gave confusing or negative results; but the last two have been effective, and TEM in particular has been studied in some detail, both for dominant lethal and translocation induction.

3. *Effect of germ-cell stage on induction of chromosome aberrations.* It was already shown by the pioneer workers in the field of mammalian radiation genetics that there is a change in dominant lethal and translocation frequencies with time after irradiation of the male (W. L. Russell, 1954, review). Since that time, dominant lethals have been used extensively to compare sensitivities of various male germ-cell stages to radiation (W. L. Russell and co-workers, Bateman), and to TEM (Cattanach and Edwards, Bateman); and translocations have been similarly used, but to a lesser extent, by Auerbach and co-workers, and by Griffen. Both of these types of aberrations have also been studied in the female with regard to oocyte stage irradiated by L. B. Russell and co-workers. (For detailed discussion and references, see L. B. Russell, 1962, review.) Specific-locus experiments have provided information concerning the relative frequencies of deficiencies induced by irradiation in various germ-cell stages of both sexes (L. B. Russell and Russell, 1960). Cytological studies have been used to compare frequencies of chromosome aberrations induced in various stages of the primary spermatocyte (Oakberg and Di Minno, 1960). Most recently, the sex-chromosome anomalies have been used extensively for germ-cell stage comparisons (L. B. Russell and Saylors, 1960, 1961, 1962, 1963; L. B. Russell, 1961). Included with germ-cells is the pronuclear stage

of the "zygote", on the rationale that fertilization is not completed until syngamy occurs (just prior to the first cleavage).

All of the studies on the induction of chromosome aberrations in relation to germ-cell stage treated have, in recent years, become much more meaningful as the result of the information obtained by Oakberg (1963) and others in extensive studies on time relations in spermatogenesis and oogenesis. Oakberg's work has also provided a great deal of information on sensitivities of the various stages to direct killing effects (i.e. death presumably from causes other than aneuploidy). The various germ-cell comparisons that have been made are summarized in a semi-quantitative comparison in Table 1.

TABLE 1. SEMI-QUANTITATIVE COMPARISON OF GERM-CELL STAGES IN THE MOUSE WITH REGARD TO RADIATION-INDUCED "NONGENETIC" CELL DEATH AND CHROMOSOME ABERRATIONS. SUMMARY OF RESULTS OF SEVERAL INVESTIGATORS*

		"Non-genetic" death (from causes other than aneuploidy)	Chromosome breakage in surviving cells
Spermatogonia A		+ + + + + +, +	0 to +
Spermatogonia B		+ + + + + +	not recovered
Spermatocytes, prophase	early	+ +	+
	mid	+ + +	+ + (?)
	late	+ +	+
metaphase I		+	?
Spermatids		0	+ + +
Spermatozoa, testis †		0	+
Spermatozoa, vas		0	+ +
Pronucleus, early zygote		0 (?)	+ + + + + +
Pronucleus, mid zygote		0 (?)	+ + +
Oogonia		?	?
Oocytes, prophase	very early	+ (?)	0 (?)
	early to mid	+ (?)	+ + (?)
	through diplotene	+ + (?)	0 (?)
	dictyate	+ + + + + + →0	+ + (mature)
metaphase I		0	+ + + + + +
Pronucleus, early zygote		0 (?)	+ + + + + +
Pronucleus, mid zygote		0 (?)	0 (?)

* From L. B. Russell and C. L. Saylors, 1963.
† According to a convention adopted recently, all stages of spermiogenesis in the testis are classified as spermatid stages.

The chromosome aberration results may be summarized as follows. The most extreme sensitivity occurs in meiotic metaphase-I of the oocyte and spermatocyte, and in both paternally and maternally contributed chromosomes of the early pronuclear stage of the zygote. At least two of these highly sensitive stages are separated by only a few hours from relatively insensitive ones. Thus, dominant lethal frequency induced in oocytes is smaller by a factor of 5 or more when one irradiates about 8 hr prior to metaphase-I (dictyate stage) (L. B. Russell and Russell, 1956); similarly, sex-chromosome loss frequency from irradiation of the pronuclei of the *mid*-zygote is only one-tenth that obtained from irradiation of the early zygote (Russell and Saylors, 1960; L. B. Russell, 1961).

By far the smallest yield of all chromosome aberrations is obtained from spermatogonia. During spermatogenesis, spermatids yield the highest rate of chromosome-breakage; and spermatocytes, as a group, are approximately equal to spermatozoa in aberration yield, although spermatocytes irradiated in the middle period of development may approach spermatids in induced XO frequency. There are, however, a number of factors that complicate the comparison between spermatocytes and postreductional stages. Prophase oocytes (for which one has to irradiate fetal stages) may resemble spermatocytes in sensitivity, but the information is not very extensive to date. The whole problem of germ-cell comparisons in the mouse has been discussed in considerable detail in another recent publication (L. B. Russell and Saylors, 1963).

B. *Translocations as Tools in Chromosome Mapping*

Two prerequisites had to be fulfilled before translocations could be used in genetic mapping. One of these was adequate cytological analysis of translocations; the other was the genetic localization of translocation breaks in known linkage-groups. Cytologically, translocations have, since the time of Koller's work (1944), been studied in the first meiotic division of the male, in stages from late diplotene through anaphase. An improved rapid technique has recently been reported (Welshons, Gibson and Scandlyn, 1962). For certain more detailed cytogenetic studies, pachytene analyses have been carried out by Slizynski and by Griffen and have most recently been perfected by J. Valencia (this symposium). Unequal translocations can also be seen in mitotic metaphases where they have been described by Ford and co-workers, and by L. B. Russell and co-workers (Fig 3). Genetic localization of translocation breaks was first achieved by Snell (1946), who "tagged" three translocations, and, later, by Carter and co-workers (1955, 1956) who tagged eleven with genes having visible phenotypes.

By using the tagged translocations, Slizynski (1957a) was able to show that ten different linkage groups in the mouse were actually located in ten different chromosomes. This was accomplished by making almost all the possible crosses between the different translocation lines and then studying meiotic metaphase of the offspring (heterozygous for two different tagged translocations) to see if two, three, or four chromosomes were involved in translocation configurations. Slizynski was also able to associate particular linkage groups with particular pachytene chromosomes, which he had characterized earlier on the basis of their chromomeric patterns. This was accomplished by identifying the chromosomes involved in the typical cross-type configuration found at pachytene in translocation heterozygotes. Among other things, this method quickly showed itself useful in disproving an earlier suggestion that one of the linkage groups was partially sex-linked. As a final refinement, Slizynski tentatively located several of the genes that had been used in tagging the translocations in certain chromomeres of the pachytene chromosomes. He also attempted to determine position of the centromeres in the pachytene chromosomes and, from this, to draw conclusions concerning their relation to the mapped loci. The centromere locations are, however, doubtful.

To a limited degree, it will, perhaps, soon be possible to locate linkage groups in certain mitotic metaphase chromosomes also. This may be possible for at least some of the very unequal translocations involving known linkage groups, such as Carter's T6 (studied by Ford *et al.*, 1956) and our six sex-linked translocations (Section I, J, above).

C. *Chromosome Aberrations as Tools in Studying Gene Action*

1. *Evidence from X-autosome translocations and theories of genetic activity of the X.* The finding that females heterozygous for T(X;A) but lacking the standard X (i.e. XO with respect to sex-chromosomes) were wild-type rather than variegated, resembling in this respect male translocation heterozygotes (L. B. Russell and Bangham, 1960, 1961), led us to suggest that, in the mouse, two X chromosomes were necessary to produce the V-type position effect. This suggestion was later strengthened by the finding of a complementary type (Cattanach, 1961a, b), i.e. translocation heterozygous males which were XXY and variegated. By relating these findings to certain cytological observations (particularly the n-1 rule for sex chromatin, and the heteromorphic nature of the X chromosomes in cell divisions), we developed the following hypothesis (L. B. Russell, 1961): the mammalian X has the potentiality of being largely heteropycnotic in somatic cells; however, genic balance requires the action of *one* X so that only *additional* X's present assume the heteropycnotic properties, one of these being the production of V-type position effect. Influences from X heterochromatin

suppress nearby autosomal genes, allowing the recessives on the standard autosome to express themselves. Shortly afterwards, Lyon (1961) proposed a somewhat similar theory which suggested that one or the other X chromosome is entirely inactive in all somatic cells, this differentiation to inactivity occurring early during embryological development. Lyon explains the V-type position effects by assuming that any portions of autosome attached by translocation to portions of X completely share that X's characteristic inactivity in half the cells of the body.

The single-active-X hypothesis, in its simplest form, would imply that, for any given autosomal locus, variegation characteristics should be *independent* of the position of the X and autosome break points. In the work with our six X-autosome translocations, however, we have obtained evidence to the contrary (L. B. Russell, Bangham, and Saylors, 1962; L B. Russell, 1963).

According to present indications, the position of rearrangement points in linkage groups I and VIII may tentatively be assigned as shown in Fig. 5.

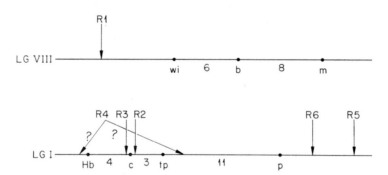

FIG. 5. Tentative location of autosomal break points for the six X-autosome translocations reported by L. B. Russell and co-workers. The X chromosome break point in the case of R1 gives 7 per cent crossing over with *Ta*.

The amount of variegation with various loci has been tested in different crosses and any case of failure of variegation has been checked to rule out other possibilities. All of these studies indicate that variegation is *not* independent of location of break points as would be implied by the single-active-X hypothesis in its simplest form.

(a) Apparently, not the entire X has inactivating functions. Thus, the c-locus, which shows typical variegation in four of the translocations involving linkage-group I (R3, R4, R5, and R6), fails to do so in the fifth (R2), even though the break point is less than 0·2 cross-over units from the locus. (Similarly there is no variegation for m in R1. However, in the case of m, it is not known whether gene action is such that variegation can be expressed. Furthermore, the locus is quite distant from the breakpoint — see below.)

(b) Inactivating portions of the X exert their influence along a gradient. Thus, the *amount* of variegation for a given locus differs for different translocations, one factor being distance of locus from rearrangement point. Furthermore, we observed a typical spreading effect for three of the translocations in that most mutant patches appear to be the color of the marker nearest to the break, and some the color of both markers, but none, to date, the color of the distant marker only. Such an effect has also been reported by Cattanach (1961b).

The finding that part of the X has no ability to inactivate translocated autosome suggests that this part may itself never become inactive and, therefore, not fit the single-active-X hypothesis. Thus, the results with the X-autosome translocations suggest that only certain regions of the X are inactivating and that this inactivation proceeds in a gradient from these regions.

2. *Influence of the Y chromosome on gene action in other chromosomes.* While in *Drosophila* the presence of an extra Y chromosome can suppress variegation, Y seems to have no such action in the mouse. Furthermore, the Y chromosome affects neither the hemizygous expression of the X-linked markers *scurfy* (W. L. Russell *et al.*, 1959), *Tabby* (Welshons and Russell, 1959), or *Blotchy* (L. B. Russell, 1960); nor the heterozygous expression of *Tabby* (L. B. Russell and Chu, 1961).

3. *Time of death of various aneuploid states.* Clues to gene action can be obtained from the relative lengths of survival of different aneuploid states. Heterozygous deficiencies may be fully viable and normal, as shown for certain *d se* types (L. B. Russell and Russell, 1960). Other *d se* heterozygotes are of small size and some are poorly viable. These presumably involve somewhat longer deficiencies. Heterozygous deficiencies combined with heterozygous duplications, such as found in the unbalanced segregants of translocation heterozygotes, can die at various stages of development — from early embryonic to late fetal — probably depending on the lengths of the deleted and duplicated pieces. In rare, special cases, such unbalanced types may be viable. Deletions of entire chromosomes, which probably make up the bulk of the "dominant lethal" category, are apparently invariably lethal by the time of, or shortly after, implantation. Finally, preliminary results of Miss Hunsicker's at our laboratory indicate that homozygous deficiencies, even if short enough to have no noticeable effect in the hetero-

zygous state, kill during the preimplantation period, and are, therefore, at least as damaging, or more so, than heterozygous losses of whole chromosomes.

D. *Miscellaneous Uses of Chromosome Aberrations*

Unequal translocations have been employed as cell markers in transplantation studies (Ford *et al.*, 1956; Welshons, this symposium). A translocation has been used as a means of artificially reducing littersize in a study on the effect of littersize on gene penetrance (Lyon, 1954). Aberrations are beginning to be utilized for the study of interchromosomal effects. XO and XXY mice, as mentioned (Section I, C), have strongly indicated that production of male antigen is indeed associated with the Y chromosome. The sex-chromosome anomalies may become more widely useful in elucidating possible chromosomal bases for sexual dimorphisms.

REFERENCES

AUSTIN, C. R., 1960, Anomalies of fertilization leading to triploidy. *J. Cell. Comp. Physiol.* (Suppl. 1), **56**, 1–15.

BATEMAN, A. J., 1958, The partition of dominant lethals in the mouse between unimplanted eggs and deciduomata. *Heredity*, **12**, 467–475.

BATEMAN, A. J. and CHANDLEY, A. C., 1962, Mutations induced in the mouse with tritiated thymidine. *Nature*, **193**, 705–706.

BEATTY, R. A., 1957, Parthenogenesis and polyploidy in mammalian development. *Monogr. in Experimental Biology, Cambridge*, **7**, University Press.

BRADEN, A. W. E., 1957, Variation between strains in the incidence of various abnormalities of egg maturation and fertilization in the mouse. *J. Genet.* **55**, 476–486.

CARTER, T. C., LYON, M. F. and PHILLIPS, R. J. S., 1955, Gene-tagged translocations in eleven stocks of mice. *J. Genet.* **53**, 154–166.

CARTER, T. C., LYON, M. F. and PHILLIPS, R. J. S., 1956, Further genetic studies of eleven translocations in the mouse. *J. Genet.* **54**, 462–473.

CATTANACH, B. M., 1959, The sensitivity of the mouse testis to the mutagenic action of triethylenemelamine. *Ztschr. Vererb.* **90**, 1–6.

CATTANACH, B. M., 1961a, XXY mice. G*enet. Res.* **2**, 156–158.

CATTANACH, B. M., 1961b, A chemically-induced variegated-type position effect in the mouse. *Ztschr. Vererb.* **92**, 165–182.

DUNN, L. C., BENNETT, D. and BEASLEY, A. B., 1962, Mutation and recombination in the vicinity of a complex gene. *Genetics*, **47**, 285–303.

EDWARDS, R. G., 1961, Induced heteroploidy in mice: effect of deacetylmethylcolchicine on eggs at fertilization. *Exper. Cell Res.* **24**, 615–617.

FORD, C. E., HAMERTON, J. L., BARNES, D. W. H. and LOUTIT, J. F., 1956, Cytological identification of radiation-chimaeras. *Nature.* **177**, 452–454.

GARTLER, S. M., WAXMAN, S. H. and GIBLETT, E., 1962, An XX/XY human hermaphrodite resulting from double fertilization. *Proc. Nat. Acad. Sci. U.S.* **48**, 332–335.

GRÜNEBERG, H., 1952, *The Genetics of the Mouse*, 2nd ed., Martinus Nijhoff. The Hague.

HAMERTON, J. L., COWIE, V. A., GIANNELLI, F. and POLANI, P. E., 1961, Differential transmission of Down's syndrome (mongolism) through male and female translocation carriers. *Lancet*, **ii**, 956–958.

KOLLER, P. S., 1944, Segmental interchange in mice. *Genetics*, **29**, 247–263.

LEA, D. E., 1947, Effects of radiation on germ cells: dominant lethals and hereditary partial sterility. *Brit. J. Radiol.* (Suppl. 1), 120–141.

LEJEUNE, J., 1963, Abnormalities of autosomes. (This symposium.)

LÜNNING, K. G., FRÖLEN, H., NELSON, A. and RÖNNBÄCK, C., 1963, Genetic effects of strontium-90 injected into male mice. *Nature*, **197**, 304–305.

LYON, M. F., 1954, Stage of action of the litter-size effect on absence of otoliths in mice. *Z. indukt. Abstamm. u. Vererbungslehre* **86**, 289–292.

LYON, M. F., 1960, Effect of X-rays on the mutation of t-alleles in the mouse. *Heredity,* **14**, 247–252.

LYON, M. F., 1961, Gene action in the X-chromosome of the mouse (*Mus musculus* L.). *Nature*, **190**, 372–373.

OAKBERG, E. F., 1963, The influence of germ cell stage on reproductive and genetic effects of radiation in mammals. Monogr. Suppl., *Diseases of the Nervous System* (in press).

OAKBERG, E. F., and DI MINNO, R. L., 1960, X-ray sensitivity of primary spermatocytes of the mouse. *Internal. J. Rad. Biol.* **2**, 196–209.

OHNO, S., 1963, Sex Chromatin: its origin and nature. (This symposium.)

RUSSELL, L. B., 1960, Blotchy. *Mouse News Letter*, **23**, 58.

RUSSELL L. B., 1961, Genetics of mammalian sex chromosomes. *Science*, **133**, 1795–1803.

RUSSELL, L. B., 1962, Chromosome aberrations in experimental mammals. In *Progress in Medical Genetics*, Eds. A. G. Steinberg and A. G. Bearn. Grune and Stratton, New York, pp. 230–294, Vol. 2.

RUSSELL, L. B., 1963, Evidence from six X-autosome translocations bearing on the single-active-X hypothesis. *Proc. XI International Congress of Genetics*. The Hague (in press).

RUSSELL, L. B., and BANGHAM, J. W., 1959, Variegated-type position effects in the mouse. *Genetics*, **44**, 532.

RUSSELL, L. B. and BANGHAM, J. W., 1960, Further analysis of variegated-type position effects from X-autosome translocations in the mouse. *Genetics*, **45**, 1008-1009.

RUSSELL, L. B. and BANGHAM, J. W., 1961, Variegated-type position effects in the mouse. *Genetics*, **46**, 509–525.

RUSSELL, L. B., BANGHAM, J. W. and SAYLORS. C. L., 1962, Delimination of chromosomal regions involved in V-type position effects from X-autosome translocations in the mouse. *Genetics*, **47**, 981–982.

RUSSELL, L. B., BANGHAM, J. W. and SAYLORS, C. L., 1963, Evidence from six X-autosome translocation bearing on the single-active-X hypothesis. USAEC Report ORNL-3427 (in press).

RUSSELL, L. B. and CHU, E. H. Y., 1961, An XXY male in the mouse. *Proc. Nat. Acad. Sci. U.S.* **47**, 571–575.

RUSSELL, L. B. and RUSSELL, W. L., 1954, Pathways of radiation effects in the mother and embryo. *Cold Spring Harbor Symp. Quant. Biol.* **19**, 50–59.

RUSSELL, L. B. and RUSSELL, W. L., 1956, The sensitivity of different stages in oogenesis to the radiation induction of dominant lethals and other changes in the mouse. In *Progress in Radiobiology*, Eds. J. S. Mitchell, B. E. Holmes, and C. L. Smith. Oliver and Boyd, Edinburgh pp. 187–192.

RUSSELL, L. B. and RUSSELL, W. L., 1960, Genetic analysis of induced deletions and of spontaneous nondisjunction involving chromosome 2 of the mouse. *J. Cell. Comp. Physiol.* (Suppl. 1), **56**, 169–188.

RUSSELL, L. B. and SAYLORS, C. L., 1960, Factors causing a high frequency of mice having the XO sex-chromosome constitution. *Science*, **131**, 1321–1322.

RUSSELL, L. B. and SAYLORS, C. L., 1961, Spontaneous and induced abnormal sex-chromosome number in the mouse. *Genetics*, **46**, 894.

RUSSELL, L. B. and SAYLORS, C. L., 1962, Induction of paternal sex chromosome losses by irradiation of mouse spermatozoa. *Genetics,* **47,** 7–10.

RUSSELL, L. B. and SAYLORS, C. L., 1963, The relative sensitivity of various germ-cell stages of the mouse to radiation-induced nondisjunction, chromosome losses and deficiencies. In *Repair from Genetic Radiation Damage and Differential Radiosensitivity in Germ Cells,* Ed. by F. Sobels, Pergamon Press, Oxford (in press).

RUSSELL, W. L., 1951, X-ray-induced mutations in mice. *Cold Spring Harbor Symp. Quant. Biol.* **16,** 327–336.

RUSSELL, W. L., 1954, Genetic effects of radiation in mammals. In *Radiation Biology,* Ed. by A. Hollaender. McGraw-Hill, New York, pp. 825–859, Vol. 1.

RUSSELL, W. L., RUSSELL, L. B. and GOWER, J. S., 1959, Exceptional inheritance of a sex-linked gene in the mouse explained on the basis that the X/O sex-chromosome constitution is female. *Proc. Nat. Acad. Sci. U.S.* **45,** 554–560.

RUSSELL, W. L., RUSSELL, L. B. and KELLY, E. M., 1960, Dependence of mutation rate on radiation intensity. *Intern. J. Rad. Biol.* (Suppl.), pp. 311–320.

RUSSELL, W. L., RUSSELL, L. B. and KIMBALL, A. W., 1954, The relative effectiveness of neutrons from a nuclear detonation and from a cyclotron in inducing dominant lethals in the mouse. *Am. Naturalist,* **88,** 269–286.

SCHULTZ, J., 1947, The nature of heterochromatin. *Cold Spring Harbor Symp. Quant. Biol.* **12,** 179–191.

SLIZYNSKI, B. M., 1957a, Cytological analysis of translocations in the mouse. *J. Genet.* **55,** 122–130.

SLIZYNSKI, B. M., 1957b, Chromosomal mechanism in translocation infertility. *Proc. Roy. Phys. Soc. Edinburgh,* **26,** 49–60.

SNELL, G. D., 1946, An analysis of translocations in the mouse. *Genetics,* **31,** 157–180.

THULINE, H. C. and NORBY, D. E., 1961, Spontaneous occurrence of chomosome abnormality in cats. *Science,* **134,** 554–555.

VALENCIA, J. I., 1963, Radiosensitivity of mature germ cell and fertilized eggs in *Drosophila Melanogaster.* (This symposium.)

WELSHONS, W. J., 1963, Detection and use of cytological anomalies in the mouse. (This symposium.)

WELSHONS, W. J., GIBSON, B. H. and SCANDLYN, B. J., 1962, Slide processing for the examination of male mammalian meiotic chromosomes. *Stain Technology,* **37,** 1–6.

WELSHONS, W. J. and RUSSELL, L. B., 1959, The Y-chromosome as the bearer of male determining factors in the mouse. *Proc. Nat. Acad. Sci. U.S.* **45,** 560–566.

CHROMOSOME BREAKAGE *in vitro*

M. A. BENDER

Biology Division, Oak Ridge National Laboratory,* Oak Ridge, Tennessee, U.S.A.

INTRODUCTION

The development of methods for producing well-spread metaphase figures from mammalian cells grown in tissue culture has led to wide interest in mammalian cytogenetics. Among the many facets of this field which have been studied is the production of chromosomal aberrations by radiation. Mammalian somatic cells in culture are, in many ways, well suited to such investigations. The cells are easily manipulated, either in suspension or attached to a glass surface such as a cover glass. They are readily accessible to chemical agents, such as colchicine, which may be added to the liquid growth medium surrounding them. In addition, the use of mammalian, and especially human cells is particularly appealing because of the wide interest in radiation damage to humans.

It must be remembered, however, that cells in culture do not necessarily respond in the same way as cells *in vivo*. Obviously, cultured cells are maintained in an abnormal environment. In many cases the cells themselves are demonstrably abnormal. For example, long-established cell lines, such as HeLa, do not have a normal diploid complement of chromosomes. Other cell lines having the proper diploid chromosome number for the species of origin may have more subtle alterations in their karyotypes. Even when cells with normal karyotypes are used, it is possible that their response to radiation is not typical of that of normal somatic cells *in vivo*. Also, the cells of most interest from the point of view of radiation hazards are the meiotic and pre-meiotic cells of the germ line, while the cultured cells used for chromosomal aberration studies so far have all been derived from somatic tissues. Data from cultured cells must thus be used with caution, and evidence must be obtained on whether or not the response of particular cells *in vitro* are the same as those of cells *in vivo*.

*Operated by Union Carbide Corporation for the United States Atomic Energy Commission.

Nevertheless, even if a given cell line, or all cultured cells for that matter, are shown to have a more or less abnormal radiation sensitivity relative to cells *in vivo*, it seems probable that the mechanisms of chromosomal aberration production must be similar for all cells. Thus, one- and two-hit aberrations should show the expected kineitcs, and aberration types seen *in vivo* should also be seen *in vitro*. Cultured cells may then be legitimate subjects for the study of chromosomal aberration production, even in cases where their radiation response is known to be quantitatively different from that of mammalian somatic cells *in vivo*.

A large number of reports of investigations of chromosomal aberration production *in vitro* have accumulated since 1957. In many cases the results

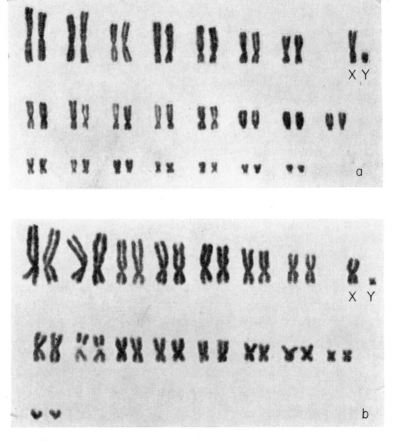

FIG. 1. Karyotypes of mammalian cells commonly used for *in vitro* chromosomal male: (a) human male; (b) *Ateles* monkey male; (c) Chinese hamster embryos

of these studies appear to be in conflict. Frequently, however, these differences are more apparent than real. In this paper I shall try to review
all of the work in this field to date, and to analyze the conflicts in the reported results. In addition, I shall compare the accumulated *in vitro* results
with those of the available studies of radiation-induced chromosomal
aberrations in mammalian somatic cells *in vivo*.

   Materials. Only four mammals have been used as donors of cells for *in
vitro* studies of chromosomal aberration production by radiation. These
are man, a monkey *(Ateles,* the South American spider monkey), the mouse,
and the Chinese hamster *(Cricetulus griseus)*. The reasons for the choice
of human material are obvious, and the human chromosome number
(2n = 46) and karyotype (Fig. 1a), although they leave much to be desired,
are not entirely unsuited to chromosome aberration work. The high diploid

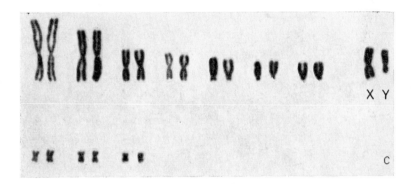

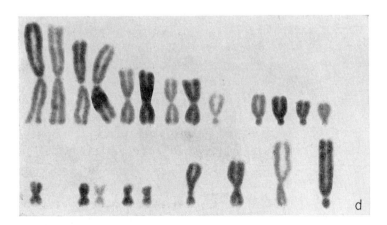

of the Chinese hamster. (d) karyotype of a cell from a cell line derived originally from
aberration studies. All four karyotypes are magnified about 3500.

number, which makes scoring tedious, to say the least, is somewhat compensated for by the identifiability of a number of the chromosomes. Thus, pairs number 1, 2, and 3, the groups of pairs 13, 14 and 15, 19 and 20, and 21, 22 and the Y (Denver classification, 1960) are easily identified by visual inspection. Many other pairs can easily be identified by karyotype analysis. A monkey was chosen as a primate that could be used for experimental radiation work. The spider monkey was selected because it has a diploid chromosome number of only 34, the lowest number yet recorded for a primate (Bender and Chu, 1962), together with a very favorable karyotype (Fig. 1b). The mouse, in spite of its chromosome number (2n = 40) and a karyotype that can only be termed undistinguished, is an obvious choice. Inbred lines are available, and a vast background of genetic information is available. The Chinese hamster offers both a very low chromosome number for a mammal (2n = 22) and an extremely favorable karyotype (Fig. 1c). There are only two places in the karyotype where one pair might be confused with another. Unfortunately, very little is known of the genetics of the Chinese hamster. Inbred lines, however, are now available.

Normal diploid cells from all four species have been used by various authors. Aneuploid permanent tissue culture lines of human and of Chinese hamster cells have also been used in a few cases. These aneuploid lines have either the normal chromosome number or one close to it, but one or more chromosomes are different from those of the normal karyotype. The karyotype of such a Chinese hamster line is shown in Fig. 1d.

Methods. Three basic culture methods have been used for chromosome aberration studies. Primary cultures are sometimes started by embedding bits of tissue, frequently skin, in a chick plasma clot on a glass surface such as a cover glass. An outgrowth of cells into the clot and onto the glass surface may be used directly, or to start secondary cultures on cover slips. Alternatively, bits of tissue such as kidney may be subjected to the action of trypsin or of versene to obtain a cell suspension which is planted directly on glass without any plasma clot. Such primary cultures may also either be used directly for experiments or used to make secondary cultures. With either method, a liquid medium covers and nourishes the cells. This medium consists of one of the usual culture fluids (such as Mixture 199) with added serum, frequently either human or fetal calf. From 10 to 50 per cent serum is commonly used. With skin or with medium containing fetal calf serum, cultures of "fibroblast-like" cells are the usual product. "Epithelioid" cells usually arise from kidney tissue. While the two morphological cell types are not completely distinct, there seems to be a basic difference between them which is reflected particularly in their spontaneous chromosomal aberration rates. Either type of culture continues to contain mainly diploid cells through many passages in culture; only the first few culture passages have been used for most aberration experiments. Diploid cultures almost always become moribund and eventually die after a number of passages, but occasionally a diploid culture gives rise to a permanent cell line which seems inevitably to be aneuploid. Such lines are easy to maintain, usually grow rapidly, and are suitable for some types of aberration work in spite of their abnormal karyotypes.

A third type of culture, the blood culture, is becoming increasingly popular. The method makes use of the fact that peripheral leukocytes, when placed in a culture medium containing phytohemagglutinin, will divide *in vitro* (Hungerford *et al.*, 1959; Moorhead *et al.*, 1960). The leukocyte culture is particularly attractive for aberration work for several reasons. The tissue is easily obtained, particularly from humans. Whole blood may be irradiated *in vitro* and the results compared with those of experiments in which the subject was irradiated before the blood was drawn, thus providing an *in vitro–in vivo* comparison with the same type of cell. Other advantages will be mentioned below.

The preparation of the well-spread metaphase figures needed for aberration analysis is usually accomplished with the aid of several technical tricks. More often than not the cultures are exposed to the action of colchicine, which arrests cells coming to metaphase. This technique not only increases the number of metaphases available, but its prevention of spindle formation also seems to produce better spreading of the chromosomes. Care must be exercised, however, that the figures do not become over-contracted from too much colchicine or too long a treatment. Just prior to fixation the well-known treatment with a hypotonic solution is given to swell the mitotic cells and further aid chromosome spreading. Usually diluted balanced salt solution or 1 per cent sodium citrate are used for a period of 10–20 min. The cells are most frequently fixed in 3:1 alcohol–acetic acid fixative. Either methyl or ethyl alcohol can be used. Sometimes advantage is taken of the fact that very dilute acetic acid further swells the cells. This is done either by a very brief immersion of the cells in a very dilute fixative mixture or, in the case of cells in suspension, by packing the cells in the bottom of a centrifuge tube and layering the fixative on top without disturbing the "button" of cells. The acid seems to penetrate the cell mass faster than the alcohol in the latter case, thus giving them a dilute acid pretreatment.

Fixed cells can be flattened and mounted by several different techniques. Some authors have flattened cells grown on cover slips by pressure or prepared suspended cells by the squash technique. Recently, however, there has been a widespread adoption of the air-drying technique first introduced by Rothfels and Siminovitch (1958). The advantages of this method are particularly striking in the case of human leukocyte preparations (Moorhead *et al.*, 1960). Acetic-orcein is the most common stain for mammalian chromosomes, although the Feulgen reaction, Geimsa, and other stains have also been used.

Scoring of preparations involves scanning the slides under relatively low magnification and selecting well-spread, apparently unbroken cells for detailed analysis. It is important that an unbiased selection be made, and cells once selected should not be discarded. Under high magnification the chromosomes are counted, and the number and types of aberrations are recorded. The figure may also be photographed for a karyotype analysis. A partial karyotype analysis may be made by visual inspection. A good knowledge of the karyotype of the material being scored is essential, in order to accurately distinguish between aberrations and artifacts due to overlap, too much colchicine, etc.

Aberration types. The aberration types seen may be grouped into two categories: chromatid type and chromosome type aberrations. Chromatid breaks are induced when the cell is irradiated after the chromosomes have "split" into chromatids (after DNA synthesis, for practical purposes). The aberration types usually seen are the chromatid deletion (Fig. 2a) in which a single break occurs in one chromatid, the isochromatid deletion (Fig. 2b), in which both chromatids are broken at the same level, and the chromatid exchange, in which recombination occurs between breaks in chromatids of two different chromosomes. The deletions are usually single-hit events and these increase roughly as the first power of the dose, while the exchanges require two "hits" and increase approximately as the square of the dose. In addition, rarer multi-hit types such as ring chromatids are seen. Isochromatid breaks may be further classified by whether the broken ends of the chromatids have undergone sister fusion. Thus, we have the "nonunion proximal" (NUP), the "nonunion distal" (NUD), the "nonunion" (NUPD), and the "sister union" (SU) types. In addition to true breaks, a class of damage in which a clear area appears in one chromatid is also seen. These are called "achromatic lesions" or "gaps." Although some authors include these in the deletion class, there is a serious question about whether they involve a real break in the chromatid continuity (Revel, 1959). The criterion used in our laboratory for separating the chromatid deletions from the achromatic lesions is whether or not the "deleted" fragment has moved from its normal position relative to the other chromatid.

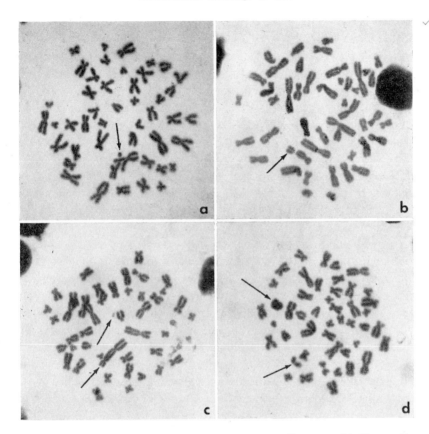

FIG. 2. X-ray-induced aberrations (arrows) in human cells *in vitro*. (a) Chromatid deletion; (b) isochromatid deletion (NUPD); (c) dicentric chromosome with fragments; (d) ring chromosome with fragments. All figures are from female leukocyte cultures. (a) and (b) received X-irradiation 6 hr before fixation; (c) and (d) were treated as whole blood prior to making the cultures. Magnified about 1350.

Chromosome type aberrations are seen when the cell is irradiated before the chromosomes replicate. Breaks induced in the single-strand pre-DNA-synthesis period are replicated when the chromosomes replicate. Thus, chromosome deletions are analogous to both chromatid and isochromatid types. The broken chromatids, however, do not undergo sister fusion, so that all chromosome type deletions look like the NUPD isochromatid class. The chromosome type two-hit aberrations analogous to the chromatid exchange are the dicentrics (Fig. 2c). As is the case with chromatid aberrations, other less frequent aberrations such as rings (Fig. 2d) are seen.

The most frequent stage scored in mammalian chromosome aberration work has been the metaphase of the first post-irradiation division. Anaphase and telophase have also been used, however. Also, in at least one case, divisions following the first post irradiation division have been used. Postmetaphase scoring has the advantage of being much quicker than metaphase scoring, thus allowing many more cells to be scored. Its disadvantage is that many aberrations are missed. Acentric fragments are frequently lost in the first division, due to their failure to move to the poles and thus to be included in the daughter nuclei. Isochromatid deletions with proximal sister-fusion, and some types of multi-hit aberrations, such as dicentrics, can cause anaphase bridge formation. These bridges and fragments are the only abnormalities scored postmetaphase. Postmetaphase scoring is frequently further complicated by the phenomenon of chromosome stickiness which may produce what looks like a bridge when there is no recombination present at metaphase.

Following the first division, chromatid aberrations are still single-stranded. After replication they appear at the next metaphase as chromosome type aberrations, recognizable as being of chromatid origin only by the absence of the expected acentric fragments. Thus, a chromatid exchange, if it is not lost through bridge formation, will appear as a dicentric chromosome, probably without fragments, at the next division. Also, deletions of either the chromatid or the chromosome types are easily recognized by the presence of fragments in the first post-irradiation division. If these are lost in a division occurring before scoring, the deletion is usually not recognized, and it may not even be obvious on karyotype analysis. It is thus essential to score the first post-irradiation division; later divisions cannot give quantitative results.

In recording and comparing aberration data, the frequency of breaks, of aberrations, or of abnormal cells may be used. Estimates of breakage rates are convenient, and at low doses fairly accurate. Since there is an appreciable incidence of multi-hit aberrations at higher doses, however, the use of a linear regression of breaks on dose becomes increasingly inaccurate as the dose increases. At low doses, the frequency of aberrations is virtually the same as the frequency of breaks; at higher doses the multi-hit aberrations make a greater and greater contribution and the two functions diverge. The scoring of abnormal cells is similarly inaccurate at higher doses, both because cells have more and more chance of having multi-hit aberrations and because they have a greater chance of having more than one aberration as the dose increases. The most valid comparisons can be made by using "coefficients of aberration production" for each type of aberration (Lea, 1955). These coefficients allow for the nonlinear kinetics of multi-hit aberrations.

SPONTANEOUS ABERRATION RATES

Curiously, almost all of the spontaneous aberrations seen in tissue cultures are of the chromatid type. In some cell lines the spontaneous aberration rates are high enough so that some of the chromatid aberrations should be seen in later divisions as chromosome type aberrations lacking fragments. This is not the case, however. Some mechanism must, then, operate to weed out the aberrant cells. The nature of this mechanism is, unfortunately, still a subject for speculation.

Various types of cultures show widely differing spontaneous metaphase aberration rates. Rates ranging from 0·009 to 0·35 breaks per cell per generation have been reported for various cell types from different species (Bender, 1957, 1960; Bender and Gooch, 1962a, b, c; Bender, Gooch and Prescott, 1962; Puck, 1958; Chu, Giles and Passano, 1961; Wakonig and Ford, 1960; Hsu, Dewey and Humphrey, 1962; Chu and Monesi, 1960 and personal communication). The reported values are listed in Table 1, together with the cell type and the investigators. Although the variation is wide, it is evident that the values for epithelioid cells from kidney are about 1 per cent, for leukocytes about 2 per cent, and for "fibroblast" cells from 4 per cent for established aneuploid cell lines to a high of almost 22 per cent for cells in their first few culture passages. One explanation for this variation is the fact that some authors have included achromatic lesions, while others have not. Even allowing for this, however, it is evident that some "fibroblast" cells have extraordinarily high aberration rates.

Postmetaphase aberration rates also vary widely. This is shown in Table 1. The reported values range from a low of 0·006 to a high of 0·201 aberrations per division (Lindsten, 1959; Fraccaro, 1960; Dubinen, Kerkis, and Lebedeva, 1960; Sax and Passano, 1961; Levan and Biesele, 1958). In the study reported by Sax and Passano, the cultures were sampled periodically over 4 $1/2$ months, and the aberration frequency rose steadily to a high of 0·201 aberrations per cell. Variation in spontaneous aberration frequency *in vitro* may, then, be a function not only of observer, and of cell type and culture method, but also of time in culture. It appears unlikely, however, that it is a function of species (Table 1) or of the sex or age of the donor (Bender, 1960; Chu, Giles and Passano, 1961).

TABLE 1. SPONTANEOUS CHROMOSOMAL ABERRATION RATES IN MAMMALIAN CELLS *in vitro*

	Species	Tissue	Cell type	Breaks/cell*	Reference
Metaphase	Human	Kidney	Epithelioid	0·009	Bender, 1957, 1960
	Ateles	Kidney	Epithelioid	0·014	Bender, 1960
	Human	Blood	Leukocytes	0·022	Bender and Gooch, 1962a, b, c; Bender et al., 1962
		Skin	Fibroblasts	0·216	Puck, 1958
		Kidney, skin	Mainly fibroblasts	0·100	Chu et al., 1961
	Mouse	Embryos	Mixed	0·01–0·35	Chu and Monesi, 1960 and personal communication
	Chinese hamster	Cell line	Fibroblasts	0·040	Wakonig and Ford, 1960
		Cell line	Fibroblasts	0·210	Bender, 1960
		Cell line	Fibroblasts	0·040	Hsu et al., 1962
Postmetaphase	Human	Fetal lung	Fibroblasts	0·006–0·009	Lindsten, 1959; Fraccaro, 1960
		Fetal brain	?	0·02–0·03	Lindsten, 1959; Fraccaro, 1960
		Embryos	?	0·015	Dubinin et al., 1960
	Mouse	Skin	Fibroblasts	0·036–0·201	Sax and Passano, 1961
		Fetal skin	Fibroblasts	0·109	Levan and Biesele, 1958

* Aberrations per cell for postmetaphase scoring.

RADIATION-INDUCED ABERRATIONS

X- and γ-rays. X-ray-induced metaphase chromatid type aberration rates reported for cells grown and irradiated *in vitro* range from 0·0032 to about 0·24 breaks per cell per r (Bender, 1957, 1960; Bender and Gooch, 1962c; Puck, 1958; Chu, Giles and Passano, 1961; Wakonig and Ford, 1960; Hsu, Dewey and Humphrey, 1962; Chu and Monesi, 1960 and personal communication). The data available are summarized in Table 2. As was the case for spontaneous aberrations, some authors have included achromatic lesions in the totals, while others have not. Allowing for this, the "fibroblast" cultures again seem to have higher rates than the epithelioid cells. The chromatid breakage values available from postmetaphase scoring range from 0·0018 to 0·14 aberrations per division per r (Table 1). The data of Dubinin *et al.* (1960) and of Sax and Passano (1961) for postmetaphase scoring agree well with each other and with most of the metaphase-scored "fibroblast" work. The range of breakage rates reported by Lindsten (1959) is, however, much higher. Thus the reports on breakage rates for "fibroblasts" scored either at metaphase or postmetaphase all agree reasonably well, allowing for differences in the inclusion of achromatic lesions in the breakage data, except for two reports of much higher values. In one case (Wakonig and Ford, 1960) only one relatively high dose of X-rays was given. A high frequency of multi-hit aberrations in appreciable numbers will, of course, lead to a high breakage value because the approximation of a linear function of dose used is increasingly inaccurate as dose increases. The other high values reported (Lindsten, 1959) are for postmetaphase scoring of Co^{60}-irradiation of fetal lung "fibroblasts" and cells from fetal brain which were reported to resemble glial elements (Fraccaro, 1960). While it seems possible that unusual stickiness might account for the unusually high aberration frequencies, it is also possible that the glial-like cells have an inherently high breakage rate.

Other factors which can explain some of the variation in the results reported are variation in the energy of the X- and γ-rays used and in the dose rates at which they are administered. The quality or "hardness" of the radiation used is of possible significance in two ways. First, in most of the experiments reported, the cells were irradiated while attached to or lying on a glass surface. The doses were reported in roentgens, measured in air. Thus the actual absorbed doses, measured in rad, undoubtedly varied from experiment to experiment. The data of Morkovin and Feldman (1959) on mammalian cell survival show that the absorbed dose may have varied by as much as a factor of 1·5 from the air dose. Also, it is possible that the

TABLE 2. CHROMOSOMAL BREAKAGE RATES INDUCED IN MAMMALIAN TISSUE CULTURE CELLS BY X-RAYS

Only the rate for the shortest irradiation-fixation interval is given in cases where more than one time was used. Breakage is considered to be a linear function of dose for the purpose of calculating the rates listed.

	Species	Tissue	Cell type	Breaks/cell/r*	Reference
Chromatid					
Metaphase					
	Human	Kidney	Epithelioid	0·0032	Bender, 1957, 1960
	Ateles	Kidney	Epithelioid	0·0036	Bender, 1960
	Human	Blood	Leukocytes	0·0026	Bender and Gooch, 1962c
		Skin	Fibroblasts	0·02	Puck, 1958
		Kidney and skin	Mainly fibroblasts	0·022	Chu et al., 1961
	Mouse	Embryos	Mixed	0·021	Chu and Monesi, 1960 and personal communication.
	Chinese hamster	Cell line	Fibroblasts	0·241	Wakonig and Ford, 1960
		Cell line	Fibroblasts	0·005	Bender, 1960
		Cell line	Fibroblasts	0·012	Hsu et al., 1962
Postmetaphase	Human	Fetal lung and brain	Mixed	0·008–0·14	Lindsten, 1959
		Embryos	?	0·0025	Dubinin et al., 1960
		Skin	Fibroblasts	0·0018	Sax and Passano, 1961
Chromosome					
Metaphase					
	Human	Kidney and skin	Mainly fibroblasts	0·009	Chu et al., 1961
		Blood	Leukocytes	0·0024	Bender and Gooch, 1962b
		Blood	Leukocytes	0·0039	Bell and Baker, 1962
	Mouse	Embryos	Mixed	0·012	Chu and Monesi, 1960 and personal communication
	Chinese hamster	Cell line	Fibroblasts	0·003	Hsu et al., 1962

* Aberrations per cell for postmetaphase scoring.

production of breaks or the recombinability of the broken ends might vary with X-ray beam in this material although such variation does not occur in other material. Dose rate is expected to affect the frequency of multi-hit aberrations and, indeed, this has been shown for chromosome type aberrations in mammalian cells *in vitro* by Bell and Baker (1962). A dose rate of 1·6 r per min yielded less than half as many aberrations as a dose rate of 160 r per min. Other factors, such as temperature at the time of irradiation and oxygen concentration, probably affect the breakage rates reported for mammalian cells. Unfortunately, these factors have yet to be investigated.

X-ray-induced chromosome type breakage frequencies have been measured only at metaphase for mammalian cells in culture. Breakage frequencies ranging from 0·0024 to 0·009 breaks per cell per r have been reported (Chu *et al.*, 1961; Bender and Gooch, 1962b; Bell and Baker, 1962; Hsu *et al.*, 1962). These values are presented in Table 2. All of the breakage rates reported are in fairly good agreement. Comparing the results reported by Chu *et al.* (1961) with their chromatid type breakage rates in the same system, a more than two-fold increase in sensitivity is evident in the replicated (post-DNA-synthesis) chromosomes. This sort of increase has been reported for other kinds of material. Direct comparison of pre- and post-replication breakage rates is not possible in the system used by Chu *et al.*, however, because the samples containing cells with "nonsplit" chromosomes also contain some cells with some or all of their chromosomes already "split" and, hence, capable of chromatid type breakage. As this fraction is not known, the chromosome type breakage estimate is certainly too low. Hsu *et al.* (1962) have used an autoradiographic technique to avoid this difficulty. A pulse of ^{3}H-thymidine was given immediately before irradiation. Cells were scored for breakage in two groups: those that were labeled and those that were not. It was found that the DNA-synthetic period was one-third to one-fourth as sensitive as the postsynthetic stage. The frequency of chromosome type breaks was also approximately one-third that of chromatid breaks, or about the same as of breaks induced during the DNA-synthetic period.

Experiments with human leukocyte cultures are also pertinent to the question of stage sensitivity in mammalian cells *in vitro*. In experiments in which the leukocytes were irradiated in whole fresh blood immediately prior to culture (Bender and Gooch, 1962b) and in cultures only a few hours old (Bell and Baker, 1962), only chromosome type breaks were found. This is in accord with autoradiographic evidence that virtually all of the cells which ultimately divide in leukocyte cultures are in the pre-DNA-synthesis stage at the time that the blood is drawn (Bender and Prescott, 1962; Lima De Faria, Reitalu, and Bergman, 1962; MacKinney, Stohlman, and Brecker, 1962), and thus must synthesize DNA and replicate their chromosomes in culture. If the leukocyte cultures are irradiated 4–6 hr before fixation, however, only chromatid breaks result (Bell and Baker, 1962; Bender and Gooch, 1962c). This allows a direct comparison between chromatid and chromosome type breakage rates to be made in the leukocyte system. Comparing the figures given in Table 2, no difference between chromatid and chromosome type breakage rates is evident in this system. It is possible, however, that the expected difference in sensitivity is compensated for by a decrease in radiosensitivity associated with *in vitro* culture. Further experiments will be necessary before the question of the relation of breakage rate to stage in the cell cycle of mammalian cells is fully answered.

The aberration types observed in all of the studies reported are the same as those reported for other systems. All of the expected types have been seen, including rings, pericentric inversions, and even tricentric chromosomes (Ohnuki, Awa and Pomerat, 1961). The kinetics of aberration production observed also agree with those seen elsewhere. Thus one-hit aberrations rise roughly as the first power of dose, and two-hit aberrations appear to increase as the square of dose. Isochromatid deletions seem to increase at slightly more than the first power of dose. Unfortunately, none of the samples scored to date are large enough to establish these relationships for mammalian cells. There is no reason to believe, however, that they will not hold when larger samples are eventually obtained.

It has been observed that both endoreduplication and tetraploidy increase markedly when human leukocytes are irradiated after some time in culture (Bell and Baker, 1962; Ohnuki et al., 1961). The sensitive period for the first division appears to be at about 16–24 culture hours (Bell and Baker, 1962) or near the time of DNA synthesis in this system (Bender and Prescott, 1962). The mechanism of this effect is not yet understood.

The distribution of breaks in mammalian cells *in vitro* on a "per cell" basis has been analyzed by Bender and Wolff (1961). No evidence of loss (through either delay or failure to divide) of heavily damaged cells was observed. Distributions of numbers of breaks per cell followed the Poisson function in most cases, and where they did not the deviation was in the direction of "over-dispersion" in which cells contained too many, rather than too few breaks. One explanation for the observed over-dispersion might be that a few cells in the populations studied were much more sensitive than the rest. Further investigation is necessary before the existence of such sensitive subpopulations can be established.

Neutrons. In addition to X-rays, the effects of a few other radiations have been studied. The effects of 14 MeV neutrons on the chromosomes of human leukocytes have been investigated (Bender and Gooch, unpublished data). Whole fresh blood was irradiated and then put into culture. The first *in vitro* division was scored. Chromosome type aberrations only were induced. The yield of deletions rose approximately linearly with dose, while, unexpectedly in this case, the yield of two-hit aberrations rose roughly as the square of the dose. The raw data suggest that the RBE for 14 MeV neutrons in this system is approximately two.

Tritium. Bender *et al.* (1962) studied the effects of tritium incorporated into either DNA or RNA (as ^{3}H-thymidine and ^{3}H-uridine, respectively) on the chromosomes of human leukocytes in culture. Although the results cannot be interpreted in terms of breakage per r of beta irradiation, due to the uncertainties of dose estimation, it is clear that the level of damage observed is compatible with the amount of radation which must have been received. The effects of incorporation of both precursors were qualitatively similar. In addition to the expected types, a type of chromosomal damage not previously recorded for mammalian material was seen in this material. It consisted of symmetrically placed "gaps" on both chromatids, giving almost the appearance of a dicentric chromosome without fragments. The distribution of aberration types was also different from that of aberrations induced by X-rays, as might be expected due to the very low dose rate. No correlation between the distribution of breaks and the distribution of tritium in autoradiographs of the scored figures was evident, though more aberrations occurred, as would be expected, in heavily labeled cells. Thus it would appear that the chromosomal damage induced by tritium incorporated into the cell is due only to the ionization produced by the β-particle produced, and not to recoil or transmutation.

Ultraviolet. Chu (1962) has investigated the effect of various wavelengths of monochromatic ultraviolet radiation on the chromosomes of an aneuploid (see Fig. 1d) Chinese hamster cell line [a clonal derivative of one used previously for X-ray studies (Bender, 1960)]. Unexpectedly, only chromatid aberrations were found during the first 24 hr following doses as low as 25 ergs/mm^2. Chromosome type aberrations were not seen until 30 hr after irradiation. Since the post-DNA-synthesis period was shown by means of autoradiography to be only 2–4 hr under the conditions of these experiments, even the low doses of ultraviolet used must have induced considerable mitotic delay. The aberrations induced, of both chromatid and chromosome type, were the same as those induced by X-rays, as were the dose-effect kinetics observed. Wavelengths of 2652 and 2804 Å were the most effective for chromosomal breakage. Experiments with visible light give no evidence of either photoprotection or photoreactivation of the ultraviolet-induced chromosomal aberrations (Chu, personal communication).

Ozone. Fetner (1962) has measured the chromosome breakage induced by ozone treatment of the KB human cell line. Eight ppm for 5 or 10 min produced as many chromosome breaks as X-ray doses in the range of 100–200 r. Since the chromosome number is variable in the KB line, the breakage rate per cell was not calculated. Chromatid deletions were produced as an exponential function of dose (time), which was interpreted as being a function of the time required for penetration of active radicals to the chromosomes.

COMPARISON WITH OTHER SYSTEMS

As mentioned earlier, the most accurate way to compare aberration rates in different materials is to compute "coefficients of aberration production" for each aberration class. The yield, Y, of one-hit aberrations is related to radiation dose, D, as:

$$Y = a + bD.$$

a is, of course, the spontaneous frequency, and b is the coefficient of aberration production. For two-hit aberrations,

$$Y = a + cD^2,$$

where c is the coefficient of aberration production per unit dose squared.

In some cases, authors have computed coefficients of aberration production for X-ray-treated mammalian cells *in vitro*. These may be compared with each other and with similar coefficients for the classical plant material, *Tradescantia* microspores (Table 3). It will be seen than there is general agreement between the mammalian results and those for *Tradescantia*. While they agree well with each other, the coefficients of chromatid deletion production for epithelioid cells are significantly different from that for *Tradescantia*. The coefficient for human "fibroblasts," however, is not different from the value for the microspores. The difference between the two sets of values is about one order of magnitude. The coefficients of chromatid exchange production for the epithelioid cells are lower than those for both *Tradescantia* and human "fibroblasts", which agree closely. In human leukocyte cultures, the coefficient of chromosome deletion production is significantly higher than the *Tradescantia* value, although their coefficients

TABLE 3. COEFFICIENTS OF ABERRATION PRODUCTION FOR MAMMALIAN CELLS *in vitro* AND FOR *Tradescantia* MICROSPORES

Material	Chromatid deletions per cell/r (10^{-2} X)	Isochromatid deletions per cell/r (10^{-2} X)	Chromatid exchanges per cell/r² (10^{-5} X)	Chromosome deletions per cell/r (10^{-2} X)	Dicentrics per cell per r² (10^{-5} X)	Reference
Tradescantia microspores	0·725±0·008	0·271±0·02	1·81±0·21	0·06±0·01	0·52±0·08	Lea, 1955
Human kidney cells	0·066±0·10	0·246±0·16	0·55±0·35			Bender and Wolff, 1961
Monkey kidney cells	0·043±0·21	0·237±0·49	0·38±0·34			
Chinese hamster fibroblasts	0·047±0·16	0·409±0·20	0·45±0·29			
Human kidney, skin cells	0·601±0·07	0·316±0·19	2·16±0·50			Chu *et al.*, 1961
Human leukocytes				0·11±0·01	0·45±0·07	Bender and Gooch, 1962b

of dicentric production are very similar. In spite of the differences from each other and from *Tradescantia* shown by the mammalian cells, the over-all similarity of results is almost surprising .

In addition to the data from plant materials, there also exist some data for mammalian somatic cells irradiated *in vivo* to which the *in vitro* results may be compared. Femoral bone marrow cells from the monkey, *Ateles*, have been scored for chromatid aberrations after the animal's legs had been irradiated with X-rays (Bender, 1960). No aberrations were seen in a total of 261 control cells. The induced breakage rate was 0·0017 chromatid breaks per cell per r. In view of the uncertainty about the generation time of marrow cells, and the small number of cells scored, it was felt that the agreement with the *in vitro* data was quite good.

Bone marrow cells from Chinese hamsters given whole body X-irradiation have also been scored for chromosomal aberrations (Bender and Gooch, 1961). Again, no aberrations were seen in a total of 299 control bone marrow cells. The chromatid breakage frequency was highest shortly after irradiation and fell rapidly with time. The maximum chromatid breakage rate was calculated to be 0·0051 breaks per cell per r. The maximum chromosome type breakage rate found was 0·0016, or about one-fourth of the chromatid breakage rate.

Brewen (1962) has investigated chromatid breaks in the X-irradiated corneal epithelium of Chinese hamsters. Two deletions were seen in a total of 236 control cells, yielding a spontaneous chromatid breakage frequency of 0·009 breaks per cell. An induced breakage frequency of 0·0035 breaks per cell per r was observed 6 hr after irradiation.

In addition to the *in vivo* work with experimental animals, several radiation accidents have recently provided the opportunity of studying the chromosome breakage rates induced by irradiation of human leukocytes *in vivo* (Bender and Gooch, unpublished data). As mentioned earlier, only chromatid type breaks have been seen in control material, with the exception of a few deletions which could equally well have been NUPD isochromatid deletions. The spontaneous chromosome breakage rate is certainly below 0·0025 breaks per cell. Only chromosome type aberrations were induced by the whole-body irradiation. Preliminary data from six irradiated people strongly suggest that the induced breakage rate is approximately the same for *in vivo* irradiation as for *in vitro* irradiation of human blood; about 0·0024 chromosome type breaks per cell per r.

All of the information available for *in vivo* irradiation of mammalian somatic cells is, then, in good agreement with the results of work with epithelioid cells and leukocytes *in vitro*. X-ray-induced breakage rates are commonly of the order of 0·002 to 0·004 breaks per cell per r. Like cells *in vitro*, mammalian somatic cells *in vivo* rarely contain spontaneous chromosome type aberrations. In mammalian cells *in vivo*, however, spontaneous chromatid type aberration rates appear to be much lower than those found *in vitro*.

CONCLUSIONS

The following generalizations seem justified in the light of the accumulated data on mammalian somatic chromosome aberrations:

1. Spontaneous aberration rates vary widely *in vitro*, but appear always to be higher *in vitro* than *in vivo*. Spontaneous breakage rates may be influenced by the type of cell in which they are measured, and they are almost certainly influenced by their *in vitro* environment and history.
2. X-ray-induced aberration rates in mammalian cells *in vitro* are very similar to those seen *in vivo*.
3. The induced chromosomal aberration rates in mammalian somatic cells are similar to those observed in the classical systems studied, such as *Tradescantia* microspores. They are certainly not (as has been suggested at various times) either very much more sensitive or very much more resistant to radiation damage.

The field of mammalian somatic cell radiation cytology is still extremely young. We are only now beginning to understand the peculiar advantages and the inevitable disadvantages of the *in vitro* approach. If it has become clear that cells do not necessarily behave in exactly the same way in culture as in the animal, it is also equally clear that they sometimes do, at least in particular and sometimes extremely useful ways. Thus it seems certain that the study of cytological phenomena in mammalian cells *in vitro* will continue to contribute to our understanding of mammalian cells *in vivo*.

REFERENCES

BELL, A. G. and BAKER, D. G., 1962, Irradiation-induced chromosome aberrations in normal human leukocytes in culture. *Canad. J. Genetics and. Cytol.* **4**, 340–351.

BENDER, M. A., 1957, X-ray-induced chromosome aberrations in normal diploid human tissue cultures. *Science*, **126**, 974–975.

BENDER, M. A., 1960, X-ray-induced chromosome aberrations in mammalian cells *in vitro* and *in vivo*. In *Immediate and Low Level Effects of Ionizing Radiations* (A. A. Buzzati-Traverso, ed.), pp. 103-118, Taylor and Frances, London.

BENDER, M. A. and CHU, E. H. Y., 1962, The chromosomes of primates. *Evolutionary and Genetic Biology of the Primates* (John Beuttner-Janusch, ed.), Academic Press, New York, in press.

BENDER, M. A. and GOOCH, P. C., 1962a, Spontaneous and X-ray-induced somatic chromosome aberrations in the Chinese hamster. *Intern. J. Rad. Biol.* **4**, 175–184.

BENDER, M. A. and GOOCH, P. C., 1962b, Types and rates of X-ray-induced chromsome aberrations in human blood irradiated *in vitro. Proc. Natl. Acad. Sci. U.S.* **48**, 522–532.

BENDER, M. A. and GOOCH, P. C., 1962c, Chromatid type aberrations induced by X-rays in human leukocyte cultures. *Cytogenetics*, in press.

BENDER, M. A. and PRESCOTT, D. M., 1962, DNA synthesis and mitosis in cultures of human peripheral leukocytes. *Exp. Cell Research*, **27**, 221–229.

BENDER, M. A., GOOCH, P. C. and PRESCOTT, D. M., 1962, Aberrations induced in human leukocyte chromosomes by ^{3}H-labeled nucleosides. *Cytogenetics*, **1**, 65–74.

BENDER, M. A. and WOLFF, S., 1961, X-ray-induced chromosome aberrations and reproductive death in mammalian cells. *Amer. Naturalist*, **95**, 39–52.

BREWEN, J. G., 1962, X-ray-induced chromosome aberrations in the corneal epithelium of the Chinese hamster, *Cricetulus griseus. Science*, **138**, 820–822.

CHU, E. H. Y., 1962, Photoreactivation and action spectrum of ultraviolet-induced mammalian chromosome aberrations. *Rec. Genet. Soc. Am.* **31**, 79 (abstract).

CHU, E. H. Y. and MONESI, V., 1960, Analysis of X-ray-induced chromosome aberrations in mouse somatic cells *in vitro. Rec. Genet. Soc. Am.* **29**, 63 (abstract).

CHU, E. H. Y., GILES, N. H. and PASSANO, K., 1961, Types and frequencies of human chromosome aberrations induced by X rays. *Proc. Natl. Acad. Sci. U.S.* **47**, 830–839.

Denver Classification, 1960, *Lancet* i, 1068.

DUBININ, N. P., KERKIS, YU. YA. and LEBEDEVA, L. T., 1960, The effects of small doses of radiation on chromosome reorganizations during the irradiation of cells in human embryonic tissue cultures. *Akademiya Nauk SSSR*, 1–14.

FETNER, R. H., 1962, Ozone-induced chromosome breakage in human cell cultures *Nature*, **194**, 793–794.

FRACCARO, M., 1960, Discussion of Bender, p. 117.

HSU, T. C., DEWEY, W. C. and HUMPHREY, R. M., 1962, Radiosensitivity of cells of Chinese hamster *in vitro* in relation to the cell cycle. *Exptl. Cell. Research*, **27**, 441–452.

HUNGERFORD, D. A., DONNELLY, A. J., NOWELL, P. C. and BECK, S., 1959, The chromosome constitution of a human phenotypic intersex. *American J. Human Genetics*, **11**, 215–236.

LEA, D. E., 1955, *Actions of Radiation on Living Cells*, 2nd ed., Cambridge University Press, Cambridge, England.

LEVAN, A. and BIESELE, J. J., 1958, Role of chromosomes in cancerogenesis, as studied in serial tissue culture of mammalian cells. *Ann. N. Y. Acad. Sci.* **71**, 1022–1053.

LIMA DE FARIA, A., REITALU, A. J. and BERGMAN, S., 1962, The pattern of DNA synthesis in the chromosomes of man. *Hereditas*, **47**, 695–704.

LINDSTEN, J., 1959, Chromosomal aberrations inducted by ionizing radiation in human cells grown *in vitro. Uppsala Läkfören Förh.* **64**, 8–9.

MACKINNEY, A. A., STOHLMAN, F. and BRECKER, G., 1962, The kinetics of cell proliferation in cultures of human peripheral blood. *Blood*, **19**, 349–358.

MOORHEAD, P. S., NOWELL, P. C., MELLMAN, W. J., BATTIPS, D. M. and HUNGERFORD, D. A., 1960, Chromosome preparations of leukocytes cultured from human peripheral blood. *Exptl. Cell. Res.* **20**, 613–616.

MORKOVIN, D. and FELDMAN, A., 1959, Dosimetry in living cells irradiated on glass: a correction. *Brit. J. Radiol.* **32**, 282.

OHNUKI, Y., AWA, A. and POMERAT, C. M., 1961, Chromosomal studies on irradiated leukocytes *in vitro.* USAF School of Aerospace Medicine, 61–104.

PUCK, T. T., 1958, Action of radiation on mammalian cells. III. Relationship between reproductive death and induction of chromosome anomalies by X-irradiation of euploid human cells *in vitro*. *Proc. Natl. Acad. Sci. U.S.* **44**, 772–780.

REVELL, S. H., 1959, The accurate estimation of chromatid aberrations and its relevance to a new interpretation of chromatid aberrations induced by ionizing radiations. *Proc. Roy. Soc. London (B)*, **150**, 563–589.

ROTHFELS, K. H. and SIMINOVITCH, L., 1958, The chromosome complement of the Rhesus monkey *(Macaca mulatta)* determined in kidney cells cultured *in vitro*. *Chromosoma*, **9**, 163–175.

SAX, H. J. and PASSANO, K. N., 1961, Spontaneous chromosome aberrations in human tissue culture cells. *Am. Naturalist*, **95**, 97–102.

WAKONIG, R., and FORD, D. K., 1960, Chromosome aberrations in irradiated cells of Chinese hamster grown in tissue culture. *Can. J. Zool.* **38**, 203–207.

XX/XXX MOSAIC IN A PATIENT WITH OLIGOPHRENIA AND OLIGOMENORRHEA ✓

J. C. C. DE ALMEIDA, L. C. PÓVOA and
J. RODRIGUES

Departamento de Endocrinologia Hospital Moncorvo Filho, Rio, and Instituto Fernandes Figueira, Departamento Nacional da Criança Rio, Brazil

A 20-YEAR-OLD feeble-minded, obese woman was referred to the Endocrine Department because of obesity and oligomenorrhea.

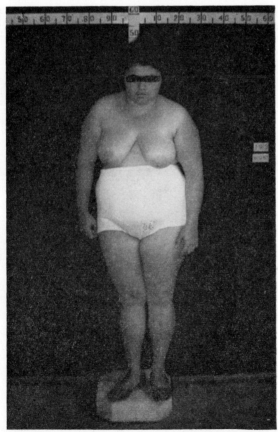

FIG. 1. The patient.

She had her first period by the age or 11. Up to the age of 19 she had regular menses. She had been overweight since she was 15.

Her mother's and father's age by the time of her birth was 33 and 36 years, respectively. They had had 4 normal children by then.

Physical examination showed an obese (Ht. 143 cm, Wt. 75·5 kg), mentally retarded woman with normal secondary sexual characters.

Her body hair distribution was normal.

Gynaecological examination revealed a normal external genitalia and no hypertrophy of the clitoris. Palpation of the ovaries was impaired because of the patient's obesity.

F.S.H.	− 10 M.U./24 hr	Total estrogens	−28·9/24 hr
17 Ks.	− 4mg/24 hr	D.H.E.	− 0·7/24 hr

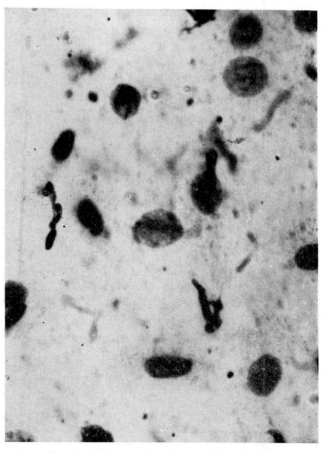

Fig. 2. Oral smear showing two Barr bodies.

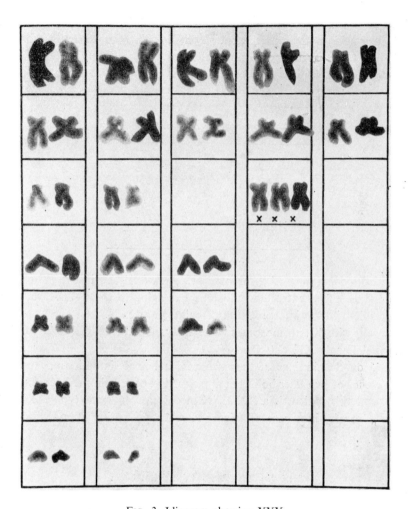

FIG. 3. Idiogram showing XXX.

Vaginal cytology showed a normal estrogenic smear.

Skull X-ray showed no abnormality.

A blind analysis of her buccal smear, using coded slides, as we normally do, revealed that 4–5 per cent of the cells contained two Barr bodies. There was a proportion of 74 per cent of cells containing a single Barr body.

Nuclear sexing of the peripheral blood showed the presence of a drumstick in 7 out of 260 neutrophils counted.

Chromosomal studies were performed using Bottura's technique.[1]

No. of chromosomes	No. of cells counted
less than 44	2
45	0
46	59
47	7
more than 47	0
	Total 68

The cells containing 47 chromosomes, when analysed in detail, showed the presence of an extra chromosome belonging to the 6–12-XX group, compatible with the interpretation of being an extra X.

The cells with 46 chromosomes were analysed and classified as presenting a normal female XX pattern.

Based on the findings of the chromosomal analysis and supported by the presence of two Barr bodies in a proportion of cells in the buccal smear we assume this patient is a XX/XXX mosaic; of the same type described by De Grouchy in a case of oligomenorrhea presenting Stein–Leventhal ovaries.

THE No. 18 TRISOMY SYNDROME

Example

As we consider it important to stress the 18 Trisomy as a separate and well-characterized condition,[3-6] we would like to report another case.

A negro male infant, born in November 1961, was referred to the Endocrine Department because of multiple congenital anomalies. He was born at the end of a full and uneventful pregnancy. His birth weight was 2·150 g. His father was 39 and his mother 33 years old by the time of his conception. He is the eighth child. One and a half years before his birth the mother

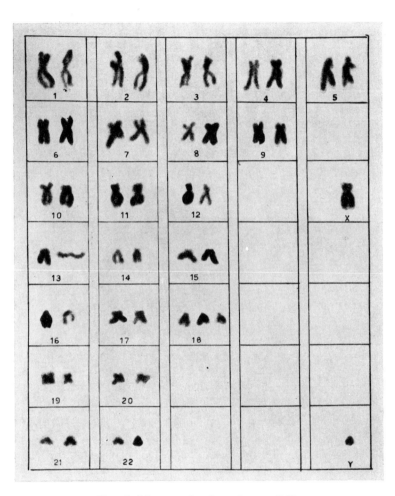

FIG. 4. Idiogram showing trisomy of 18.

delivered male twins who died very early due to intestinal infections. An older brother died at 5 months following an acute respiratory infection. None of his sibs present or seemed to have presented any noticeable congenital malformations. No maternal history of exposition to X-ray just before or at any time during pregnancy. The infant has had repeated episodes of respiratory infections.

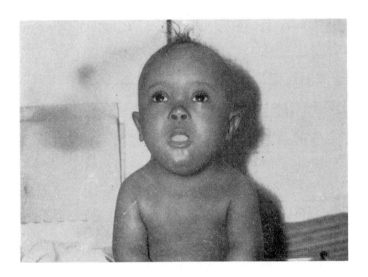

FIG. 5. The patient.

Physical examination. Poor physical and mental development. Low set and malformed ears. Small mandible. Bonnevie–Ulrich type of neck. Moderate generalized hypertonicity. Slight diastasis recti above the umbelicus. Fingers tightly flexed over hands. Index overlapping the third finger. Simian crease. Bilateral equinovarus feet. Dorsiflexion of the big toes.

Heart auscultation showed no abnormality.

Prominent occiput.

Slight delay of bone age.

Congenital dislocation of the hip.

Chromatin negative.

E.C.G.: normal.

Cytologic examination. We employed the technique described by Bottura[7].

No. of chromosomes	Cells counted
46	1
47	66
48	0
49	1
51	2
	70

We selected several karyotypes and the extra chromosome was constantly classified as belonging to the eighteenth pair.

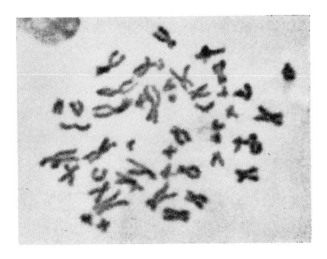

FIG. 6. Metaphase plate with 47 chromosomes.

The maternal age of our patient was of 33 in agreement with the average of the other cases published up to now, which is 34.

The analysis of the dermal patterns revealed a high palmar triradius and all ten digits with arches as Dr. Uchida[8] has found in this syndrome.

As for the soles we found a well-developed pattern of a whorl but entirely displaced to the external edge, which we do not usually find in normal infants.

ACKNOWLEDGEMENTS

We wish to express our appreciation for the help Dr. C. Bottura, Dr. I. Ferrari and Dr. M. Jardim have given to our work.

REFERENCES

1. BOTTURA, C. and FERRARI, I., *Nature*, **186**, 904, 1960.
2. DE GROUCHY, J., LAMY, M. M., YANEVA, H., SALOMON, Y. and NETTER, A., *Lancet*, II, 777, 1961.
3. SMITH, D. W., PATAU, K., THERMAN, E. and INHORN, S. L., *Pediatrics*, **57**, 338, 1960.
4. PATAU, K., THERMAN, E., SMITH, D. W. and DE MARS, R. I., *Chromosoma*, **12**, 280, 1961.
5. SMITH, D. W., PATAU, K. and THERMAN, E., *J. Pediatrics*, **60**, 513, 1962.
6. UCHIDA, I. A., BOWMAN, J. M. and WANG, H. C., *N. England J. Med.* **266**, 1198, 1962.
7. BOTTURA, C. and FERRARI, I., *Nature*, **186**, 904, 1960.
8. UCHIDA, I. A., PATAU, K. and SMITH, D. W., Abstract 31st Meeting Soc. Pediat. Res. 131, 1961.

SURVIVAL OF HUMAN CELLS IN TISSUE CULTURE AFTER IRRADIATION WITH DENSELY AND SPARSELY IONIZING RADIATION

G. W. BARENDSEN

Radiobiological Institute of the
Organization for Health Research T.N.O.,
151 Lange Kleiweg, Rijswijk Z.H.,
Netherlands

INTRODUCTION

During the last few years quantitative studies of the damage induced by ionizing radiations on the reproductive capacity of mammalian cells have become possible by the development of a plating technique for single mammalian cells, whereby each cell grows into a separate clone of macroscopic size.[1] Since the introduction of this technique by Puck *et al.*, a number of investigations has been reported concerning dose-response curves of different types of cultured mammalian cells obtained with X-rays. Though differences of a factor of two or three have been found, all of these cell types were shown to be very sensitive to ionizing radiations with an LD_{37} of the order of 100 r.[2-5]

The purpose of this paper is to describe results of experiments in which the sensitivity to ionizing radiation of cells derived from a human kidney was measured in relation to the type of radiation employed and as a function of various experimental conditions. Experiments will be described in which cells were irradiated with α-particles and deuterons of various energies, X-rays and β-particles. The values obtained for the relative biological effectiveness (RBE) as a function of the linear energy transfer (LET) will be presented in relation to the levels of damage considered.

Results of further experiments have shown that the effects of sparsely ionizing radiations can be modified to a considerable extent by various factors, whereas this is much less so in the case of densely ionizing radiations.

The insight, gained from these experiments in the effects of various experimental conditions on survival curves has important consequences for the appraisal of RBE data obtained with radiations of different LET's.

MATERIALS AND METHODS

In all experiments an established line of heteroploid cells derived from a human kidney was used, subcultured routinely in glass bottles during the past four years in our laboratory.[6] The culture medium consisted of Hank's solution with 0·5 per cent lactalbumine hydrolysate and 6 per cent calf serum, supplemented with 100 IU of penicillin and 0·10 mg of streptomycin per ml. The incubator, at 37°C, was continuously flushed with air, which was saturated with water vapour and contained 3 per cent of CO_2 in order to maintain the pH of the culture fluid at about 7·4. The cells used for irradiation experiments were obtained from 4 days old flask cultures in proliferation phase. They were detached from the glass and dispersed by gentle trypsinization[1] followed by vigorous pipetting to break up clumps of cells. The single-cell suspension thus obtained was counted in a hemocytometer and dilutions were made with tissue culture fluid. Microscopic inspection showed that not more than a few per cent of the cells were present in groups of two or three cells.

The standard procedure used in our experiments can be summarized as follows. The cells were plated in modified Petri dishes which consist of glass rings, 45–50 mm in diameter, with a Melinex bottom, 6 μ thick.[7] Puck's "feeder layer" technique was employed, using 150,000 "feeder cells" per dish in 3 ml medium. These cells were made incapable of unlimited proliferation by 4000 rad of 250 kVp X-rays. About 18 hr after the feeder layer was plated, 200 or more cells from the single-cell suspension, diluted to 1 ml culture medium, were added to the dishes. After about 4 hr of incubation at 37°C, more than 99 per cent of these cells adhered to the bottom of the culture dishes. Subsequently the culture dishes were taken out of the incubator and allowed to attain room temperature during 10 min (18–22°C). The irradiation and other treatments were carried out at room temperature. After irradiation the cells were incubated at 37°C for 12–14 days. Medium was replaced every five days. After 12–14 days the cells were stained *in situ* and the number of clones containing more than 50 cells was counted. This number of clones has been taken to represent the number of surviving cells. In each experiment the mean value was taken of at least three and usually four or more culture dishes, each of which had received the same dose of radiation and treatment. The fraction of cells surviving after irradiation was calculated as a percentage of the unirradiated controls, which had received exactly the same treatment except for the irradiation.

Plating efficiencies of unirradiated controls ranged from 70 to 110 per cent of the values determined from counting in a hemocytometer the single-cell suspension before dilution. This apparent variation in plating efficiency is presumably in a large part due to statistical variation inherent in the determination of the initial cell concentration by the counting of about 100 cells in a hemocytometer and to variations introduced by the dilution of a suspension from about 10^6 cells per ml to 200 cells per ml. Therefore the true plating efficiency was presumably very close to 100 per cent in all experiments. Standard deviations were calculated from the variation between the dishes which received the same treatment and radiation dose. If this value was smaller than the square root of the total number of clones counted per group, the latter value was taken. The feeder layer technique was used in all experiments, although without this layer plating efficiencies could be attained of between 50 and 100 per cent, if culture medium with 20–30 per cent calf serum, instead of 6 per cent, was used. The results on survival after irradiation were found to be more reproducible, however, with the feeder layer present.

Details of the irradiation techniques and dosimetry have been published elsewhere.*[7,8]

THE RELATION BETWEEN RBE AND LET

In previous papers results have been described of experiments on inhibition of clone formation by α-particles from ^{210}Po, by cyclotron accelerated α-particles and deuterons, by 20 kVP X-rays, 250 kVp X-rays and β-radiation from ^{90}Y.[8,9] The results are summarized in Fig. 1. For a discussion of the accuracy of the individual curves, reference may be made to the earlier publications. [8−10] It will be clear from these results that densely ionizing α-particles give rise to experimental survival curves, whereas with sparsely ionizing radiations sigmoid survival curves are obtained whereby the effectiveness per unit dose increases with increasing dose.

From the curves presented it is possible to derive values for the RBE of the radiations, compared to 200 kV X-rays, which are, as a consequence of the differences in shape between the survival curves, dependent on the

---

* In part of the experiments a 200 kVp X-ray machine was used and in later experiments a 250 kVp X-ray machine. Both radiations had a HVL of about 2·0 mm Cu. The survival curves obtained with standard conditions were identical for both radiations.

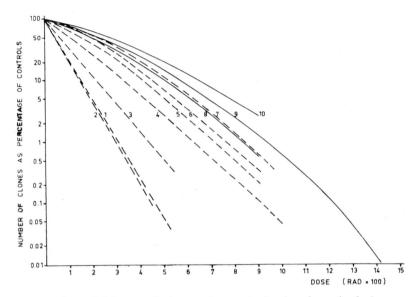

Fɪɢ. 1. Effects of different radiations on the capacity for clone formation by human kidney cells in culture. Curves obtained with:

1. ^{210}Po α-particles (3·4 MeV, 140 keV/μ of tissue). 2. Cyclotron accelerated α-particles (5·2 MeV, 85·8 keV/μ of tissue). 3. Cyclotron accelerated α-particles (8·3 MeV, 60·8 keV/μ of tissue). 4. Cyclotron accelerated α-particles (26·8 MeV, 24·6 keV/μ of tissue). 5. Cyclotron accelerated deuterons (3·45 MeV, 17·4 keV/μ of tissue). 6. Cyclotron accelerated deuterons (6·3 MeV, 11·0 keV/μ of tissue). 7. Cyclotron accelerated deuterons (14·87 MeV, 5·6 keV/μ of tissue). 8. 20 kV X-rays (average LET about 6 keV/μ of tissue). 9. 200 kV X-rays (average LET about 2·5 keV/μ of tissue). 10. β-particles from ^{90}Y (E$_{\beta\,max}$ = 2·2 MeV, average LET about 0·3 keV/μ of tissue).

level of damage considered. The RBE of a radiation Y is defined as the ratio of two absorbed doses of radiation, namely:

$$\text{RBE (Y)} = \frac{\text{dose of ``standard'' radiation required for specified effect}}{\text{dose or radiation Y required for equal effect}}$$

This definition has been used to calculate RBE's corresponding to 80, 20, 5 and 0·5 per cent survival. The pertinent data are given in Table 1 and summarized in Fig. 2, from which a few conclusions can be drawn. First, the general shape of the RBE vs. LET curves is the same for various levels of damage and agrees with published results concerning other mammalian systems.[11] Between 0·3 and 10 keV/μ of tissue the RBE increases but slowly with LET, followed by a more rapid rise above 10 keV/μ of tissue till at about 100 keV/μ of tissue a maximum is found with a subsequent

TABLE 1. RELATIVE BIOLOGICAL EFFECTIVENESS OF DIFFERENT RADIATIONS FOR VARIOUS LEVELS OF DAMAGE, CORRESPONDING TO DIFFERENT PERCENTAGES OF SURVIVING CELLS

Radiation	Energy MeV	LET keV/μ of wet tissue	Percentage survival, i.e. level of damage							
			80%		20%		5%		0·5%	
			dose in rad	RBE	dose in rad	RBE	dose in rad	RBE	dose in rad	RBE
α-particles	3·4	140	14·5	6·9	105	4·24	194	3·53	344	2·98
α-particles	5·2	85·8	14·3	7·0	104	4·28	192	3·57	340	3·02
α-particles	8·3	60·8	24	4·2	150	2·97	250	2·74	420	2·44
α-particles	26·8	24·6	44	2·27	260	1·71	430	1·57	670	1·53
Deuterons	3·45	17·4	60	1·67	320	1·39	520	1·32	775	1·32
Deuterons	6·3	11·0	80	1·25	345	1·29	540	1·27	795	1·29
Deuterons	14·87	5·6	95	1·05	390	1·14	580	1·18	860	1·19
X-rays	0·02[a]	6[b]	90	1·11	380	1·17	610	1·11	915	1·12
X-rays	0·2[a]	2·5[b]	100	1·00	445	1·00	685	1·00	1025	1·00
β-particles	2·2[a]	0·3[b]	120	0·84	500	0·83	780	0·88	1130	0·91

a Maximum energy.
b Average linear energy transfer.

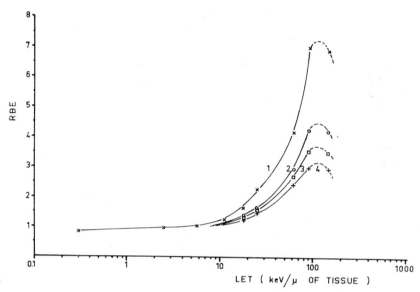

FIG. 2. RBE of different radiations for inhibition of clone formation as a function of LET at various levels of damage: Curve 1 corresponds to 80 per cent survival, Curve 2 corresponds to 20 per cent survival, Curve 3 corresponds to 5 per cent survival, Curve 4 corresponds to 0·5 per cent survival.

decrease at higher LET's. The high LET part of the curves is ill-defined as shown by the dotted parts of the curves.

A second characteristic shown by Fig. 2 is the increase of the RBE with decreasing level of damage, i.e. at low doses corresponding to high percentages survival, the maximum RBE is found. The curve obtained for 80 per cent survival shows a maximum RBE of about 7, derived from a dose of 100 rad of 200 kV X-rays and about 14 rad of α-radiation with a LET between 80 and 120 keV/μ of tissue. The question arises whether this maximum RBE may increase indefinitely at still lower doses or whether there will be some limiting value. Arguments have been advanced elsewhere which show that, with low LET radiations, there is a definite, though small, probability that damage is produced through a "single event" type of mechanism.[10] The conclusion must be drawn that there will be a limiting value for the RBE of densely ionizing radiations; the absolute value may depend on several factors however.

Finally it might be pointed out that the results given in Fig. 2 can be used to estimate an "effective LET" of a type of radiation for which an "average LET" is usually calculated on a theoretical basis.[12] This can be applied for instance to our results with 20 kV X-rays. The efficiency of this radiation is about equal to the value obtained from 14·8 MeV deuterons with a LET of 5·6 keV/μ of tissue. This agrees perhaps fortuitously with the LET value usually quoted as 6 keV/μ, which can be derived from the mean electron energy of about 6 keV.[13] It is significantly smaller, however, than the value of about 18 calculated by Burch.[12]

A similar comparison can be made for the estimation of the effective LET of other radiations. If for instance with doses of about 300 rad of fast neutrons an RBE is obtained of 2, for a specified type of damage, i.e. the same effect is produced by 600 rad of 200 kV X-rays, then it can be deduced from curve 3 in Fig. 2 that these neutrons have an effective LET of about 38 keV/μ in tissue. By comparison of curves 1 and 3 of Fig. 2 it can further be estimated that at low doses the same neutrons will have a considerably higher RBE. This high RBE will presumably also apply if very low dose rates are considered, because this is equivalent to a low dose in each cell generation.

It will be clear that in this way the relation between dose, dose-rate, LET and RBE can in principle be derived from the curves given in Fig. 2. The results thus obtained can be compared with RBE values from animal experiments. Agreement between these RBE's may give confidence in conclusions to be drawn from cell culture experiments in application to conditions where no animal experiments are as yet available or feasible. It will be clear, however, that cells irradiated in an organism are in quite different experimental conditions than cells irradiated in the standard conditions as described above. Thus, apart from differences in cell types, a comparison of results on RBE's in animal experiments and cell culture experiments will only be of significance if the influence of various factors has been evaluated. Although the general characteristics of the relation between LET and RBE may not be affected, the absolute values obtained might well depend on various culturing conditions as will be discussed in the next section.

MODIFICATION OF THE RADIATION RESPONSE

A. *Effects of the Time Interval between Plating and Irradiation*

The experiments on survival of cells after irradiation with different doses of various types of radiations and with different experimental conditions, involved handling of between 60 and 120 dishes and usually lasted a few hours. For the comparison of results obtained in one experiment, it was necessary first to investigate whether cells irradiated at 4 hr after plating would have the same radiosensitivity as cells irradiated 8 or more hours after plating. Therefore a number of experiments were carried out in

which the time interval between plating and irradiation was varied. The cells
were taken out of the incubator at 0, 2, 6, 8, 12, 20, 28, 52, 76 and 100 hr
after plating respectively and irradiated with different doses of either 250
kVp X-rays or α-radiation from ^{210}Po. The results are shown in Fig. 3.
The curve at zero hours could not be measured with α-particles as the cells
have to attach to the bottom before irradiation with α-particles is possible.
At 2 hr after plating a curve identical with curve 1 of Fig. 3 was obtained.

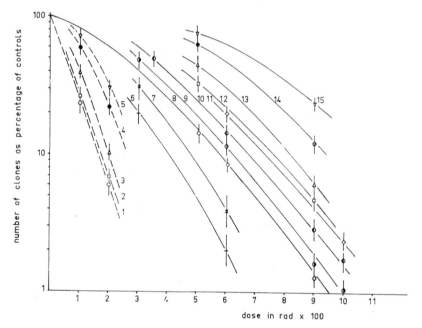

Fɪɢ. 3. Inhibition of clone formation as a function of the radiation dose in relation
to the interval between plating of the cells and irradiation. Curves 1, 2, 3, 4 and 5:
survival curves obtained with ^{210}Po α-radiation administered 4, 28, 52, 76 and 100 hr
after plating respectively. Curves 6 to 15: survival curves obtained with 250 kVp X-
rays administered 0, 2, 4, 8, 12, 20, 28, 52, 76 and 100 hr after plating respectively.

Not all of the doses and time intervals could be used in the same experiment,
as this would involve the handling of more dishes at a time than was feasible.
In order to ensure that the results of different experiments could be compared, a control curve corresponding to a time interval of 4 hr between plating
and irradiation was included in each experiment. As these curves were the
same within experimental errors in four experiments, the data of all these
four experiments were combined in Fig. 3. The results show that in experiments with α-particles the time interval between plating and irradiation is

important only if the interval is increased to more than about 30 hr. Consequently a period of at least 24 hr is available for reproducible experiments. Furthermore these results indicate that only a small percentage of the cells divide during the first 24 hr after plating, because in case significant division had occurred this would most likely have influenced the percentage survival significantly.

Quite different results were obtained with 250 kVp X-rays. Immediately after plating the effect of irradiation is most severe, i.e. the cells are most sensitive and the percentage survival found after a given dose is lowest. During the first few hours after plating the sensitivity decreases rapidly, i.e. appreciably higher percentages survival are found if the irradiation takes place 4 hr after plating as compared with, for instance, 2 hr after plating (see Fig. 3, curves 7 and 8). This change in percentage survival is presented in a different way in Fig. 4 as a function of the interval between plating and irradiation for a dose of 150 rad of α-radiation (curve 1) and a dose of 550 rad of 250 kVp X-radiation (curve 2). Curve 1 of Fig. 4 shows again clearly that with α-particles the sensitivity does not change significantly between 2 and 30 hr after plating, followed by an increase of the percentage survival presumably due to multiplication of the cells. An indication that multiplication is the cause here can also be obtained from Fig. 3, curves 3, 4 and 5, which clearly show a "sigmoid" or "multi-event" character.

Curve 2 of Fig. 4 shows that, after a sharp increase during the first 4 hr, the percentage survival after a dose of 550 rad of 250 kVp X-rays changes less rapidly, till starting at 30–40 hr after plating a more pronounced increase is found, presumably due to multiplication of the cells.

A satisfactory explanation of the differences in shape between curves 1 and 2 of Fig. 4 cannot as yet be given. The change in sensitivity to 250 kVp X-rays cannot be due to an appreciable extent to cell multiplication, as in this case the apparent sensitivities to X-rays and α-particles should decrease in about the same way. One possible explanation is that the sensitivity to X-rays is influenced by the trypsinization procedure, used to prepare the single-cell suspension. A "recovery" from this treatment during the period after plating might result in a decrease in the sensitivity to X-rays, whereas the sensitivity to α-particles is likely to remain constant. As explained in a previous paper the damage produced by one α-particle passing anywhere through a sensitive area of about 40 μ^2 in the nucleus is so severe that inhibition of clone formation will result even if the cell has completely recovered from the trypsinization treatment.[5] Some evidence that the trypsinization plays a part was obtained by comparison of the sensitivity of cells which were treated with trypsin during 5 and 15 min respectively. The longer

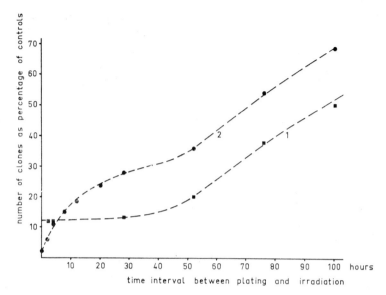

FIG. 4. Effect of the interval between plating and irradiation of cells on the capacity for clone formation after (1) 150 rad of α-radiation from ^{210}Po and (2) 550 rads of 250 kVp X-radiation. These doses were chosen because the percentages survival are about equal for both doses of radiation if administered 4 hr after plating.

treatment resulted in a higher sensitivity immediately after plating, but 8 hr after plating both groups of cells were equally sensitive within experimental errors.

A second explanation for the decrease of the sensitivity to X-rays with the time interval between plating and irradiation may be given by the assumption that the trypsinization and plating procedure, which is carried out at room temperature (18–22°C), results in a partial synchronization of the cells plated. Changes in the sensitivity to X-rays in relation to the division cycle have been described for HeLa cells with the same criterion of clone formation.[14] The most likely explanation at present seems to be that both factors mentioned play a part.

B. Effects of Temperature before and after Plating

Besides the time interval between plating and irradiation, the temperature at which the cells are maintained during this interval and after irradiation has been found to influence the radioresponse of the cells considerably. Although the general trend was the same in all experiments, these effects were found to vary in magnitude. The results of the 4 experiments carried out, could therefore not be pooled and in Table 2 only one experiment is represented. In this experiment groups of dishes were irradiated either immediately after plating (Table 2, group 1) or kept at 20°C during 4 hr

TABLE 2. SURVIVAL OF CULTURED CELLS AFTER 350 RAD AND 700 RAD OF 250 KVP X-RADIATION IN RELATION TO THE TEMPERATURE BEFORE AND AFTER IRRADIATION

Treatment after plating	Percentage survival		
	Controls	350 rad	700 rad
1. Irradiation immediately after plating and			
a. after irradiation 4 hr at 37°C	104·6±4·2	30·6±2·3	3·8±0·5
b. after irradiation 4 hr at 20°C	96·9±4·0	8·9±1·2	0·2±0·1
2. Irradiation 4 hr after plating; in this interval the cells were kept at 20°C			
a. after irradiation 4 hr at 37°C	101·7±4·2	30·7±2·3	3·2±0·7
b. after irradiation 4 hr at 20°C	93·2±4·0	17·4±1·7	0·3±·01
3. Irradiation 4 hr after plating; in this interval the cells were kept at 37°C			
a. after irradiation 4 hr at 37°C	98·1±4·1	36·7±2·5	5·6±0·9
b. after irraditaion 4 hr at 20°C	101·8±4·2	21·9±2·0	2·5±0·6

after plating and subsequently irradiated (Table 2, group 2), or kept at 37°C during 4 hr after plating and subsequently irradiated (Table 2, group 3). In each of these groups two types of post-irradiation treatments were employed: the cells were either kept at 20°C during 4 hr and subsequently transferred to the incubator at 37°C (Table 1, groups 1b, 2b and 3b) or the dishes were transferred to the incubator at 37°C immediately after irradiation (Table 2, groups 1a, 2a and 3a). Unirradiated controls for all groups were the same within the statistical variation and the average is taken as 100 per cent. From the results the following conclusions can be drawn:

(a) A significant difference is found between results obtained with pre-irradiation treatment of the cells at 20°C as compared with 37°C. Cells kept at 20°C for 4 hr after plating are more sensitive than cells kept at 37°C, i.e. lower percentages survival are found in group 2 as compared with group 3 after corresponding doses of radiation.

(b) A significant effect of post-irradiation treatment of the cells is found in all groups. Cells maintained at 20°C during 4 hr after irradiation show lower percentages survival as compared with cells maintained at 37°C after irradiation.

(c) The effect of post-irradiation treatment at 20°C on the survival of irradiated cells is more pronounced if the cells are irradiated immediately after plating or are kept at 20°C during 4 hr after plating as compared with cells kept at 37°C during 4 hr between plating and irradiation.

C. *Effects of Culture Fluids*

A next factor, the importance of which for survival of irradiated cells was evaluated, is the culture medium. An experiment was carried out in which cells derived from one flask culture, grown on the standard medium, were plated in two groups of dishes. One half of the initial single-cell suspension obtained by trypsinization of a flask culture was diluted by a factor of 100 in Eagle's medium and plated, whereas the other half served as

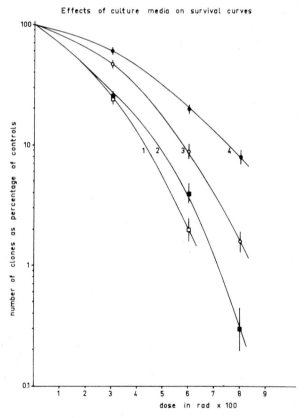

FIG. 5. Effects of culture media on survival of cells obtained from a monolayer culture after irradiation with 250 kVp X-rays. Curves 1 and 2: Cells cultured in Eagle's medium, irradiated 2 and 7 hr after plating respectively. Curves 3 and 4: Cells cultured in the standard medium, irradiated 2 and 7 hr after plating respectively.

a control and was diluted in the standard medium. Survival curves were determined for both groups of dishes. The irradiations were carried out either 2 or 7 hr respectively after plating for both media. Results are shown in Fig. 5. With the standard medium the usual pattern was observed, whereby the dishes irradiated 7 hr after plating show higher percentages survival as compared with those irradiated 2 hr after plating. With the cells plated in Eagle's medium, significantly lower percentages survival were obtained both at 2 and 7 hr after plating as compared with cells plated in the standard medium. However, the differences in survival due to different time intervals between plating and irradiation are smaller in Eagle's medium as compared with the standard medium. A comparable effect of the culture medium on survival of irradiated cells was observed with cells derived from a suspension culture. The T_1 cells have been routinely subcultured in 500 ml suspension cultures, using the modified Eagle's medium.*[15] An important difference in the experimental procedure used for these cells as compared with cells

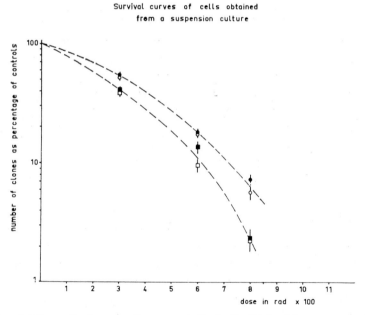

FIG. 6. Effects of culture media on survival of cells obtained from a suspension culture after irradiation with 250 kVp X-rays. Open and closed squares: Cells cultured in Eagle's medium, irradiated 2 and 7 hr after plating respectively. Open and closed circles: Cells cultured in the standard medium, irradiated 2 and 7 hr after plating respectively.

* I wish to thank Dr. J. C. Klein for putting these cultures at my disposal.

derived from monolayer cultures is that no trypsinization is required. After vigorous pipetting to break up clumps, the cells obtained from the stock culture were simply diluted in either Eagle's medium or the standard medium and subsequently plated. Irradiations were carried out either 2 hr or 7 hr after plating for both cultures. From the results which are shown in Fig. 6 two conclusions can be drawn. First the survival of cells plated in Eagle's medium is after irradiation again lower as compared with cells plated in the standard medium. Furthermore, neither in the standard medium nor in Eagle's medium is an effect of the time interval between plating and irradiation observed. This provides another indication that the trypsinization procedure used in the experiments with cells derived from monolayer cultures is the cause of the important effect of the time interval between plating and irradiation as described in one of the preceding paragraphs. Cells detached from the glass by trypsin are likely to be damaged by trypsinization and to recover during the first hours after plating corresponding with a decrease in radiosensitivity.

D. *Effects of Anoxia and Cysteamine on Survival of Cells after Irradiation*

The effects of these factors will not be discussed in detail, but the results described elsewhere will be summarized briefly to show differences in response of the cells to densely and sparsely ionizing radiations.

Anoxia has been shown to protect many biological systems from effects of X-rays. Equilibration of T_1 cells with different mixtures of O_2 and N_2 has been found to influence the sensitivity of these cells to 250 kVp X-rays significantly, whereas the sensitivity to α-particles changed very little.[9] As has been described in detail elsewhere, with very pure nitrogen dose-reduction factors of 2·6 and 1·15 were obtained with 250 kVp X-rays and ^{210}Po α-particles respectively.

A considerable number of substances have been found to protect different biological systems from the action of ionizing radiations. The action of cysteamine on radiation induced inhibition of clone formation has been compared for α-radiation and 250 kVp X-radiation in experiments in which 25 mM cysteamine was applied during 30 min before irradiation. Details of the experimental procedure are described elsewhere.[16] It was found that a dose reduction factor of 3·7 could be achieved for 250 kVp X-rays and a factor of only 1·20 for α-particles from ^{210}Po.

DISCUSSION

It will be clear that a general conclusion can be drawn from the results described, namely that survival of cells after irradiation can be influenced considerably if sparsely ionizing radiations are used, whereas with densely ionizing radiations experimental conditions and metabolic or physiological factors seem to be much less important. This implies that whenever results on the relative biological effectiveness of different radiations are to be compared, one should consider in detail the experimental conditions involved. The RBE of a given type of densely ionizing radiations may vary to various factors not because its own effectiveness changes so much, but as a result of the variation in effectiveness of the standard reference, usually taken as 200 kVp X-rays, which has a relatively low mean LET.

The values given in Table 1 and Fig. 2 should be considered in the light of these results. The treatment of the cells with cysteamine which gave the largest difference, resulted in a dose modifying factor of 3·7 for 250 kVp X-rays and of only 1·2 for α-particles from ^{210}Po. The RBE of the latter particles is thereby increased by a factor of about 3. Thus in these conditions a maximum RBE of about 20 may be observed at low levels of damage. Other factors, such as culturing conditions, may modify the RBE values to a lesser extent but differences of 50 per cent may well be found.

Finally a last point should be made, RBE data are sometimes used to derive conclusions about the mechanism by which radiation damage is produced. Any comparison of RBE's observed for a particular radiation in biological systems should include however consideration of the various factors mentioned. Different RBE's do not have to imply different mechanisms while identical RBE values do not have to indicate a similar basic mechanism by which radiation damage is produced.

SUMMARY

Effects of ionizing radiations on the capacity for clone formation by kidney cells of human origin was studied in relation to the LET of the radiations employed.

The RBE of various radiations was found to change with the level of damage considered, the highest RBE's being found at low doses. For all levels of damage the results show that between 0·3 and 10 keV/μ of tissue the RBE increases slowly with LET, followed by a more rapid rise above 10 keV/μ of tissue, till at about 100 keV/μ of tissue a maximum is found with a subsequent decrease at higher LET's.

The values obtained for the RBE's of various radiations were further studied in relation to the possibilities of modifying the radiation response of the cells by various conditions. It was found that the effectiveness of densely ionizing radiations is much less affected by various treatments than the effectiveness of sparsely ionizing radiations. Thus the RBE's of densely ionizing radiations may vary due to several factors, including normal culturing conditions, not because their own effectiveness changes so much, but as a result of variations in effectiveness of the standard of reference, 200 kVp X-rays, which has a relatively low mean LET.

REFERENCES

1. PUCK T. T., MARCUS P. I. and CIECIURA S. J., Clonal growth of mammalian cells *in vitro*. *J. Exptl. Med.* **103**, 273–284, 1956.
2. PUCK T. T. and MARCUS P. I., Action of X-rays on mammalian cells. *J. Exptl. Med.* **103**, 653–666, 1956.
3. HOOD S. L. and NORRIS G., Sensitivity of human cells to soft X-rays. *Biochim. et Biophys. Acta*, **36**, 275–278, 1959.
4. ELKIND M. M. and SUTTON H., Radiation response of mammalian cells grown in culture (I). *Radiation Res.* **13**, 556–593, 1960.
5. BARENDSEN G. W., BEUSKER T. L. J., VERGROESEN A. J. and BUDKE L., Effects of different ionizing radiations on human cells in tissue culture. II. Biological experiments. *Radiation Res.* **13**, 841–849, 1960.
6. VAN DER VEEN J., BOTS L. and MES A., Establishment of two human cell strains from kidney and reticulasarcoma of lung. *Arch. ges. Virusforsch.* **8**, 230–238, 1958.
7. BARENDSEN G. W. and BEUSKER T. L. J., Effect of different ionizing radiations on human cells in tissue culture. I. Irradiation techniques and dosimetry. *Radiation Res.* **13**, 832–840, 1960.
8. BARENDSEN G. W., WALTER H. D. M., FOWLER J. F. and BEWLY D. K., Effects of different ionizing radiations on human cells in tissue culture. III. Experiments with cyclotron accelerated alpha particles and deuterons. *Radiation Res.* **18**, 106–19, 1963.
9. BARENDSEN G. W., Damage to the reproductive capacity of human cells in tissue culture by ionizing radiations of different linear energy transfer. In *The Initial Effects of Ionizing Radiations on Cells*, ed. by HARRIS J. R. G., pp. 183–194, Academic Press, London, 1961.
10. BARENDSEN G. W., Dose-survival curves of human cells in tissue culture irradiated with α-, β-, 20 kV X- and 200 kV X-radiation. *Nature*, **193**, 1153–1155, 1962.
11. STORER J. B., HARRIS P. S., FURCHNER J. E. and LANDHAM W. H., The relative biological effectiveness of various ionizing radiations in mammalian systems. *Radiation Res.* **6**, 188–288, 1957.
12. BURCH P. R. J., Some physical aspects of relative biological efficiency. *Brit. J. Radiol.* **30**, 524–529, 1957.
13. LEA D. E., *Action of Radiations on Living Cells*, p. 24, 2nd ed., Cambridge University Press, London, 1956.
14. TERASIMA T. and TOLMACH, L. J., Changes in X-ray sensitivity of HeLa cells during the division cycle. *Nature*, **190**, 1210–1211, 1961.
15. EAGLE H., Amino-acid metabolism in mammalian cell cultures. *Science*, **130**, 432–437, 1959.
16. BARENDSEN G. W. and WALTER H. D. M., Effects of different ionizing radiations on human cells in tissue culture. IV. Modification of radiation damage. To be published.

OBSERVATIONS ON THE MORPHOLOGY AND BEHAVIOR OF NORMAL HUMAN CHROMOSOMES*†

D. A. HUNGERFORD‡§

The Institute for Cancer Research, Philadelphia, Pa., U. S. A.

INTRODUCTION

The many milestones of discovery in the development of human cytogenetics since 1956 are well known, and almost all have been independently confirmed and exhaustively documented. Included among these are abnormalities of chromosome number and/or structure in a variety of abnormal individuals and in some cases in normal ones, as well as apparently normal complements in abnormal individuals.

The major themes and an ever-growing number of variations on them have been catalogued in many reviews, almost exclusively concerned with the relationship of such findings to problems of medical interest. Among the more recent of these are reviews by Bearn and German, 1961; Bőők, 1961; Ferguson-Smith, 1961; Ford, 1961; Hamerton, 1961; Harnden and Jacobs, 1961; Hauschka, 1961; Hirschhorn and Cooper, 1961; Hsu, in press; Lejeune and Turpin, 1961; and Robinson, 1961. Some of these include as well brief treatments of some of the major historical and technical developments in this field.

* Parts of this paper constituted a portion of a dissertation in zoology presented to the Faculty of the Graduate School of Arts and Sciences of the University of Pennsylvania in partial fulfilment of the requirements for the degree of Doctor of Philosophy.

† Supported in part by terminal year predoctoral research fellowship CF-11,168 and grant C-5903 from the National Cancer Institute, National Institutes of Health, Public Health Service, and earlier by a junior research fellowship from The Institute for Cancer Research, Philadelphia.

‡ Travel to the Symposium on Mammalian Tissue Culture and Cytology, São Paulo, Brazil, was enabled by grant NSF-G22888 from the National Science Foundation, Washington, D. C.

§ The author is indebted to Dr. Peter C. Nowell for providing much of the material used in these studies, to Dr. Jack Schultz for constructive criticism of the manuscript, and to Miss Joyce Wagner for valuable technical assistance.

Increase in knowledge of the morphology and behavior of the human chromosome complement has kept pace with growth in the rest of the field. In general the principles employed in the formulation of the Denver system ("A proposed standard system of nomenclature of human mitotic chromosomes" has appeared in the following places among others: *Lancet*, **i**, 1063–1065, 1960; *Am. J. Human Genet.* **12**, 384–388, 1960; *J.A.M.A.* **174**, 159–162, 1960) have been borne out, and while it is apparently still not possible unequivocally to distinguish all of the chromosome pairs, increasing numbers of criteria useful in making such distinctions have become available. Some of these will be among the subjects of this paper.

The author's observations on normal human chromosomes have been made almost entirely on metaphases from cultures of leukocytes from peripheral blood; all preparations have been made by the method of Moorhead *et al.* Since air-drying often results in greater distortion of the chromosomes than the squash method, emphasis has been placed on recognizing individual chromosomes on sight, and direct measurements for the determination of percentage haploid length and arm ratios have not been generally employed. Whether the criteria adopted here are useful in examining chromosomes derived from skin and other organ cultures remains to be determined.

Materials and Methods

The contemporary use of short-term cultures of leukocytes derived from human peripheral blood for chromosome analysis was begun in 1957 (Nowell *et al.*, 1958. Note, however, the much earlier studies, beginning in 1931, on the same material — see Chrustschoff (1935) for a full account) with a method derived from the work of Li and Osgood (1949) and Osgood and Kripphaene (1955). Our initial studies were made on leukemic blood. Subsequently, Nowell (1960) demonstrated that leukocytes in *normal* blood can be stimulated to divide in culture by the presence of phytohemagglutinin (PHA) in the medium. The original peripheral blood method (see Hungerford *et al.*, 1959) was later modified (Moorhead *et al.*, 1960) such that air-drying replaced squashing and preparations of considerably improved technical quality resulted. We have continued to use this method, essentially unchanged except for the substitution of hypotonic serum (Lejeune *et al.*, 1959) for hypotonic balanced salt solution in prefixation treatment.

Because of its speed and convenience, the method has become widely adopted in other laboratories, and a number of workers have further modified the technique. Miller and Breg (1962) have employed various fixatives and have compared squashing with air-drying; Hastings *et al.* (1961) have

used fine iron powder and a magnetic field to remove polymorphs —
responsible for clotting sometimes observed — from the inoculum; Nichols
and Levan (1962) have used dextran instead of PHA for separation and have
extended the method to a variety of species; and Edwards (1962) has developed semi-micro methods for use with very small blood samples such as
those obtained from infants and very young children.

The method of Moorhead *et al.* was developed just preceding the Denver
conference, and the majority of observations to be discussed here were
made during a short interval immediately following the adoption of the new
method. This method conferred the advantages of high numbers of mitoses,
little or no over-contraction of chromosomes, and better fixation and spreading. It may be noted that these advantages alone would have permitted
the recognition of the Ph^1 chromosome as an autosomal derivative, even if
females had not been included in the series studied (Nowell and Hungerford,
1960b). The earlier interpretation of this chromosome had been confused
(Nowell and Hungerford, 1960a).

OBSERVATIONS AND DISCUSSION

The Denver system has been severely criticized, notably by Patau (1961,
see also 1960), who has based his objections on statistical analysis of linear
measurements used in characterizing the chromosomes. However, few
investigators rely solely on this parameter in identifying chromosomes,
and as Patau himself has said (1960) " . . . the experienced cytologist may
at times even draw valid distinctions where these do not show up with
sufficient clarity in measurements". Such features as shape (estimation of
which involves the visual integration of area and volume) and density
(variation in which may indicate heteropycnosis or, alternatively, rotation
of the object in a plane perpendicular to that of the preparation are
important factors.

Group 1–3. No uncertainty has existed concerning the identification of
individual chromosomes in this group, and it will not be discussed further,
except to remark on the characteristic presence of a secondary constriction
in one arm of No. 1, close to the centromere (Fig. 1). This marker has been
noted by de la Chapelle (1961).

Group 4–5. No consistently reliable method of distinguishing readily
between these chromosomes has appeared. Often the four chromosomes
can be arrayed in two apparently homologous pairs on the basis of a slight
difference in length of the short arms. However, in view of the variability
in the centromere position of known homologues (mentioned below in

reference to No. 16), and in view of the fact that the difference is so slight, this procedure seems of doubtful value.

Group X–6. These are often distinguishable as a group from members of the following group on the basis of overall length. Discrimination between X and 6 is difficult if not impossible. We have attempted to learn whether such discrimination is possible on the basis of direct measurement and calculation of arm ratios. Were differences between the two chromosomes

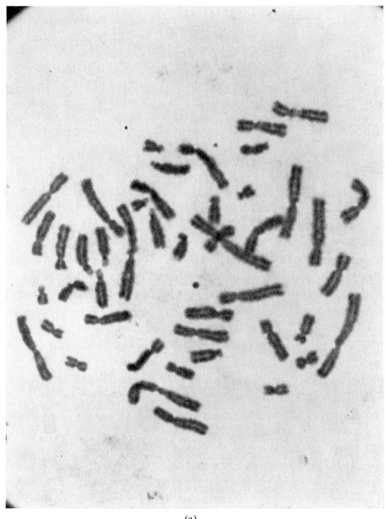

(a)

Fig. 1a, b. Metaphase and karyotype analysis

sufficiently distinct, two classes would be expected; ideally in males one class would be twice as large as the other. However, in a group of 132 meta-phases, all from normal males, the arm ratios of the three chromosomes of group X–6 formed a distribution from which there did not emerge two such classes. The author had earlier been of the opinion that visual discrimination between X and 6 on the basis of arm ratio was possible (Hungerford, 1961).

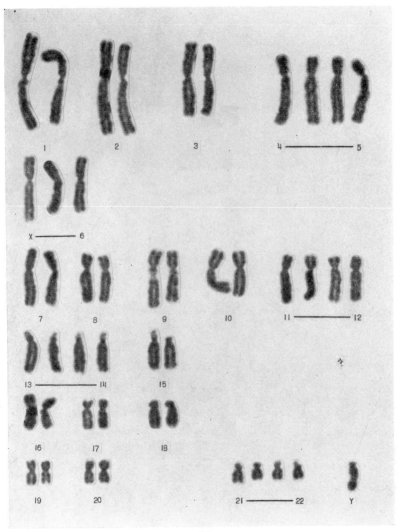

(b)

from normal male (case 135H). See text for details.

Neither have we been able to detect in our studies the presence of the X-allocycly observed by Sandberg *et al.* (1960) and by Hauschka (1962). While it is difficult to judge such matters from published photomicrographs, it would seem in the paper by Sandberg *et al.*, a perhaps better interpretation of some of the configurations illustrating "X-allocycly" is that the appearance of these chromosomes results from sister chromatids not lying in the

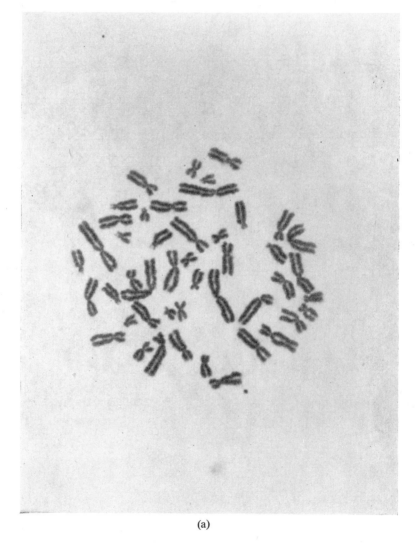

(a)

F<small>IG</small>. 2a, b. Metaphase and karyotype analysis

same plane and being partially overlapped (their Figs. 11, 13). The identification of many of these as X's seems questionable.

Group 7–12. It is in the identification of chromosomes within this group that a great deal of progress was made shortly after the adoption of the technique of Moorhead *et al.* For a period of almost three years, we have used the following convenient and reliable – if somewhat arbitrary in terms of numbering – system in the classification of this group (Hungerford, 1961). It is stressed that in general the centromere position has been considerably more helpful than estimates or relative length (differences in which

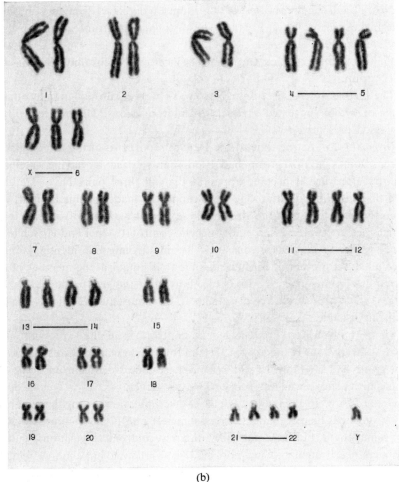

(b)

from normal male (case 189H). See text for details.

are slight and easily distorted by preparative manipulation) in assigning numbers within the 7–12 group.

No. 7: the longest of the group, having the second most nearly median centromere (after 10).

No. 8: nearly as long as 7, but having a more submedian centromere position.

No. 9: often bears a pronounced secondary constriction in the long arm, near the centromere; expression varies among individuals.

No. 10: longer (?) than 11 and 12, has decidedly the most nearly median centromere position in the group.

Nos. 11 and 12: the shortest of the group, having closely similar arm ratios (the highest in the group); cannot be distinguished from each other with any assurance.

Figures 1b and 2b illustrate the classification of chromosomes in the 7–12 group.

The secondary constriction in No. 9 was observed subsequently by others, some of whom suggested a variety of interpretations. This matter will be discussed presently.

Group 13–15. At the time of the Denver report two of the three pairs of chromosomes in this group had been characterized as having satellites. Shortly afterward it became apparent that all three pairs have satellites, and that discrimination among them cannot be made on this basis. It has been reported also that the sizes of these satellites and the frequency with which they are expressed are under genetic control (Cooper and Hirschhorn, 1962; Miller *et al.*, 1962), thus their use in chromosome identification is precluded. At present, it is often possible to distinguish one member of the group as chromosome No. 15 as the shortest of the group and having the largest short arm (exclusive of satellites). Chromosomes 13 and 14 remain indistinguishable.

Figure 1 illustrates apparent genetic control of satellite expression. Ten analyses were done in this case, 135H; in four of these, five chromosomes in this group had satellites. In all ten metaphases one No. 15 chromosome did not, and its short arm was proportionately larger.

Group 16–18. In the majority of cases discrimination among the members of this group is readily made. Chromosomes 16 and 17 are of approximately the same length, but have markedly different centromere positions, that of 16 being nearly median. Chromosome 18 is shorter and has a more submedian centromere position than No. 17. Figure 3 illustrates this group in a typical normal individual.

There are however two sets of observations which taken together tend

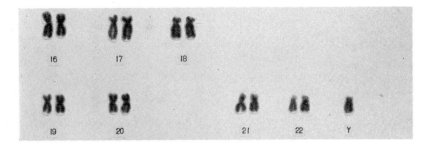

FIG. 3. Portion of karyotype from normal male (case 177H). Differences among members of group 16–18 and 21–22 are particularly clear. See text for details.

to render these identifications somewhat less certain. Chromosome 16 occasionally shows polymorphism in size and/or in centromere position; this does usually not interfere with its specific recognition. It is relevant to recall that there has been disagreement on identification of the extra chromosome (No. 17 vs. No. 18) in the trisomy syndrome involving this group (see Patau *et al.*, 1961), and it suggests itself that polymorphism may sometimes extend to these chromosomes as well, limiting in such cases the precision with which the distinction between them can be made.

Group 19–20. The members of this group are remarkably similar, and in fully contracted and over-contracted metaphases are difficult to distinguish from each other. However, in less contracted metaphases, the distinction can often be made on the basis of 19 being longer than 20, due mainly to attenuation in the region of the centromeric constriction, as well as on the basis that 19 is often perceptibly more asymmetrical than 20 (Fig. 4c). The numerical order of this designation is entirely arbitrary, based on the convention of relative length. Chromosome No. 20 may very well have greater total mass. It must be stressed that the ability to discriminate between these chromosomes is easily lost when they are contracted.

Group 21–22. In the Denver report, chromosome 21 was distinguished from 22 on the basis of its being satellited. Since then both 21 and 22 have proved to be satellited. Again, in uncontracted metaphases, one pair of these two appears longer than the other. On closer examination, the greater portion of this length differential is confined to the short arms of the chromosomes. The longer of the two has been taken to be No. 21 (Nowell and Hungerford, 1961). An identical interpretation was made earlier by Patau (1960a).

Most of the above comments are general ones, and undoubtedly exceptions have, can, or will be found to these "rules". However, they are consis-

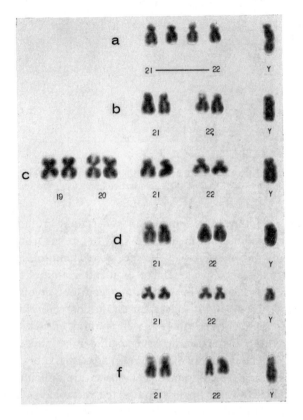

Fig. 4. Chromosomes 21, 22, and Y. Note varying degrees of condensation of the unusually large Y chromosome in four different metaphases from normal case 135H (4a-d), a Y chromosome of the more usual size from normal case 149H (4e) — see also Fig. 2b — and another unusually large Y from normal 191H (4f). Although the short arms of the Y in Fig. 4f have an appearance similar to that of satellites, they are not, judged from other metaphases in this case. Figure 4c includes chromosome pairs 19 and 20 and illustrates the differences between them (see text).

tent enough to have constituted in our hands a useful working procedure. Less frequently seen markers have been omitted, since up to the present they have not been useful.

The Y chromosome. In the Denver report the Y chromosome was characterized as being similar to autosomes 21 and 22, which it often is. In general, as the degree of metaphase contraction increases, the distinction between Y and the small acrocentric autosomes becomes increasingly less clear just as it does between chromosomes 21 and 22. Otherwise, several features distinguish the Y. One is that it is usually perceptibly longer than 21 and 22. In some normal males it is *much* longer. Figure 4 illustrates some of the variability in the Y within and among normal males. Tjio (1961) has observed a very long Y chromosome similar to that in our cases 135H and 191H, described here. The usually long Y chromosome illustrated by Bender and Gooch (1961) is by comparison somewhat less extreme. One unusually small and two unusually large Y chromosomes have been described by van Wijck *et al.* (1962) — these, however, were in individuals with problems of sterility.

Another criterion which has been extremely useful is that, while autosomes often show chromatid separation (usually but not always excepting the centromere) following the prefixation treatment used here, the Y chromosome seldom does. Ford (1962) has also commented recently on this feature of the Y chromosome. This close approximation of the chromatids throughout their length might easily be interpreted as positive heteropycnosis, whereas in fact in our material the Y is often isopycnotic and occasionally negatively heteropycnotic (Fig. 4a–d). True positive heteropycnosis has been well demonstrated (Tjio, 1961; Krooth and Tjio, 1961), and positive heteropycnosis has been stated to be generally characteristic of the Japanese population studied by Makino and Sasaki (1961).

ROSETTE FORMATION, NUCLEOLUS-ORGANIZATION, AND CHROMOSOME No. 9

Since the secondary constriction in chromosome No. 9 is regularly observed, there is some likelihood that it is a, if not "the", nucleolar organizer. Several lines of evidence tend to support this idea.

It was suggested some time ago by Chu and Giles (1959) on the basis of their having found two pairs of autosomes with satellites and basically four spherical nucleoli in somatic interphase nuclei *in vitro*, that these two autosomal pairs were probably nucleolus organizing chromosomes. However, Tjio *et al.* (1960) subsequently established that three pairs of autosomes were satellited, which threw some doubt on the earlier interpretation.

Levan and Hsu (1959) observed that a small acrocentric autosome "often shows remnants of a nucleolus on its shorter arm". It had been well known for some time that acrocentric autosomes are often associated by their short arms in configurations which we have termed "rosettes" (Hungerford, 1961). Based on such observations, an argument is advanced by Polani *et al.* (1960) that satellited chromosomes bear nucleolar organizers and become associated by nucleolar fusion. This view was questioned at that time by Hungerford (1961), who proposed the alternative to be given below.

Ferguson-Smith and Handmaker (1961a) — see also Petersen and Therkelsen (1961) and Ferguson-Smith and Handmaker (1961b) — in a subse-

quent discussion of the matter, thought it likely that satellited autosomes —
of which they described five pairs (see also Hungerford, 1961; Therman *et
al.*, 1961; Hamerton, 1961) — are nucleolar chromosomes (a view shared
by Therman *et al.)* and stated, "It no longer seems necessary to relate the
number of satellited chromosomes directly to the number of nucleoli visible
in the intermitotic nucleus."

Shortly afterwards Ohno *et al.* (1961) treated the subject further, stating
that the nucleolus-organizing region in man is always located near the end
of a chromosome, and explained that the absence of all ten chromosomes
in association with nucleolus formation at prophase may be due either to
the fact that "some of the satellited pairs are not true nucleolus-organizing
chromosomes" or that "not all nucleolus-organizing regions are functional
at the same time".

Edwards (1961), however, mentions the probability that a sixth chromosome pair, No.18, is satellited and suggests that "the probability that a nucleolus is likely to require, or even to survive, the ministrations of (six pairs
of) organizers can no longer be regarded as implied".

Specific objections to the hypothesis that satellited acrocentrics bear
nucleolar organizers were advanced on the following bases. A study (Hungerford, unpublished) of rosette configurations in blood cultures — a
phenomenon observed well before the modifications of Moorhead *et al.* —
has shown that the chromosome associations are apparently completely
at random, i.e. a variable number of rosettes may be present in a given
metaphase plate, and each rosette may be composed of from two to eight
or possibly more chromosomes (Fig. 5). In addition almost any combination of large and small acrocentrics may be present in a rosette. Finally,
the variability in number and type (i.e. long or short acrocentrics) of chromosome in rosettes and in total number of rosettes does not correspond
to the basic regularity in nucleolar number and size frequently observed in
interphase nuclei.

The possibility remains that rosettes composed of acrocentric autosomes
may very well be associated with nucleoli, if not with their organization.
In such a case the satellites might be wholly or partially responsible for
nucleolus-associated chromatin.

(Recently, Lima-de-Faria and Reitalu (1962) have observed early pro-
phases in human leukocyte cultures which show, associated with the nucleoli,
blocks of heterochromatin composed of the positively heteropycnotic regions
of six chromosome segments. Earlier, Ohno *et al.* (1961) had seen a maximum
of six chromosomes with constrictions and adjacent satellites associated
with a single large nucleolus. These chromosomes were interpreted as parti-

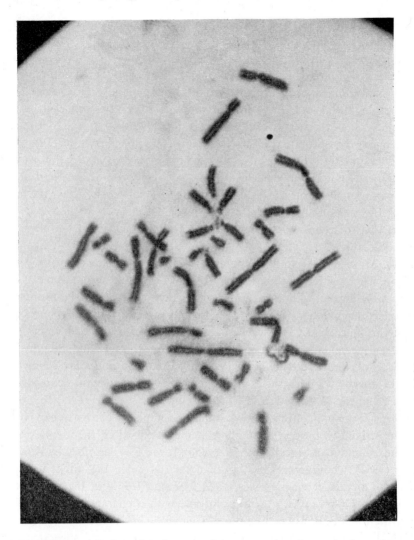

FIG. 5. A rosette configuration of acrocentric autosomes in an incomplete metaphase from leukemia case 145T. Such associations are typical of metaphases from normal individuals as well.

cipating in nucleolar organization. However, Lima-de-Faria and Reitalu state regarding the segments they observed associated with the nucleolus that, " . . .this does not mean that they necessarily participate in the formation of this organelle. The phenomenon may simply represent a non-homologous heterochromatin association, such as that observed in many plant and animal species.")

One further factor to be considered in discussing rosette formation is the following. The short arms of acrocentrics are obviously located in close proximity to centric heterochromatin, if indeed not composed primarily of it. The non-homologous association of centric heterochromatin is a well-known phenomenon, e.g. in *Drosophila* salivary gland cells. Observations concerning the association of the short arms of acrocentrics with centromeres of other, non-acrocentric, chromosomes (Shaw, 1961 — see also Edwards, 1961) may constitute a further example of this phenomenon. Telomeric heterochromatin responsible for such non-homologous association as that seen in the bouquet stage of meiosis is also likely to constitute part of the short arm of acrocentrics and may serve to accentuate even further the tendency toward non-homologous association.

Finally, there has existed for many years information on the nucleolar chromosome at pachytene (Schultz and St. Lawrence, 1949; Yerganian, 1957). More recent photomicrographs of this chromosome are shown in Fig. 6. The position of the nucleolar organizer on this chromosome agrees very well indeed with that of the secondary constriction in metaphase chromosome number 9 (Figs. 1, 7). (It is of some interest in this connection that chromosome IX of the rhesus monkey is characterized by a pronounced secondary constriction, interpreted by Rothfels and Siminovitch (1958) as "almost certainly associated with the main nucleolus". Nowhere in the rhesus complement is there an acrocentric autosome comparable with numbers 13–15, and 21–22 of the human.)

The secondary constriction in human metaphase chromosome No. 9 came strikingly to one's attention immediately after the development of the technique of Moorhead *et al.* (1960). It was first described by Hungerford (1961), who interpreted it in the manner given in the foregoing paragraph. Later, brief mention was made by Patau (1961) of the presence in group 6–12 ("group C") of an autosome with a characteristic secondary constriction. Following this, de la Chapelle (1961) and simultaneously Muldal and Ockey (1961) described the chromosome, and suggested that it might be the X. This, however, is ruled out by its presence homozygously in males (Figs. 1, 7). Dobson and Ohnuki (1961) found three chromosomes with secondary constrictions, which they interpreted as abnormalities, in a child with a convulsive disorder. Two of these, however, have the morphology of normal chromosomes No. 9. Patau *et al.* (1961b) have published a full description of this chromosome, which they designate chromosome C'.

Mindful of Kodani's unpublished map of a second nucleolar chromosome at pachytene (see Neel and Schull, 1954, p. 11) one should consider the

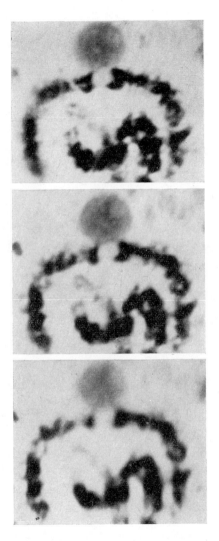

FIG. 6. The pachytene nucleolar chromosome of man described by Schultz and St. Lawrence (1949). These three focal levels were taken at 0·5 μ intervals with light of wavelength 257 mμ.

Orchiectomy was performed in 1955 on this individual (case 101H), whose disease was diagnosed as adenocarcinoma of the prostate. The author is indebted to Dr. Charles A. Uhle for the specimen, and to Dr. George T. Rudkin for the use of his ultraviolet microscope.

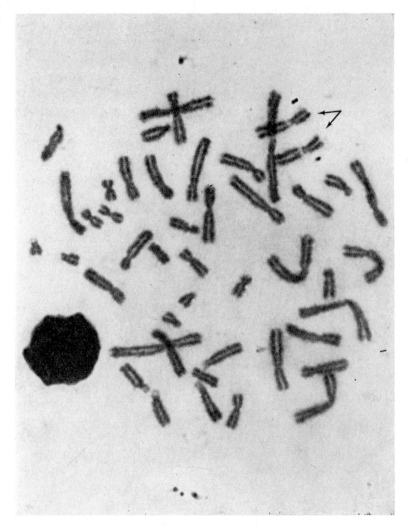

FIG. 7. Metaphase from normal male (case 135H). Note association of homologous
chromosomes number 9 (arrows).

possibility that the secondary constriction in chromosome No. 1 or one
elsewhere may also play a role in nucleolar organization. (It is an interesting coincidence that chromosome I of the rhesus monkey also exhibits a
secondary constriction.) If in fact there are two pachytene nucleolar organizers in the human complement their specific correspondence with metaphase
chromosomes 1 and 9 can only be guessed at on the basis of the relative
lengths involved, since the slightly asymmetrical location of the secondary

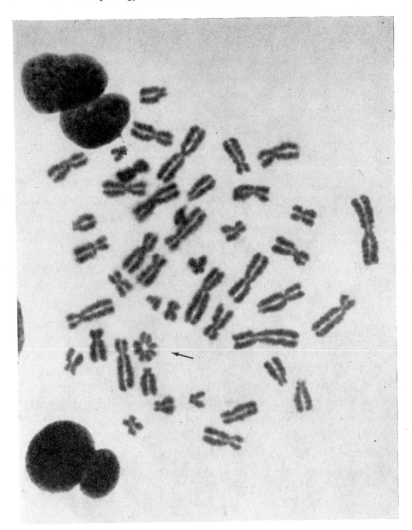

FIG. 8. Metaphase from normal female (case 111H). It is possible to interpret as somatic pairing the configuration indicated by the arrow (see text).

constrictions in both 1 and 9 is compatible with the location of the nucleolar organizer in the chromosome described by Schultz and St. Lawrence. Unfortunately, centromeres have not yet been identified in human pachytene chromosomes.

Thus, cytological evidence accumulated to date seems to leave the burden of proof with the proponents of the theory of large numbers of nucleolar organizers in the human karyotype.

SOMATIC ASSOCIATION

The association of homologous metaphase chromosomes in somatic cells — commonly seen in lower forms — has been observed and commented upon in human somatic cells by Hungerford et al. (1959). The author's attention had earlier been drawn to the presence of this phenomenon in the figures of Andres and Navashin (1936) by Schultz (1955). Such association (Fig. 7) is often in an approximately parallel configuration and is distinct both from the essentially non-homologous end to end association involved in rosette formation and from true somatic pairing (pairing in the meiotic sense). It seems to involve the larger chromosomes, which are normally situated with their centromeres on the equator of the spindle. Since hypotonic solutions as well as colchicine cause serious disorganization of the spindle, whatever somatic association persists in hypotonically pretreated and physically manipulated metaphases must be a pale reflection of the usual orientation of chromosomes in the intact spindle. With such observations at hand it is tempting to speculate concerning the origin and significance, with respect to the possibility of differentiation within the spindle apparatus, of such patterns of arrangement.

What apparently constitutes the first definitive study of somatic association in mammalian cells has been made by Ruddle (1960), who used metaphases from primary kidney cultures of the pig, Sus scrofa. Chromosomes were scored in squash preparations of cells pretreated with colchicine and hypotonic solutions, and close spatial relationship between the homologues studied was statistically significant at the 0·01–0·005 level.

Rothfels and Siminovitch (1958) noted a tendency for homologous chromosomes to lie together in air dried, hypotonically pretreated metaphases of cells cultured from the kidney cortex of rhesus monkeys, but state that "quantitative study of this somatic pairing was not undertaken".

Somatic association of human metaphase chromosomes has been studied recently by statistical methods by Barton and David (1962) and by Schneiderman and Smith (1962).

Somatic pairing. Instances of configurations which suggest true somatic pairing are seen in extremely low frequency. The metaphase shown in figure 8 may be a case in point. The chromosomes involved are either two No. 19's, two No. 20's, or one of each. The technical quality of the preparation does not allow this distinction to be made with any great certainty. However, since the four chromatids in the pairing figure are more symmetrical than the two remaining small metacentric chromosomes, it is assumed that two No. 20's are paired. If this is the case two interpretations are possible.

One is a direct pairing, analogous to that which takes place during zygotene. The other involves equal reciprocal translocation, with a break point very close to the centromere, of non-sister chromatids. Even if this were the case, the homologues must have been closely approximated (associated or paired) at the time at which the translocation took place.

Sandberg *et al.* (1960) claim to have illustrated somatic pairing (their Figs. 4 and 5). In spite of the poor quality of these preparations, the chromosomes are well enough depicted so that it is obvious that it is not possible to arrange this group of chromosomes into a haploid karyotype. Since this could readily be done were true somatic pairing involved, the demonstration remains unconvincing.

SUMMARY AND CONCLUSIONS

It is difficult to be faced with the problem of dealing with the recognition of individual human chromosomes, not to say intrachromosomal regions, when techniques have only begun to advance toward the cytogenetic ideals represented for example by *Drosophila* and maize. Nevertheless, it is perhaps useful to attempt to define the limitations of present techniques.

In doing so, one is required to deal with exceptionally good cells and to use them as demonstrations. Logically one must restrict his statements to observations made on such cells and assume that they hold for others less well prepared and to make such statements with this reservation. And, as Patau (1961) has remarked, "...after all, who wants to confess that he has no very favorable preparations?" However, such procedures are not without precedent. A great many preparations were employed by Bridges in the construction of his masterful cytogenetic maps of the salivary gland chromosomes of *Drosophila melanogaster*. In some of these, only small regions constituted good (thus exceptional) demonstrations. The validity of these maps, constructed from pooled observations made on ideal demonstrations, has not been seriously questioned. In similar fashion piecemeal observations of satellited human chromosomes have led many workers to the belief that all ten acrocentric autosomes are satellited, although no one has yet published a metaphase in which this is unquestionably the case.

In this paper useful criteria in addition to those given in the Denver report are given for the recognition of individual chromosomes. These are given with the following reservations.

(1) They are known to hold only for preparations from blood made by a particular method (Moorhead *et al.*, 1960); their applicability to other material remains to be demonstrated.

(2) Demonstrations are made with ideal, thus often exceptional, examples. Once having been established, the criteria can often be applied to less favorable material, and are thus thought in general to be valid.

(3) The question of structural chromosomal polymorphism has not been adequately studied in human populations, and the frequency of exceptions to the criteria which may arise from such sources is not known.

(4) The degree of genetic control over the phenotype of human chromosomes is not well known. The expression of satellites has been studied and pedigrees established (Cooper and Hirschhorn, 1962; Miller *et al.*, 1962). Our own observations suggest that there may also be genetic influences bearing on the expression of secondary constrictions such as the one in chromosome 9.

(5) Metabolic intrachromosomal differentiation known to exist in other organisms and to be correlated with cellular differentiation (see, for example, the review by Beermann, 1959) may be present in human chromosomes. While this is presently by no means apparent in human material, it could nonetheless affect the chromosome phenotype even at the present level of observation.

It is felt that in general the criteria adopted here often permit the individual recognition of chromosomes 1, 2, 3, 7, 8, 9, 10, 15, 16, 17, 18, 19, 20, 21, 22 and Y and the recognition as discrete groups of 4 and 5, X and 6, 11 and 12, and 13 and 14. A more optimistic view is not permitted by observations made on our preparations, nor is a more pessimistic one justified.

We remain faced with the urgent necessity of devising better techniques for the examination of both gonial and somatic cells. We know that patterns of linear differentiation exist in the chromosomes of the former and that they can be mapped, although with the technique as it now stands this is extremely arduous. It is not unreasonable to hope that we will eventually be able to examine such patterns in the chromosomes of somatic cells. Developments such as those made recently by Saksela and Moorhead (1962) and reported by Moorhead elsewhere in this symposium are in this regard most encouraging.

The hypothetical role of satellited acrocentric chromosomes in nucleolus-organization in humans is examined, and a more plausible alternative suggested.

Observations of somatic association of homologous chromosomes are discussed in relation to the non-homologous association involved in rosette formation, as well as in relation to the possible existence of true somatic pairing.

REFERENCES

ANDRES, A. H. and NAVASHIN, M. S. Morphological analysis of human chromosomes. *Proc. Maxim Gorky Med. Genet. Res. Inst.* **4**, 506–524, 1936.

BARTON, D. E. and DAVID, F. N. The analysis of chromosome patterns in the normal cell. *Ann. Hum. Genet.* **25**, 232–329, 1962.

BEARN, A. G. and GERMAN, J. L. III. Chromosomes and disease. *Sci. Amer.* **205**, 66–76, 1961.

BEERMANN, W. Chromosome differentiation in insects. In *Developmental Cytology*, ed. by D. Rudnick, Ronald Press, N.Y., 1959.

BENDER, M. A. and GOOCH, P. C. An unusually long human Y chromosome. *Lancet*, **ii**, 463–464, 1961.

BÖÖK, J. A. Clinical cytogenetics. In *De Genetica Medica* – Part III, ed. by L. Gedda, Instituto "Gregorio Mendel", Rome, 1961, pp. 21–47.

CHAPELLE, A. DE LA. Constrictions in normal human chromosomes. *Lancet*, **ii**, 460–462, 1961.

CHRUSTSCHOFF, G. K. Cytological investigations on cultures of normal human blood. *J. Genet.* **31**, 243–261, 1935.

CHU, E. H. Y. and GILES, N. H. Human chromosome complements in normal somatic cells in culture. *Am. J. Human Genet.* **11**, 63–79, 1959.

COOPER, H. L. and HIRSCHHORN, K. Enlarged satellites as a familial chromosome marker. *Am. J. Human Genet.* **14**, 107–124, 1962.

DOBSON, R. and OHNUKI, Y. Chromosomal abnormalities in a child with a convulsive disorder. *Lancet*, **ii**, 627–630, 1961.

EDWARDS, J. H. Chromosome analysis from capillary blood. *Cytogenetics*, **1**, 90–96, 1962.

EDWARDS, J. H. Chromosomal association in man. *Lancet*, **ii**, 317–318, 1961.

FERGUSON–SMITH, M. A. Chromosomes in human disease. In *Progress in Medical Genetics*, ed. by A. G. Steinberg, Grune and Stratton, N.Y., 1961.

FERGUSON-SMITH, M. A. and HANDMAKER, S. D. Observations on the satellited human chromosomes. *Lancet*, **i**, 638–640, 1961a.

FERGUSON-SMITH, M. A. and HANDMAKER, S. D. Observations on the satellited human chromosomes. *Lancet*, **i**, 1362, 1961b.

FORD, C. E. Methodology of chromosomal analysis in man. National Cancer Institute Monograph No. 7, pp. 105–117, 1962.

FORD, C. E. Human cytogenetics. *Brit. Med. Bull.* **17**, 179–183, 1961.

HAMERTON, J. L. Sex chromatin and human chromosomes. *Internat. Rev. Cytol.* **12** 1–68, 1961.

HARNDEN, D. G. and JACOBS, P. A. Cytogenetics of abnormal sexual development in man. *Brit. Med. Bull.* **17**, 206–212, 1961.

HASTINGS, J., FREEDMAN, S., RENDON, I., COOPER, H. L. and HIRSCHHORN, K. Culture of human white cells using differential leukocyte separation. *Nature*, **192**, 1214–1215, 1961.

HAUSCHKA, T. S. Identification of X and Y chromosomes of man. In *Methodology in Human Genetics*, ed. by W. J. Burdette, Holden-Day, San Francisco, 1962.

HAUSCHKA, T. S. The chromosomes in ontogeny and oncogeny. *Cancer Res.* **21**, 957–974, 1961.

HIRSCHHORN, K. and COOPER, H. L. Chromosomal aberrations in human disease. A review of the status of cytogenetics in medicine. *Am. J. Med.* **31**, 442–470, 1961.

HSU, T. C. Genetic cytology. In *The Biology of Cells and Tissues in Culture*, ed. by E. N. Willmer, Academic Press, N.Y., in press.

HUNGERFORD, D. A. A study of the chromosomes in leukocytes from the peripheral blood of children with leukemia. Doctoral dissertation, Univ. of Pennsylvania, February 1961.

HUNGERFORD, D. A., DONELLY, A. J., NOWELL, P. C. and BECK, S. The chromosome constitution of a human phenotypic intersex. *Am. J. Human Genet.* **11**, 215–236, 1959.

KROOTH, R. S. and TJIO, J. H. The biosynthesis of poliovirus by euploid "fibroblasts" of non-neoplastic origin. *Virology,* **14**, 289–292, 1961.

LEJEUNE, J. and TURPIN, R. Chromosomal aberrations in man. *Am. J. Human Genet.* **13**, 175–184, 1961.

LEJEUNE, J., TURPIN, R. and GAUTIER, M. Le mongolisme premiere exemple d'aberration autosomique humaine. *Ann. Génét.* **1**, 41–49, 1959.

LEVAN, A. and HSU, T. C. The human idiogram. *Hereditas,* **45**, 666–674, 1959.

LI, J. G. and OSGOOD, E. E. A method for the rapid separation of leukocytes and nucleated erythrocytes from blood or marrow with a phytohemagglutinin from red beans *(Phaseolus vulgaris). Blood,* **4**, 670–675, 1949.

LIMA-DE-FARIA, A. and REITALU, J. Heterochromatin in human male leukocytes. *J. Cell Biol.,* **16**, 315–322, 1963.

MAKINO, S. and SASAKI, M. A study of somatic chromosomes in a Japanese population. *Am. J. Human Genet.* **13**, 47–63, 1961.

MILLER, O. J. and BREG, W. R. A blood cell culture technique for the study of the satellites and secondary constrictions of 10 pairs of human chromosomes. *Blood,* **20**, 102–103 (abstract), 1962.

MILLER, O. J., MUKHERJEE, B. B. and BREG, W. R. Normal variations in the human karyotype. *Trans. N. Y. Acad. Sci.,* Ser. II, **24**, 372–382, 1962.

MOORHEAD, P. S., NOWELL, P. C., MELLMAN, W. J., BATTIPS, D. M. and HUNGERFORD, D. A. Chromosome preparations of leukocytes cultured from human peripheral blood. *Exp. Cell Res.* **20**, 613–616, 1960.

MULDAL, S. and OCKEY, C. H. The Denver classification and group III. *Lancet,* **ii,** 462–463, 1961.

NEEL, J. V. and SCHULL, W. J. *Human Heredity,* University of Chicago Press, Chicago, 1954.

NICHOLS, W. W. and LEVAN, A. Chromosome preparations by the blood tissue culture technique in various laboratory animals. *Blood,* **20**, 106 (abstract), 1962.

NOWELL, P. C. Phytohemagglutinin: an initiator of mitosis in cultures of normal human leukocytes. *Cancer Res.* **20**, 462–466, 1960.

NOWELL, P. C. HUNGERFORD, D. A. and BROOKS, C. D. Chromosomal characteristics of normal and leukemic human leukocytes after short-term tissue culture. *Proc. Am. Assoc. Cancer Res.* **2**, 331–332 (abstract), 1958.

NOWELL, P. C. and HUNGERFORD, D. A. Chromosome studies in human leukemia. II. Chronic granulocytic leukemia. *J. Nat. Cancer Inst.* **27**, 1013–1035, 1961.

NOWELL, P. C. and HUNGERFORD, D. A. Chromosome studies on normal and leukemic human leukocytes. *J. Nat. Cancer Inst.* **25**, 85–109, 1960a.

NOWELL, P. C. and HUNGERFORD, D. A. A minute chromosome in human chronic granulocytic leukemia. *Science,* **132**, 1497 (abstract), 1960b.

OHNO, S., TRUJILLO, J. M., KAPLAN, W. D. and KINOSITA, R. Nucleolus-organizers in the causation of chromosomal anomalies in man. *Lancet,* ii, 123–126, 1961.

PATAU, K., Chromosome identification and the Denver report. *Lancet,* i, 933–934, 1961.

PATAU, K., The identification of individual chromosomes, especially in man. *Am. J. Human Genet.* **12**, 250–276, 1960.

PATAU, K., THERMAN, E., SMITH, D. W. and DE MARS, R. I. Trisomy for chromosome No. 18 in man. *Chromosoma,* **12**, 280–285, 1961a.

PATAU, K., THERMAN. E., INHORN, S. L., SMITH, D. W. and RUESS, A. L. Patiratrisomy syndromes. II. An insertion as cause of the OFD syndrome in mother and daughter. *Chromosoma,* **12**, 573–584, 1961b.

PETERSEN, G. B. and THERKELSEN, A. J. Observations on satellited human chromosomes. *Lancet,* i, 1229, 1961.

POLANI, P. E., BRIGGS, J. H., FORD, C. E., CLARKE, C. M. and BERG, J. M. A mongol girl with 46 chromosomes. *Lancet*, i, 721–724, 1960.

ROBINSON, A. The human chromosomes. *Am. J. Dis. Children*, **101**, 379–398, 1961.

ROTHFELS, K. H. and SIMINOVITCH, L. The chromosome complement of the rhesus monkey *(Macaca mulatta)* determined in kidney cells cultivated *in vitro. Chromosoma*, **9**, 163–175, 1958.

RUDDLE, F. H. Chromosome variation in cell populations. Doctoral dissertation, University of California, Berkeley, 1960.

SAKSELA, E. and MOORHEAD, P. S. Enhancement of secondary constrictions and the heterochromatic X in human cells. *Cytogenetics* **1**, 225–244, 1962.

SANDBERG, A. A., KOEPF, G. F., CROSSWHITE, L. H. and HAUSCHKA, T. S. The chromosome constitution of human marrow in various developmental and blood disorders. *Am. J. Human Genet.* **12**, 231–249, 1960.

SCHNEIDERMAN, L. J. and SMITH, C. A. B. Non-random distribution of certain homologous pairs of normal human chromosomes in metaphase. *Nature*, **195**, 1229–1230, 1962.

SCHULTZ, J. Personal communication, 1955.

SCHULTZ, J. and ST. LAWRENCE, P. A cytological basis for a map of the nucleolar chromosome in man. *J. Hered.* **40**, 30–38, 1949.

SHAW, M. Association of acrocentric chromosomes with the centromere region of chromosome No. 1. *Lancet*, i, 1351–1352, 1961.

TJIO, J. H. Personal communication, 1961.

TJIO, J. H., PUCK, T. T. and ROBINSON, A. The human chromosomal satellites in normal persons and in two patients with Marfan's syndrome. *Proc. Nat. Acad. Sci.* **46**, 532–539, 759, 1960.

WIJCK, J. A. M. VAN, TIJDINK, G. A. J. and STOLTE, L. A. M. Anomalies in the Y chromosome. *Lancet*, **i**, 218, 1962.

YERGANIAN, G. Cytologic maps of some isolated human pachytene chromosomes. *Am. J. Human Genet.* **9**, 4254–, 1957.

THE CHROMOSOMES OF THE BRAZILIAN
OPOSSUM (*DIDELPHIS MARSUPIALIS* L., 1758)

A. N. Cestari and A. L. P. Perondini

Department of Biology, Fac. Filosofia, Ciências e Letras, University of São Paulo, Brazil

THE DIPLOID number of chromosomes of the North American opossum (*Didelphis virginiana*) has been established as being 22 by means of sections of young embryos and testes of adults (Painter, 1922; Hoy, 1929). The sex chromosomes were identified as the smallest in the complement, the

FIG. 1. An adult female of the Brazilian opossum *Didelphis marsupialis*.

Y being smaller than the X. Sáez (1930) found the same diploid number in *Didelphis paraguayensis*. In Brazil, Dreyfus and Souza Campos (1939) studied the chromosomes in the spermatogenesis of *Didelphis aurita* and found also 22 chromosomes, the X and Y being similar to those in the other two species. They concluded that *D. aurita*, *D. virginiana* and *D. paraguayensis* are cytologically similar at least in what concerns the number, type and relative size of chromosomes.

The first modern studies of the karyotype of a marsupial were made by Ohno (1960) and Shaver (1962) in *D. virginiana*.

We present here the result of a study, by modern techniques, of the chromosomes of *Didelphis marsupialis* (Fig. 1), a Brazilian species very close to *D. aurita*. The South American species of *Didelphis* are known commonly by the names "gambá", "jupati", "sarigueia", "raposa" and, in Spanish, "zarigueia" or "zorra".

Materials and Methods

Tissue cultures of an adult female and two young animals found in the pouch of two females as well as squashes of testes of the two youngsters were used for the study of the chromosomes.

Tissue Culture Methods

The plasma clot method was used. The cortex of the kidney were removed aseptically. The tissue was minced with a pair of sharp scalpels and the pieces of tissue were washed in Hank's saline containing a high concentration of antibiotics and clotted on coverslips into Leighton tubes with chicken plasma and chicken embryo extract (from Difco Laboratories). One milliliter of fresh fibroblast medium suplemented with 15 per cent calf serum was added to each tube. The pH was adjusted to 7·2 with CO_2 and the culture incubated at 37°C for 1–2 weeks. The medium was changed each two or three days. When the growth was considered convenient the medium was changed again and, after 15 hr, a colchicine treatment was applied. The final concentration of colchicine was about 5×10^{-8}M. After further incubation for 4–5 hr, the medium was replaced with hypotonic saline and incubated at 37°C for 30 min. The material on the coverslips was fixed in Carnoy (absolute alcohol, chloroform and acetic acid, 6 : 3 : 1) for another 30 min and dried at room temperature. The staining was made in a solution of 2 per cent natural orcein in 45 per cent acetic acid, for about 10 min. The preparation was washed and dehydrated very quickly in absolute alcohol, cleared in xylene, and mounted in Canadian balsam.

Testes Preparation

After removing the testicular tunic, the masses of tubules were placed in 3 ml of 0·7 sodium citrate and incubated at 37°C for 15 min. The material was fixed by adding slowly (for 2 min) 3 ml of glacial acetic acid to the hypotonic citrate. Pieces of tubules were distended on slides and covered with drops of lactic acetic-orcein prepared according to Welshons (1962), for 10 min. Coverslips were placed over the tubules and those found

TABLE 1. MEASUREMENTS OF METAPHASE CHROMOSOMES OF *D. marsupialis*

Chromosomes		Chromosome length relative to the total diploid complement length*			Average chromosome lengths in micron in three metaphases
		Metaphase in Fig. 2	Metaphase in Fig. 3	Mean values for 6 chromosomes in 3 metaphases	
Large	1	7·80 7·60	7·78 7·78	7·82	10·0
	2	7·06 6·80	7·04 6·62	6·89	8·8
	3	5·86 5·86	6·13 6·13	6·07	7·7
Medium	4	4·93 4·80	4·55 4·39	4·63	6·0
	5	4·20 4·20	4·14 4·14	4·11	5·3
	6	4·13 4·13	4·05 3·97	4·02	5·2
	7	4·06 4·00	3·89 3·89	3·97	5·0
	8	3·73 3·73	3·81 3·81	3·77	4·8
	9	3·66 3·66	3·64 3·56	3·59	4·6
	10	3·60 3·06	3·29 3·23	3·32	4·2
Short (sex chromosomes)	X	1·73 1·33	1·98	1·72	2·2
	Y		1·11		1·4

* In males, the diploid complement included the X twice and no Y.

under the microscope to have dividing cells were squashed between bibolous paper. These preparations were made permanent by a treatment with absolute alcohol which detaches the coverslip and dehydrates the material. Xylene was employed for clearing and Canadian balsam for mounting.

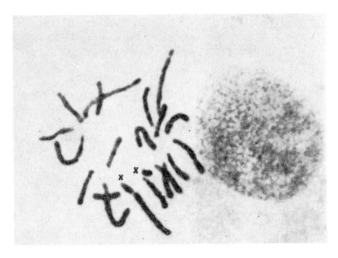

Fig. 2. Metaphase in tissue culture of kidney from a female specimen of *D. marsupialis*.

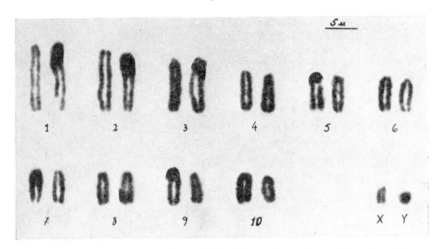

Fig. 3. Metaphase in tissue culture of kidney from male specimen of *D. marsupialis*.

Chromosome counts were made on about 15 good mitoses both from tissue cultures of the three animals and from the squashed testes. Ten of these mitoses were photographed in the phase-contrast microscope for further analysis and three of them were used for pairing the chromosomes and measuring their relative lengths (Table 1). In Fig. 3 they are arranged only according to their length, since all chromosomes are acrocentric. The lengths of the chromosomes were measured on the picture in arbitrary units and the measurements were recalculated as per cent of the total length of the diploid complement of the female. The total length of the diploid male complement was measured by including the X chromosome twice and disregarding the Y chromosome.

RESULTS

The 11 pairs of chromosomes were classified into three groups: large (chromosomes Nos. 1–3), medium (Nos. 4–10) and short (sex chromosomes). There is a sharp difference between the length of the X chromosome and the smallest autosome. The Y chromosome is approximately half the length of the X. Determinations of individual chromosomes within the two groups of autosomes is very difficult and probably not possible.

All autosomes and the X chromosome are acrocentric. The Y chromosome appears dot-like in most cases and the position of its centromere is doubtful.

DISCUSSION

Our study of spermatogonial mitoses confirmed the following findings reported by Dreyfus and Souza Campos (1939) in *D. aurita:*

(a) The diploid number of chromosomes is 22.

(b) In the spermatogonial metaphasis (polar view) the autosomes lay in general in circle around the sex chromosomes (we did not find this in all cells, probably because we studied squashed and Dreyfus and Souza Campos used only sections).

(c) All the autosomes are acrocentric.

(d) The sex chromosomes are distinguishable from the autosomes and the X from the Y, the latter being dot-like.

The karyotype of the North American opossum, *Didelphis virginiana* (Shaver, 1962), differs from that of *D. marsupialis* in the following aspects:

(a) In *D. virginiana* six pairs of autosomes (group A) have subterminal centromeres. In *D. marsupialis* all autosomes are acrocentric.

(b) In *D. virginiana* the X chromosome has subterminal centromere while in *D. marsupialis* it is probably acrocentric.

(c) In the karyotype by length, the difference in length between any two consecutive pairs of autosomes is small in both species, except for the fact that in *D. marsupialis*, but not in *D. virginiana*, the difference in size between pairs 3 and 4 is quite clear.

(d) *D. virginiana* has the X chromosome larger than *D. marsupialis*.

SUMMARY

The chromosomes of the South American opossum, *D. marsupialis*, were studied with methods of short-term tissue culture and testes preparations. The diploid number (22 chromosomes) is the same for other species of the same genus. All the chromosomes are acrocentric. The autosomes are classified into two groups according to size. The karyotypes of *D. marsupialis* and *D. virginiana*, the North American opossum, are compared.

ACKNOWLEDGEMENTS

The authors wish to express their gratitude to Dr. O. Frota-Pessoa for his interest and suggestions and to the Rockefeller Foundation for financial assistance.

REFERENCES

DREYFUS, A. and SOUZA CAMPOS, J. E., 1939, Os cromosomas na espermatogênese de *Didelphis aurita* (Wied). Bolet. Fac. Fil., Ci. Letr. XVII. Biologia Geral 3, São Paulo, 3–19.

HOY, W. E., Jr. and GEORGE, W. C., 1929, The somatic chromosomes of the opossum *(Didelphis virginiana)*. J. Morphol. **47**, 201–225.

OHNO, S., KAPLAN, W. D., and KINOSITA, R., 1960, The basis of nuclear sex difference in somatic cells of the opossum *Didelphis virginiana*. Exptl. Cell Research, **19**, 417–420.

PAINTER, T. S., 1922, Studies in mammalian spermatogenesis. I. The spermatogenesis of the opossum *(Didelphis virginiana)*. J. Exptl. Zool. **35**, 13–45.

SÁEZ, F. A., 1931, The chromosomes of the South American opossum, *Didelphis paraguayensis*. Am. Naturalist, **65**, 287–288.

SHAVER, E. L., 1962, The chromosomes of the opossum, *Didelphis virginiana*. Canad. J. Genetics and Cytology, Vol. IV, No. 1, 62–68.

WELSHONS, W. J., GIBSON, B. H. and SCANDLYN, B. J., 1962, Slide processing for the examination of male mammalian meiotic chromosomes. *Stain Technology*, **37**, 1–5.

THE CHROMOSOMES OF THE MULITA
(*DASYPUS HYBRIDUS* DESMAREST):
A MAMMALIAN EDENTATA
OF SOUTH AMERICA

F. A. SAEZ, M. E. DRETS and N. BRUM

Departamento de Citogenética, Instituto de Investigación de Ciencias Biológicas,
Montevideo, Uruguay

INTRODUCTION

This is a preliminary report forming part of a more extensive investigation dealing with the Edentates of South America.

Up to the present, very few investigations on this interesting group have been carried out. The papers by Newman and Patterson (1910) and Newman (1912) were the first to be published.

These authors used the same embryologic material, prepared for studying the polyembryony of the armadillo *Tatusia novemcinctus*, to study the chromosomes. They found 31 chromosomes in the spermatogonia and 32 in the ovogonia attributing the odd number of the male sex to the existence of an XO type of sex determination mechanism.

Several years passed before Painter (1925) in a short note found 60 somatic chromosomes in the amniotic cells in embryos of the same species.

When our paper on the South American seven banded armadillo (mulita) *Dasypus hybridus* was almost finished, we received the paper of Beath, Benirschke and Brownhill (1962) on the chromosomes of *Dasypus novemcinctus*.

The authors using the modern techniques involving the study of peripheral leukocytes and tissue cultures, found that this species has $2n = 64$ chromosomes and were able to identify morphologically, by its relative size, the five groups of chromosomes that constitute the karyotype of this species.

Thirty-seven years elapsed from Painter's paper on the armadillo, but it is only now that the subject was restudied by the above-mentioned authors and by ourselves definitively establishing the number and morphology of the chromosomes of these two species of *Dasypus*.

MATERIAL AND METHODS

Seven individuals coming from Estancia Santa Elena, Arroyo del Perdido, Departamento de Soriano, Uruguay, were studied. For the classification of *Dasypus hybridus* (Desmarest), the seven banded species commonly called "mulita", we have followed the nomenclature described by Cabrera (1957). The same species was used by Fernández (1915) for his studies on polyembryony under the name *Tatusia septemcinctus*.

One of the animals cytogenetically studied is preserved in the collection of the Museo Nacional de Historia Natural, Montevideo, with the number 1120 ♀.

Bone marrow cells were cultivated following the schedule described by Ford and Hammerton (1956). The tissue was removed from the dissected femurs and the culture was carried out in homologous serum plus saline solution and glucose (1 : 1). No other changes were introduced in the culture technique.

Germ-cells were studied by squashing small pieces of seminiferous tubuli, which were pre-treated with a 0·5 per cent NaCl solution during 15 min and afterwards fixed in a 3:1 or 2:1 alcohol–acetic acid mixture for about 30 min. The tubuli were then squashed in a drop of acetic haematoxylin (Saez, 1960) composed of haematoxylin 2 per cent in 45 per cent acetic acid.

The chromosomes were studied by (1) photographic recording of sets of chromosomes and subsequent preparation of karyotypes; (2) by drawings of individual spreads of chromosomes.

RESULTS

Somatic Chromosomes

The majority of cells examined contained 64 somatic chromosomes at mitotic metaphase (Figs. 1 and 3) Only clear well-spread preparations were selected for study. An attempt was made to group the chromosomes according to size and morphology taking account of the position of the centromere.

Individual chromosomes of a definite group could, in some instances, be identified with enough accuracy as a pair of the group by comparing their size with the size of the other member of the group. In the other instances, however, such individual identification was impossible and pairs could only be assigned to a group and numbered sequentially in order of decreasing size.

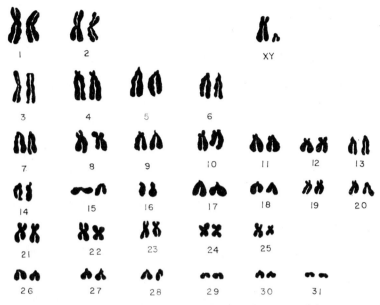

FIG. 1. The karyotype of *Dasypus hybridus* (2n = 64), prepared from a metaphase plate of a bone marrow culture, showing the morphological characteristics of the five groups of autosomes and the sex chromosomes.

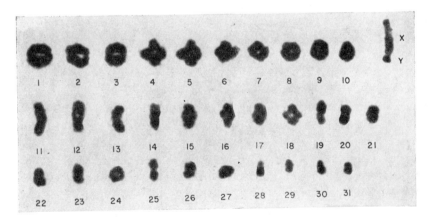

FIG. 2. Serial alignment of the 32 bivalents during first meiotic metaphase in side view. The XY pair shows different degree of heteropycnosis.

From the karyogram analysis 5 groups were arbitrarily defined based on the following characteristics (Fig. 1).

Group I   2 pairs of large *metacentrics*

Group II   4 pairs of large *acrocentrics*

Group III   14 pairs of medium *acrocentrics*
Group IV   5 pairs of medium *metacentrics*
Group V   6 pairs of small *acrocentrics*

The chromosomes of groups I and II are quite characteristic. Pair I has a median centromere, pair II has the centromere nearly in submedian position. Both pairs are of equal size. Pairs 3 to 6 of group II are all acrocentric and decrease gradually in size.

In group III the majority of the chromosomes are typically all of the acrocentric type, pair 8 and pair 12 have the small arm a little longer than the rest of the elements of the group and show a gradual decrease in size.

In group IV the 5 pairs are all metacentric. There is a difference between the homologues of pair 25 and also but not so marked between the members of pair 22.

In our material we have not found any satellited chromosome in this group. In group V the six pairs are acrocentric, they form a decreasing seriation in size.

Pairs 29, 30 and 31 are smaller and constitute a uniform group in comparison with pairs 26, 27 and 28.

There is an extra chromosome in the group II corresponding in size to this group but with submedian centromere and an extra-small chromosome in group V. They were designated the X and the Y chromosome that constitute the heteromorphic pair of sex chromosomes.

Meiotic Chromosomes

At early prophase the chromonema present a woolly appearance of indefinite individuality. They develop afterwards into many long, curved, slender, discontinuous threads. By shortening and thickening they enter into pachytene (Fig. 4). The condensation of the bivalents advances until diakinesis. The spiral structure becomes visible at first in the leptonema and can be observed until the end of diakinesis and in some cases in well-spread preparations until prometaphase (Fig. 5).

At first metaphase we find 31 bivalents and the XY heteromorphic pair. In general one or two terminal chiasmata are present in the bivalents whose configuration is shown in Fig. 2.

The sex chromosomes are in *Dasypus hybridus*, as in most mammals, precocious in their movements and have a rhythm of condensation different from that of the rest of the autosomes.

During leptonema and paquinema the sex chromosomes appear to be formed by a coiled chromonema enclosed within a vesicle of its own and

it is located, as it is characteristic of these chromosomes, at the periphery
of the nucleus (Fig. 4). Its thread, the chromonema, contracts and thickens
in the diplotene stage and becomes more evident as prophase goes on. The
chromonema is seen freed from the ground substance of the vesicle; it is
no longer coiled and becomes a complete sex bivalent composed of two

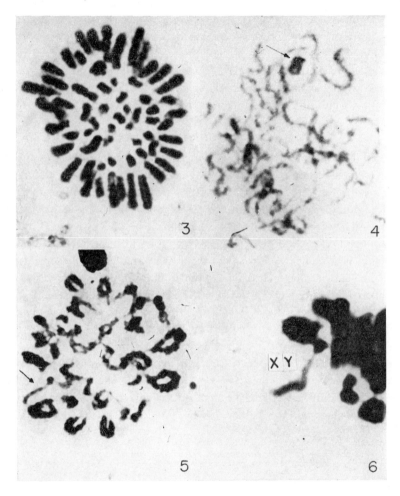

Fig. 3. Spermatogonial metaphase in polar view showing the 64 chromosomes.
From a squash stained in acetic hematoxylin.

Fig. 4. Pachytene stage showing the structure of the sex vesicle (XY bivalent) in
positive heteropycnosis.

Fig. 5. Late diplotene. The arrow indicates the sex chromosomes.

Fig. 6. First meiotic metaphase showing the different degree of heteropycnosis
between the X and the Y chromosomes.

elements. In the closing stage of prophase I, the chromatin concentration is not quite equal throughout the length of the sex bivalent, because there is a persistent concentration in a small portion set off from a larger region by a slightly achromatic interval. The small segment is the Y chromosome showing positive heteropycnosis associated by a terminal chiasma to the X chromosome which is represented by a less condensed isopycnotic large segment.

No evidence of longitudinal pairing between X and Y was observed in the course of meiotic prophase.

At metaphase the sex bivalent shows the configuration illustrated by Figs. 2 and 6. A large isopycnotic segment, the X chromosome, is seen united by a chiasma to the small positive heteropycnotic Y chromosome.

DISCUSSION

When Newman and Patterson investigated the armadillo they used a material fixed in unfavourable cytological conditions and for this reason their results were inaccurate. The authors found 31 and 32 chromosomes (diploid number) in male and female, and 10–14 (haploid number) in females. They interpret the sex mechanism to be of XO type.

Painter (1925) while describing 60 somatic chromosomes in the same species was very near the real number. In a later paper Painter (1925b) published camera lucida drawings of the somatic chromosomes of two cells in a horizontal line, placing together the elements of similar size and shape.

He points out that there are "proportionally more small chromosomes in this animal than in forms with only 48 chromosomes".

The edentates constitute an ancient group among mammalia, and it is interesting to find that most of large and median chromosomes are acrocentric, whereas metacentric ones are among the less sized median ones. There only exists 5 large metacentric chromosomes, among these the X chromosome (see Table 1, Fig. 1).

TABLE 1. NUMBER AND DISTRIBUTION OF THE DIFFERENT CHROMOSOME TYPES
IN *Dasypus Novemcinctus* AND *Dasypus Hybridus*†

Species	Ml	Mm	Al	Am	As	X	Y	Total M	Total A
D. novemcinctus	4	12	8	28	10	M	A	17	47
D. hybridus	4	10	8	28	12	M	A	15	48

† Ml — metacentrics large; Mm — metacentrics medium; Al — acrocentrics large ; Am — acrocentrics medium; As — acrocentrics short.

Beath, Benirschke and Brownhill (1962) obtained the modal number of 64 chromosomes for *Dasypus novemcinctus*. Their distribution is similar to that found by us in *Dasypus hybridus*.

In our slides the satellited chromosome could not be found as it was by the same authors corresponding to pair labelled — 26 —.

Five pairs of metacentric chromosomes in group IV and six pairs of acrocentrics were placed by us in our material in group V. Beath, Benirschke and Brownhill (1962) place 6 pairs of metacentrics in the fourth group and 5 pairs in the sixth one.

According to our view pair No. 22 of these authors could be looked at as acrocentric and thus placed in the series corresponding to the sixth group. The karyotypes of both species are therefore closely similar.

Makino and Tateishi (1951) described the existence of a diploid chromosome complex of 42 in the spermatogonia of *Manis pentadactyla*. All the autosomes in this species are acrocentric and similar to one another, constituting a gradual series decreasing in size. The sex bivalent is composed by the submetacentric X and a small Y attached to the long arm of the X. It is not surprising to find a marked difference between the chromosomes of *Dasypus* and *Manis*. The genus *Dasypus* belongs to the order Edentata and *Manis* to the order Pholidota. The center of distribution of the edentates in South America extended as far North as Central America, Mexico and in the case of *Dasypus novemcinctus* even into Texas.

The Pholidotes, or pangolins, are African and Southern Asian forms and are properly placed in a separate order for geographical as well as profound anatomical differences.

Only two species were studied up to the present. As the study of the karyotypes of other genera and species of edentates will progress, a more general vision of the chromosome evolution of this interesting group will be seen.

SUMMARY

The chromosomes of "mulita", the seven banded armadillo *Dasypus hybridus* (Desmarest), were studied by means of bone marrow cultures and male germ cells squash preparations.

The somatic and spermatogonial cells contained 2n = 64 (62+XY) chromosomes and at the first meiotic metaphase there are 31 bivalents and the XY heteromorphic pair.

According to the size and position of the centromere the karyotype is composed by five groups of autosomes and the XY sex chromosomes.

Group I contains 2 pairs of large metacentrics; group II 4 pairs of large acrocentrics; group III 14 pairs of medium acrocentrics; group IV is composed of 5 pairs of medium metacentrics; and group V contains 6 pairs of small acrocentrics.

The X chromosome corresponds in size to group II but it has a submedian centrome, the Y chromosome is acrocentric and corresponds in size to the V group.

The meiotic prophase was studied and the behaviour and configuration of the XY sex complex was followed.

X and Y chromosomes appear to be formed by a coiled chromonema enclosed within a vesicle during leptonema and pachynema, and as prophase advances the thread are free and become the sex bivalent. The X chromosome shows negative heteropycnosis at the end of prophase and in metaphase I.

The Y chromosome is small and shows positive heteropycnosis at the same stages. Both X and Y are probably united by a terminal chiasma. Side by side pairing between the sex chromosomes was not clearly observed in any stage of the meiotic prophase. During metaphase I the bivalents terminalize with one or two chiasmata. Considerations on some evolutionary correlations are discussed.

REFERENCES

BEATH, M. M. K., BENIRSCHKE and BROWNHILL L., The chromosomes of the nine-banded armadillo *Dasypus novemcinctus. Chromosomes (Berl.)* **13**, 1–15, 1962.

CABRERA, A., Catálogo de los mamíferos de América del Sur. *Rev. Mus. Arg. Cien. Nat. Serie Ciencias Biológicas Bernardino Rivadavia*, **4**, No. 1, 223, 1957.

FERNANDEZ, M., Die zur Embryologie der Gärteltiere. I. Zur Keimblätterinversion und spezifischen Polyembrionie der Mulita (Tatusiahydrida). *Morph. Jahrb. Bd.* **39**, 302–333, 1909.

FERNANDEZ, M., Die Entwicklung der Mulita. *Rev. Mus. de La Plata*, **21**, 1–156, 1915.

FORD, C. E. and HAMERTON, J. L., A colchicine hypotonic citrate squash sequence for mammalian chromosomes. *Stain Technology*, **31**, 247, 1956.

MAKINO, S. and TATEISHI, S., Notes on the chromosomes of the pangolin, *Manis pentadactyla* (Edentata). *J. Fasc. Sci. Hokkaido Univ. Ser. II* **10**, 319–323, 1951.

NEWMAN, N. H. and PATTERSON, J. T., The development of the nine-banded armadillo from the primitive streak stage to birth with special reference to the question of specific polyembryony. *J. Morph.* **21**, 359–424, 1910.

NEWMAN, H. H., The ovum of the nine-banded armadillo. Growth of the oocytes maturation and fertilization. *Biol. Bull.* **23**, 1912.

PAINTER, T. S., Chromosome numbers in mammals. *Science*, **61**, 423–424, 1925a.

PAINTER, T. S., A comparative study of the chromosomes of Mammals. *The American Naturalist*, **59**, 385–409, 1925b.

SAEZ, F. A., El empleo de la hematoxilina acética o propiónica para el estudio de los cromosomas con la técnica de aplastamiento. Comun. Soc. Biol. Montevideo, 11 de mayo de 1960.

ON HUMAN PACHYTENE CHROMOSOMES

B. M. SLIZYNSKI

Institute of Animal Genetics, Edinburgh, Scotland

INTRODUCTION

"Differences in the metaphase morphology of the various chromosomes have been established. In view of the detail required for cytogenetic map, however, the structure of metaphase chromosomes has limited uses. We have found it possible to work out the pattern of the chromomeres of one chromosome of the complement. The nucleolar chromosome at the pachytene stage of meiosis. These observations have extended to the production of a standard diagram for this chromosome which can serve as a basis for recognition of deviations from the normal pattern". So wrote Schultz and St Lawrence[19] in 1949 in the Introduction to their paper, which was the first paper on the pachytene chromosomes of man.

Since Schultz and St Lawrence's publication there was one attempt by Yerganian[27] in 1957 to continue the line of research initiated by them. Yerganian's paper contains a collection of microphotographs and drawings of nine isolated human pachytene chromosomes. These drawings could eventually be used for identification purposes, though there is no reference system given. Beyond Yerganian's paper nothing has been done in the field of mapping human pachytene chromosomes.

Under these circumstances it is very difficult to say something about pachytene chromosomes of man.

This depressing state of affairs requires rather an outline of research program, for which perhaps the results obtained from other sources may be of some use. In trying to develop such an outline several approaches could be proposed — morphological, cytogenetical, physiological and as a separate problem the study of sex chromosomes.

A. METHODS

Schultz and St Lawrence[19] in their study employed the acetocarmin technique. The improvement which they introduced permits the analysis of individual chromosomes. It consists in cutting the tubule into small fragments from which the cells are squeezed out into a drop of fixative. They also applied Feulgen stain with fast green counterstaining. They found that storing in a fixative in the frozen state for several years yields preparations almost as good as the fresh material.

Yerganian's[27] technique consisted of breaking up of nuclei and repeated centrifugation, after which single chromosomes could be easily isolated. The yield of clean single chromosomes is very large. There is, however, a danger of disconnecting nucleoli from their chromosomes and of disrupting chromocentres. The advantage of the method is that chromosomes are not stretched, their natural shape and length relations of components are preserved.

Recent improvements found in Edinburgh lead to an increase of the yield of the desired stages of spermatogenesis by selecting a region of the tubule in which they are abundant.

Parallel to Oakberg's[12] definition of stages of spermatogenesis it was found that the different frequencies of various stages occur in morphologically definable regions of the tubule.

Along the 2–5 cm long section of a tubule (the length varies with the season) there is as a rule the whole of the spermatogenetic wave contained. The piece of the tubule is selected in such a way that it starts with a wider part followed by a rapid change of the diamater. After this the tubule slowly comes to its original width. Meiotic metaphases I and II occur in large frequency just in this part which slowly regains the original diameter. This is followed by the region in which the tubule is full of secondary spermatocytes and spermatids.

Further on, low power examination of carmine stained tubule reveals two dark lines running irregularly just under the surface of the tubule. These are a multitude of spermatids attached to the Sertoli cells. At the same time leptotene and zygotene stages begin to appear.

Next, there is only one thick line in the centre of the tubule. It represents the stained heads of spermatozoa occupying the lumen of the tubule. In this region almost all remaining cells are in zygotene and pachytene stage. Incidentally the sequence of two dark lines followed by one indicates the direction in which the spermatozoa will travel and also the direction of the spermatogenetic wave.

Culturing *in vitro* undoubtedly belongs to the chapter on technique. This can be done quite easily with both testes and ovaries as a short term culture or rather storing (up to six days) in M199. In such culture the morphological effects on the chromosomes of some quickly acting substances can be studied with comparative ease.

B. MORPHOLOGY

1. *Comparison of Meiotic Prophase Chromosomes*

The comparison of meiotic prophase chromosomes of different species of animals reveals that there is very little difference in the general appearance of the chromosomes. The similarity goes much further. Whether it be plant material or animal the chromosomes in prophase of meiosis are alike if one does not go into the chromomeric pattern.

The plate shows leptotene stage in the oocyte of newly born pig and man and in both cases the chromosomes resemble those of the lily in which the leptotene stage was first described. It is almost impossible to tell, when looking at the preparation, whether it is of a plant or of an animal (Plate I (a) and (b)).

This is a very important fact as it indicates that the structural and functional principles of the chromosome organization are fundamentally the same in all higher organisms.

2. *Size of the Chromosomes*

During the division cycle of the cell the chromosomes visibly change their size. This change is brought about by spiralization. The correct idea about the dimensions of the chromosomes could be obtained by estimating their maximum length. For this purpose much information has been obtained from the study of lampbrush chromosomes from the oocytes of amphibia. The lampbrush chromosomes are at present the nearest visible approximation to the real length of the gene string.

Gall and Callan in 1962,[4] using radioisotope labelled compounds, the time and rate of their incorporation in the chromosomes and the optically determined length of the side loops, conclude that the total length of the entire haploid set of the chromosomes of a newt would be about 9 m. This tremendous figure (75 cm for an average chromosomes) is confirmed by the photometric measurements (carried out by the authors) which show that the haploid set of a new chromatid contains about 30×10^{-6} μg of DNA. This amount of DNA when calculated as a Watson–Crick double helical chain would measure just about 10 m.

The chromosome may be thus visualized as an enormously long structure, possibly differentiated in some way into active and non-active regions which are not equally spaced.

A chromosome may undergo various degrees of coiling by which it may appear as a lampbrush chromosome in amphibian oocytes, polytene chromosome of many dipteran tissues, or pachytene chromosome of meiotic prophase. Further coiling, which goes on in the course of later stages of division, obliterates almost all traces of internal differentiation.

The different types of chromosomes may be produced by different changes. For instance from mitotic prophase, a chromosome of *Drosophila* has to go through a process of uncoiling to become a salivary gland chromosome, while meiotic chromosome of leptotene becomes a pachytene chromosome after it has gone through a process of intensive coiling.

Several authors suggested that polytene chromosomes grow longitudinally during the development of the larvae by insertion of new material into the interchromomeric regions. There is no evidence for or against it at the present time.

3. *Elements of Structure*

(a) *Chromomeres.* Linear arrangement of particulate genes established by genetical methods is expected to have a morphological counterpart or basis. There are at present two main possibilities — either the chromosome fibre is regionally differentiated into separate units which correspond to the genes, the links between them being of different material — or there is no regional structural differentiation but the similarity of successive pattern of DNA produces centres of genetic activity separated from each other by a segment of less similar pattern.

In both cases the fibre undergoes coiling and in both cases chromioles or ultimate chromomeres produced by primary coiling would represent the morphological counterparts of groups of genes.

The term chromomere was originally used to describe the stainable knobs in the leptotene chromosomes of the lily. These probably correspond to the leptotene knobs of mammals, but the large and less numerous structures seen later in pachytene undoubtedly consist of several leptotene chromomeres coiled into one; they could be called gyromeres.

Among the chromomeres of pachytene chromosomes of mammals there are several morphological types differing in size, clarity of outline, intensity of staining, etc. The type and pattern of their distribution is generally constant and is used as a means of identification of chromosomes.

(b) *Centromere.* The region of the centromere is defined by Lima-de-Faria[8] by five criteria. The first is functional and leads to the recognition of the centromeric region in metaphase and in anaphase. The second is the morphological one. The centromere is in the primary constriction, which is usually poorly stained (third criterion). The relative length of arms separated by primary constriction may be used to indicate the position of the centromere in other stages, where it is functionally not definable. The fourth criterion postulates the existence of the same structure at the centromeric region in all phases of the chromosome cycle. The fifth criterion is furnished by the attachment of the sister chromatids on both sides of the centromere.

Of these criteria only the lesser stainability and the relative arm length could be used for determination of the position of the centromere in pachytene chromosomes.

Schultz and St Lawrence[19] in their description of pachytene pattern of nucleolar chromosome in man do not make any mention of the centromere. It could be that the centromere is near the nucleolar organizer, which is at the point between the two arms.

Neither does Yerganian[27] mention centromeres in his paper.

Slizynski in 1949[22] introducing a preliminary pachytene map of the mouse accepted as approximate positions of the centromeres the so-called light areas (third criterion of Lima-de-Faria). According to this determination several mouse chromosomes have subterminal, few short chromosomes have a submedian centromere (Plate I (c) and (d)).

Griffen in 1955[5] in describing details of his pachytene map of mouse chromosomes wrote "the faint areas suggested by Slizynski as centromere locations have not been observed". In the map of Griffen many chromosomes have densely stained and closely synapted cluster of chromomeres "which are remarkably similar in structure and in appearance to the centromeres of dipteran salivary gland chromosomes".

In their *Drosophila* paper Warters and Griffen[26] conclude that in the interphase the centromeres are not denuded of nucleic acid but are heavily invested with it. Beautiful drawings and microphotographs support this view strongly.

If Griffen's location of centromeres in mouse pachytene chromosomes is accepted, then again several chromosomes in mouse pachytenogram have subterminal or submedian centromeres.

On the other hand several authors studying mouse metaphase chromosome came to the conclusion that almost all mouse chromosomes are telocentric, the short arm being exceedingly small in all of them.

Against the telocentricity of all mouse chromosomes some evidence is supplied from studies of translocation fertilities in the mouse. In the case of several translocations in this animal it has been found that fertility exceeds the expected 50 per cent.

As it is known, fertility higher than 50 per cent in translocation heterozygotes can be obtained if some particular configurations are formed at metaphase of meiosis. The formation of such configurations depends on the occurrence of a chiasma in the short arm of the chromosomes

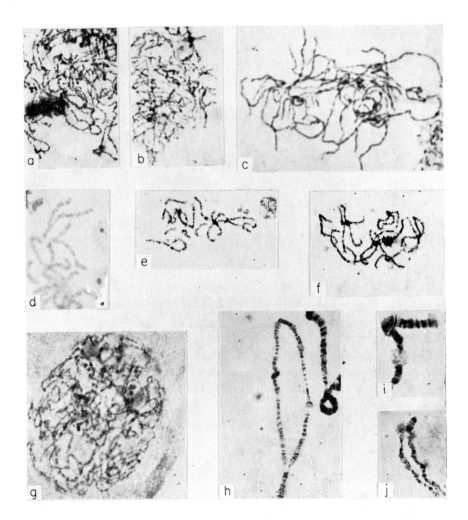

PLATE I (a—j)

(a) End of leptotene stage in an oocyte of a newly born pig.
(b) End of leptotene in an oocyte of a prematurely (6 months) born human — foetus.
(c) Pachytene stage in an oocyte of prematurely born human foetus.
(d) "Light areas" in mouse pachytene chromosomes in oocytes.
(e) Pig testis, pachytene stage light areas and chromocentre.
(f) Bull testis, chromocentres, XY complex embedded in one chromocentre.
(g) Zygotene stage in a human oocyte from a prematurely born foetus. Two nucleoli.
(h), (i), (j) Different degrees of puff formation in *Drosophila melanogaster* polytene chromosomes — (h) in division 56, (i) in 26 and (j) in division 2.

involved. The conclusion from translocation fertilities is that some mouse chromosomes must have a short arm so long as to permit a formation of a chiasma (Slizynski[23]).

Several methods have been tried to define the centromeres in pachytene stage including the interpretation of microphotographs from electron microscope.

The best method seems to be the comparison of clearly rod-shaped chromosomes with distinctly V-shaped ones both in pachytene and in metaphase in the same animal. For this purpose the pig has been chosen as it has clearly defined both rod-shaped and V-shaped chromosomes. in its karyogram.

The length of arms has been measured in four mitotic metaphase plates (from bone marrow) and in 15 pachytene chromosome complements on two assumptions — that either the so-called light areas or the dark knobs represent the site of the centromere. The first assumption had better agreement with metaphase arm ratio than the second (Plate I (e)).

For instance the largest chromosome of pig metaphase karyogram has a submedian centromere, the arm ratio being 29 : 64 (in arbitrary units as measured on the screen). The largest element of pachytene nucleus has a distinct light area delimited on both sides by darkly stained knobs.

Its pachytene arm ratio if measured from the centre of the light area is 32 : 62 and if measured from either of the dark knobs becomes 24 : 70 or 38 : 56.

Whether the centromeres are in staining or in non-staining parts of the pachytene chromosome the discrepancy between pachytene and metaphase determination of centromere in mice is not cleared up as both pachytene determinations indicate that some mouse chromosomes have submedian centromeres.

A way out of this contradiction may be that the short arm of a chromosome may change its relative length at different stages of cell life. It can be that the short arm is more coiled in metaphase than the long arm. Another possibility is that short arms have particularly high frequency of chiasma formation per unit of length.

(c) *Chromocentre*. In salivary gland preparations of many *Drosophilae* species the proximal heterochromatic regions of the chromosomes fuse to form the so-called chromocentre.

In pachytene neuclei in mammalian gametogenesis chromocentres are almost always present and there may be one or more of them in one nucleus. They may consist of 2–11 chromosomes stricking together with their dark staining ends. However, not all chromosomes are attached to it and the attachment is not obligatory for any one chromosome. This is true for mouse, rat, rabbit, two species of peromyscus, cavia, bull, pig and man. The frequency of attachment of any given chromosome has not been studied. It may be that it depends on the size of heterochromatic regions.

A peculiarity of chromocentres in bull pachytene nuclei is that they appear occasionally associated with the XY chromosome complex (Plate I (f)).

Another observation has been made in pachytene nuclei of pig, and this is that some chromosomes have sometimes both ends inserted into the chromocentre — the limb of the chromosome forming a loop. Sometimes the chromocentres in the pig may have a hole in the middle of the heterochromatic mass possibly indicating shortness of the heterochromatic region (Plate I (k)).

(d) *Nucleolus.* Very little has been done about the last constituent of the pachytene nucleus, namely about the nucleolus since Schultz and St Lawrence's paper. According to them, nucleolus of man may be considered as organized under the influence of heterochromatic segments. The nucleolus formed by the X chromosome appears to be independent of that formed by the nucleolar chromosome. The nucleolus associated with sex chromosomes differs from the autosomal nucleolus in staining less intensely with fast green and in the pattern of association with the chromomeres. There are then two separate nucleolar organizers in spermatogonial prophase in man.

This conclusion is fully confirmed by the study of pachytene stage in human oocytes. This has been done on the ovaries of three prematurely born (six lunar months of pregnancy) human foetuses who died shortly after birth (within 24 hr). In the oocyte nuclei from these ovaries there are two nucleoli present in analyzable zygo and pachytene nuclei. One nucleolus is larger than the other (Plate I (g)).

In 1961 Ferguson-Smith and Handmaker (as quoted by Ohno, Weiler and Stenius [15]) found that in tissue culture of human material in prophase of mitosis all five pairs of telocentric autosomes show nucleolus-like structures in their short arms. Ohno, Weiler and Stenius[15] have shown that six is the highest number of chromosomes which were seen to have nucleoli in mitotic prophase of man. They conclude that not every nucleolus organizer must be active all the time.

To this it could be added that nucleoli from meiotic prophase (one in the V-shaped autosome and another in the sex chromosome) are different

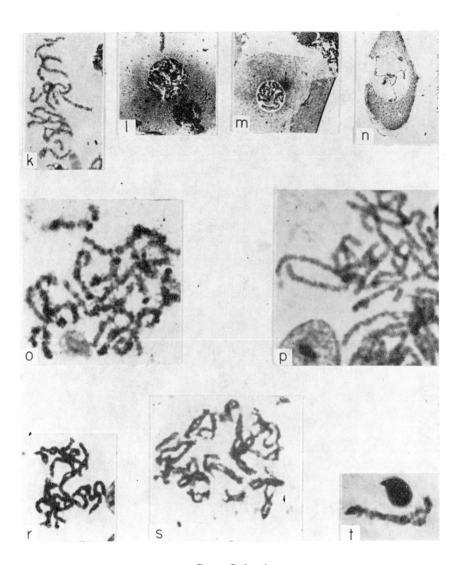

PLATE I (k—t)

(k) Pig testis, pachytene stage, one chromosome attached to the chromocentre with both ends.

(l), (m), (n) Movements of chromosomes in salivary gland nuclei.

(o), (p) Male and female pachytene chromosome of the mouse.

(r) Diakinesis of an oocyte of 18 days old mouse embryo cultured *in vitro* and superovulated.

(s) Diakinesis of an oocyte of a newly born pig.

(t) Differences among chromomeres involved in pairing.

from nucleoli from mitotic prophase (on five rod-shaped autosomes). There is then a possibility that, at different stages of cell cycle, different nucleolus organizers may be active.

4. *Morphological Variations*

Generally speaking the length of a chromosome and its arms is a species characteristic. There are, however, exceptions, for instance chromosome 15 of human karyotype[6] has an arm ratio varying between 1 : 4 and 1 : 12, although the variation of its total length is much smaller.

Another example is the difference in the length of arms between the two homologues within the same nucleus, observed in Crossley and Clarke's[3] material of cows mitotic metaphase chromosomes. There the length ratio of the arms of chromosome *c* varies from 1 : 2 to 1 : 3.

Best example of length variation is given in a paper by Ohno, Weiler and Stenius[15] on the nucleolar chromosome of the guinea pig. This chromosome has a short arm which, in relation to the other arm, is longer in mitotic metaphase than in meiotic. In mitotic prophase and in pachytene one of these chromosomes develops a long nucleolus organizing region, while the other remains small. The difference persists till diakinesis later diasappears.

Another type of variation occurs among chromomeres. This has been described in *Chironomus*, *Rhynchosciara* and *Acricotopus* by Bermann[1], Breuer and Pavan,[2] Pavan and Breuer,[17, 18] Mechelke[11] and others.

These authors described the so-called puffy regions in polytene chromosomes and found that (a) the amount of nucleic acid in a chromomere-band is indicative of how much puff it can produce and how much a given gene can influence the metabolism, (b) the puff formation depends on the stage of development of the larva, (c) puffs contain active loci, (d) there is a morphological position effect in the formation of the puff, (e) puffs can be influenced by hormones and (f) puffs move along the chromosome as the functions change.

In *Drosophila melanogaster* polytene chromosomes the (a), (b), (d) and (f) points have been established. In addition it has been found that the two homologues in the same cell may differ in the degree of puff formation, this could be called morphological heterozygotity and it may represent a case of unequal functioning of two homologous genes (Plate I (h) (i) (j)).

The first example of variation of pachytene chromomeres in man was given by Schultz and St Lawrence,[19] who found in the nucleolar chromosome a group of chromomeres paler in one strand than in the other. This and the parallel case in *Drosophila* (quoted above) seem to belong to a type of functional variation, which could perhaps be related to L. B. Russell's partial or to Lyon's total[9] inactivation hypothesis (Plate I (t)).

Another type of functional variation can be found in relation to the sex. This is strikingly evident in the morphology of the sex chromosomes in the pachytene stage. In oocytes the two X chromosomes behave like all other chromosomes, while in spermatocytes the presence of the Y chromosome changes completely the structure and behaviour of the X chromosome, its partner.

In spite of all these variations, the pachytene maps do not loose their validity. Pachytene chromosome maps of spermatocytes of the mouse can be used to identify the chromosomes in the oocytes. And in man − the nucleolar chromosome has been identified by its chromomere pattern in the oocyte. The general morphology and the pattern of pachytene chromomeres correspond quite well between the sexes, although there are some differences resembling puff formation.

The dimensions of pachytene chromosomes are slightly different, female chromosomes beeng a little longer than those of the male. Oocyte chromosomes have more compact structure, their outlines are smooth and their diameter is almost constant. In spermatocytes the chromosomes are shorter, their diameter is greatly variable and their outlines are fuzzy (Plate I (p)).

C. CYTOGENETICS

In the field of cytogenetical research connected with pachytene chromosomes, the mouse is the most advanced mammal. Up to ten chromosomes are related to their linkage groups.

Nothing has been done in this respect in any other animal or in man.

From the studies of Beermann, Pavan, Breuer, Mechelke (1c) and their co-workers it appears that a new field for a cytogenetical research is now being opened. That is the localization of genes on the polytene (and possibly on prophase) chromosomes using puffy regions as indicators of activity at various developmental stages and in various tissues.

In the last few years another cytogenetic problem, the problem of pairing and of crossing-over awakened a new interest. It is known that in meiosis the last synthesis of DNA occurs at the end of interphase. This apparently makes the theory of crossing-over as taking place in the second half of pachytene untenable, and it gives a different meaning to the zygote pairing, pachytene association and diplotene chiasmata.

However, in defence of chiasmata in their original interpretation, Schultz and Redfield[20] suggested that the last synthesis of DNA occurring in the pre-leptotene stage corresponds to the formation of new genes, while linking them up, and chiasma formation occurs in the second half of the pachytene stage. Perhaps some evidence for the Schultz and Redfield opinion may be found in the fact that in polytene chromosomes pairing and reduplication are not in any way interdependent.

Several hypotheses have been put forward to explain conditions necessary for zygotene pairing. The simplest, and one which requires the least elaboration, is the hypothesis of active movements of the chromosomes. These movements related to the metabolic activity of the chromosomes may bring the two homologues in contact in any one place. This is probably the reason why in polytene chromosome pairing Schultz and Hungerford[21] found that there are no constant regions in which pairing will occur first.

Movements of large chromosomes, namely polytene chromosomes, can be found in salivary gland nuclei of many dipteran larvae, and in analogy it is easier to accept active movements of chromosomes as a condition of zygotene pairing (Plate I (l), (m), (n)).

E. PHYSIOLOGY

The duration of zygotene and of pachytene may be estimated from the proportion of spermatocytes in these two stages in comparison with cells in other stages of meiosis. If the post-meiotic sperm differentiation phase be disregarded, spermatocytes in zygotene and in pachytene form by far the most numerous elements of spermatogenesis. This may be taken as evidence that the association of paternal and maternal chromosomes is of a very long duration.

Koller in 1936[7] found that in a quiescent testis of hibernating ferret the frequency of spermatocytes in the pachytene stage has increased to 50 per cent, as compared with 36 per cent in active testis.

This indicates that the pachytene stage is much longer in quiescent than in active testis. What is more, during the non-breeding season the diakinesis bivalents show fewer chiasmata.

Koller attributed it to a higher degree of terminalization or to a lower initial frequency of chiasmata. Higher degree of terminalization as a cause of fever chiasmata would be in line with the age-depending terminalization of chiasmata in mammalian oocytes as suggested by Slizynski in 1962.[25]

The beginning of meiotic prophase in the ovaries of mammals is variable.

In the mouse where gestation period is 20 days, the first leptotene appears at about day 15, which is after three-quarters of pregnancy have elapsed. In man the first leptotene in the oocytes was observed in a three-month-old foetus, that is after only one-third of the pregnancy (Ohno, Klinger and Atkin[16]).

The end of the first part of meiotic prophase in embryonic ovaries occurs in some organisms before birth and in others during the first few post-natal days. The relevant data are collected in Table 1 (mostly own observations, for rat and for part of man data, see Ohno, Makino, Kaplan and Kinosita[14] and Ohno, Klinger and Atkin[16]). In Table 1 the letters L, Z, P, D denote successive stages of prophase.

TABLE 1. STATE OF OOCYTES NUCLEI AT THE TIME OF BIRTH AND AFTER

Animal	End of pregnancy	Day 1	Day 2	Day 3
Mouse	L Z P	P D	D	D
Peromyscus	L Z P	P D	D	D
Rat	L Z P	L Z P D	L Z P D	D
Cavia	L Z P	D	D	D
Pig	L Z P	L Z P D	D	D
Man 3 months	L Z			
4 months	L Z			
6 months	L Z P			
7 months	L Z P D			
9 months	D			

The data on six-month-old human foetuses came from an analysis of ovarian material kindly supplied by Prof. J. Kowalczykowa (Dept. of Pathological Anatomy, Krakow University, Poland). The prophase picture of these embryos occupies an intermediate position between those of 4 months and 7 months of Ohno, Klinger and Atkin.

In the table there are two extremes, (1) rat in which on second day after birth (leptotene stage) still can be seen and (2) man where before the birth all pre-dictyotene stages of prophase have passed and all oocytes are in the diffuse stage.

In the mouse the appearance of first follicle cells around the oocyte indicates infallibly that it is in the dictyotene stage, while in man an oocyte surrounded by follicle cells may still be in zygotene.

It appears that the beginning of prophase and its interruption after the pachytene are species characteristics. There are some indications that in the mouse it may be even strain characteristic. In certain strains pachytene stage may be seen even on the second post-natal day.

For the initiation of prophase some conclusions can be drawn from the paper of Martinovitch published in 1939.[10]

Embryonic ovaries of mouse were cultured *in vitro* in embryo extract. Their oocytes went into the prophase and on addition of the extract of hypophysis (without the intervening dictyotene stage) through diakinesis to metaphase.

From these results it can be concluded that (a) either some factors contained in embryo extract or self differentiation inside the oocyte nucleus may be responsible for the initiation of prophase; (b) this initiation of prophase is not enough to carry on the whole of meiosis. Prophase stimulus evidently does not act beyond pachytene/diplotene stages of prophase; (c) the dictyotene stage represents a gap between prophase stimulation and hypophyseal stimulation of metaphase.

The mechanism, however, may be more complicated since (1) in very rare cases diakinesis and even metaphase can be seen in newly born mice or pigs (Plate I (s)). (2) Hormonal treatment *in vitro* of 19-day-old embryonic ovaries of mouse induced in their oocytes in 24 hr all stages of first meiotic division without the interval of dictyotene (Plate I (r)). (3) At the time of normal ovulation the hormonal stimulus induces preparatory changes in many more oocytes than are going to ovulate. (4) In the case of the so-called free Martin in cattle, irreversible changes are effected in the oocytes of female embryo. (5) Culturing embryonic ovaries in M-199 only, arrests the oocytes at the stages at which they were at the time of gonadectomy.

From these additional observations it follows that nuclear differentiation in exceptional cases may go very far by itself without hormonal stimulation, but hormonal stimulation can compel nuclear differentiation to proceed with high speed. In normal ovulation only these oocytes respond to metaphase stimulation which were at the highest level of nuclear differentiation, and, also, the Y chromosome of the embryonic testes may be responsible for powerful factors inhibiting meiotic prophase. Not all oocyte nuclei are in the same stage of internal differentiation as may be indicated by variation in several morphological characteristics as uneven staining of homologues, or variability in chromocentre formation, positioning of chromosomes or in resting nuclei the movement of sex chromatin which oscillates between the centre and the nuclear membrane.

ACKNOWLEDGEMENTS

The author is greatly indebted to Prof. Dr. J. Kowalczykowa, Dr. H. P. Donald and Dr. R. A. Beattie for supplying the material of human, pig and rabbit ovaries respectively, to Dr. H. Slizynska for criticism and to Prof. Dr. C. Pavan for the invitation to this conference at which this paper could be presented.

REFERENCES

1. BEERMANN W., 1961, Ein Balbiani Ring als Lokus einer Speicheldrusenmutation, *Chromosome*, **7**, 371–86.
2. BREUER M. E. and PAVAN C., 1955, Behaviour of polytene chromosomes of *Rhynchosciara angelae* at different stages of larval development. *Chromosome*, **12**, 1–25.
3. CROSSLEY R. and CLARKE G., 1962, The application of tissue-culture technique to the chromosomal analysis of *Bos taurus*. *Gen. Res. Camb.* **3**, 167–68.
4. GALL J. G. and GALLAN H. G., 1962, Uridine incorporation in lampbrush chromosomes. *Proc. Nat. Acad. Sci.* **48**, 562–70.
5. GRIFFEN A. B., 1955, A late pachytene chromosome map of the male mouse. *J. Morph.* **96**, 123–136.
6. HUMAN CROMOSOME STUDY GROUP, 1960, A proposed standard of nomenclature of human mitotic chromosomes. *Suppl. Cerebral Palsy Bull.* **2**, 1–9.
7. KOLLER P. C., 1936, Chromosome behaviour in the male ferret and mole during anoestrus. *Proc. Roy. Soc. Lond.* **121**, 192–206.
8. LIMA-DE-FARIA A., 1956, The role of the kinetochore in chromosome organisation. *Hereditas*, **42**, 85–160.
9. LYON M. F., 1961, Gene action in the X-chromosome of the mouse. *Nature (London)*, **190**, 372.
10. MARTINOVITCH P. N., 1939, The effect of subnormal temperature on the differentiation and survival of cultivated *in vitro* embryonic and infantile rat and mouse ovaries. *Proc. Roy. Soc. Lond.* **128**, 138–43.
11. MECHELKE F., 1959, Beziehungen zwischen DNA and dem Ausmass der potentiellen Oberfiachenentfaltung von Riesenchromosomen loci. *Naturwiss.* **46**, 609.
12. OAKBERG E. T., 1956, A description of spermiogenesis in the mouse and its use in analysis of the cycle of seminiferous epithelium and germ cell renewal. *Am. J. Anat.* **99**, 391–413.
13. OHNO S., KAPLAN W. D. and KINOSITA R., 1959, The centromeric and nucleolus associated heterochromatin of *Rattus norvegicus*. *Exp. Cell. Res.* **24**, 348–57.
14. OHNO S., MAKINO S., KAPLAN W. D. and KINOSITA R., 1961, Female germ cells of man. *Exp. Cell. Res.* **24**, 106–10.
15. OHNO S., WEILER G. and STENIUS CHR., 1961, A dormant nucleolus organizer in the guinea pig, *Cavia cobaya*. *Exp. Cell. Res.* **25**, 498–501.
16. OHNO S., KLINGER H. P. and ATKIN., N. B., 1962, Human oogenesis. *Cytogenetics*, **1**, 42–51.
17. PAVAN C. and BREUER M. E., 1955, in *Symposium on Cell Secretion.* **90**, Bello Horozonte, Brazil.
18. PAVAN C. and BREUER M. E., 1952, Polytene chromosomes in different tissues of *Rhynchosciara*. *J. Her.* **43**, 151–7.
19. SCHULTZ J. and LAWRENCE P. ST., 1949, A cytological basis for a map of the nucleolar-chromosome in man. *J. Her.* **40a**, 30–8.
20. SCHULTZ J. and REDFIELD H., 1951, Interchromosomal effects on crossing-over. *Cold Spring Harb. Symp.* **16**, 175–95.

21. SCHULTZ J. and HUNGERFORD D. A., 1953, in *Abstracts of Rev. Gen. Soc.* **22**, 99.
22. SLIZYNSKI B. M., 1949, A preliminary pachytene chromosome map of the house mouse. *J. Gen.* **49**, 242–5.
23. SLIZYNSKI B. M., 1957, A chromosomal mechanism in translocation fertility. *Proc. Roy. Phys. Soc. Edinb.* **26**, 49–60.
24. SLIZYNSKI B. M., 1961, The pachytene stage in mammalian oocytes. *Nature (London)*, **189**, 683–4.
25. SLIZYNSKI B. M., 1960, Sexual dimorphism in mouse gametogenesis. *Gen. Res. Camb.* **1**, 477–86.
26. WATERS M. and GRIFFEN A. B., 1959, The centromeres in *Drosophila*. *Genetica*, **30**, 152–67.
27. YERGANIAN G., 1957, Cytological maps of some isolated human pachytene chromosomes. *Am. J. Hum. Gen.* **9**, 42–54.

DISCUSSION

J. I. VALENCIA: I would like, if I may, to make a few comments on Dr. Slizynski's paper and also present a few observations made in our laboratory on human pachytene chromosomes. This work is being done by N. Cacheiro, C. Sonnenschein and myself. We are interested in studying the morphological features of these chromosomes, with the view to making a cytological map. By the combination of different staining techniques, we have been able to study the bivalents from a large number of whole nuclei with well-spread chromosomes. In addition to studying the chromomere pattern of the pachytene chromosomes, we have also made observations on the pairing of the sex chromosomes, the function of the sex vesicle and the pairs associated with the nucleolus.

First, I would like to point out that we have not detected in very well spread pachytenes anything like a chromocentral region. We wonder whether the sex vesicle might not have been mistaken for a chromocenter. In many cells, this organelle appears to be super-imposed on one or more chromosome pair, giving the impression of a chromocentral region.

In the sex vesicle, it is often possible to distinguish the X and the Y chromosomes associated end-to-end. It is not clear how this "pairing" takes place, since the two chromosomes become associated in pre-pachytene stages when they are already highly condensed. In some favorable metaphase preparations, it was possible to observe a minute knot-like structure, reminiscent of a chiasma, at the point where the X and Y chromosomes pair. Thus the formation of a terminal chiasma cannot be discarded. If such a chiasma does not exist, perhaps the X–Y pair is simply held together by being embedded in the vesicle.

The chromosome thread may be observed inside the vesicle. The X is folded in two un-equal arms, one of which is approximately one-third the length of the other. The short arm of the Y would appear to be attached to the end of the short arm of the X. The long arm of the Y ends in two minute and very deeply staining appendages which *protrude* from the vesicle.

At the end of pachytene and the beginning of diplotene, the vesicle starts to disintegrate and each chromosome shows two threads side by side. The sex pair now becomes more stainable, like the autosomes, and the nucleus regains cytologic synchrony.

It can be stated very definitely that the sex pair is not involved with the formation of the nucleolus. We have observed that cells during pachytene show a varying number of nucle-oli (from 1 to 4). Some cells have one very large nucleolus which is often associated with more than one pair (2 or 3); other cells show two medium-sized acrocentric nucleoli; others show three or four, in which case they are often rather small. In most cases the nucleoli are associated terminally or sub-terminally with small or medium-sized chromosomes. Some cells, however, show what would appear to be one very large nucleolus attached to a bivalent of large size (like number 3 or 4 of the Denver classification),

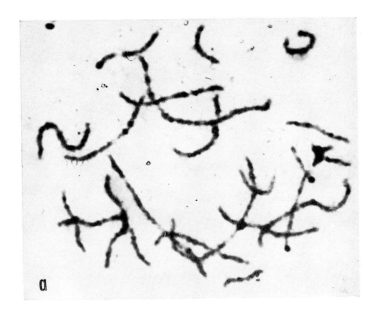

(a) **Pachytene** figure showing 22 autosomes and the sex vesicle (X-Y pair). The centromeric regions are marked by pycnotic knobs (arrows).

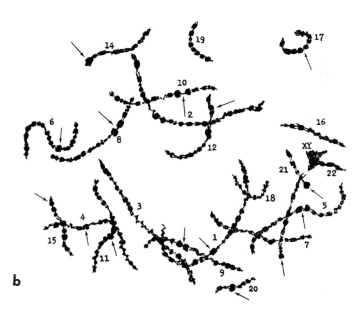

(b) Drawing of cell shown in (a). Detailed analysis of centromeres.

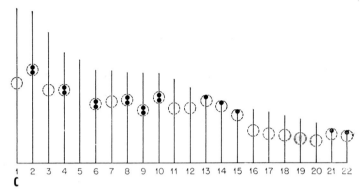

(c) Diagram of the chromosome complement indicating the determined or tentative position of the centromere for each pair. (Denver classification.)

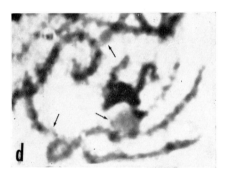

(d) Large nucleous associated with three acrocentric pairs (13, 15, 21). Notice the tip of two other acrocentrics showing small nucleoli (arrows).

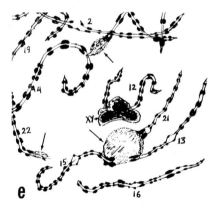

(e) A detailed drawing of (d)

a situation similar to that decribed by Schultz and St. Lawrence (1949). This is not, however, one chromosome but two chromosomes of the large acrocentric group, with sub-terminal organizers.

The centromere can be unmistakably identified in some pairs by the presence of one or two large, prominent, deeply pycnotic chromomeres. These appear terminal in the acrocentric chromosomes and are associated with nucleoli. In other chromosomes they can be seen non-terminally and not associated with nucleoli.

Taking into consideration the size of each chromosome, its relation to the nucleolus and the position of the centromere, several bivalents can already be identified tentatively with relation to the mitotic chromosomes. We do not feel at the present time that we have studied a sufficient number of bivalents to give an accurate chromomere count for each one. As is to be expected, there is considerable variation in the numbers, depending upon the degree of advancement of the pachytene stage, staining, etc. These variations are especially evident in the larger chromosomes. For example, the largest bivalent with a median centromere (apparently chromosome No. 1) shows about 57 chromomeres in early pachytene but only about 30 in later pachytene. The two smallest pairs, both acrocentrics, vary between 6 and 9 chromomeres each. One of them appears attached to a nucleolus and could be No. 21, while the other could be No. 22. Certain chromosomes, nevertheless, have given more consistent counts in the cells observed thus far. Of the 2 large acrocentrics which are in some cases jointly associated with the nucleolus, 16 chromomeres have been observed in one and 13 in the other. A third large acrocentric nucleolus-bearing pair gave a count of 18 chromomeres, some of them extremely small in size. The rest of the bivalents show chromomere numbers which vary between the above-mentioned extremes (9—57).

The morphological features of each chromosome in each nucleus are being recorded on individual maps, with the hope eventually to be able to identify each bivalent at pachytene. This would permit studying in minute detail certain modifications of the human genetic material which are otherwise undetectable.

ABNORMALITIES OF AUTOSOMES

J. LEJEUNE

Institut de Progénèse, Université de Paris, France

THE CONTINUOUS increase of human cytogenetic knowledge imposes the task of frequent reviews. To avoid the difficulty of an exhaustive catalogue, we can restrict the present talk to autosomal disorders and discuss the subject under the three main points of view of the actual research:

The definition of syndromes.

The circumstances of the production of chromosomal abnormalities and the use which can be made of the present knowledge.

DEFINITION OF AUTOSOMAL SYNDROMES

Autosomal syndromes can be viewed as three broad categories, more or less overlapping each other which are:

Excess of genetic material.

Rearrangement of normal amount of material

and loss of some part of the chromosomal set.

A. *Excess of Genetic Material*

Most of the cases now published concern numerical abnormalities, in which the presence of an extra chromosome realizes excess of genetic material, essentially by trisomy of a whole element.

Three conditions are well established and characterized by the presence of 47 chromosomes.

Mongolism due to the presence in triplicate of the chromosome 21 (Lejeune, Gautier and Turpin, 1959).

Trisomy (13) for a big acrocentric of the 13–15 group (Patau, Smith, Therman, Inhorn and Wagner, 1960).

Trisomy (17) for a chromosome of the 16–18 group, most probably the 17 (Edwards, Harnden, Cameron, Crosse and Woff, 1960).

The number of cases observed in those three trisomies is great enough to individualize each of them chromosomally, as well as phenotypically. The clinical picture of mongolism is too well known to be discussed here, but it is at least interesting to note that children affected by trisomy (13) resemble each other in a mongolian manner. The typical picture includes eye ball defects, polydactyly, congenital heart defect, and various deformities of lips, palate, skin and ears, also a severe mental retardation and an extremely poor survival expectancy, are main features of the disease.

In trisomy 17, typical deformities are also found, prominent occiput, low set ears, small mandibule, and malformations of heart, hands, and feet with severe mental retardation. The vital prognosis is also very poor.

Various other clinical syndromes have been recorded in correlation with the presence of an extra small acrocentric chromosome (like a 21 or a 22).

Sturge Weber syndrome (Hayward and Bower, 1961), schizophrenia in a child (Turner and Jennings, 1961); congenital hypotonia (Dunn, Ford, Ausberg, and Miller, 1961; Zellweger, Mikano and Opitz, 1961); mental deficiency in monozygous female twins (Biesele, Schmidt and Lawlis, 1962; Schmidt, Biesele and Lawlis, 1962); mongolism-like syndrome in two sibs (Visle, Wehn, Grosser and Mohr, 1962); and complex malformations, like trisomy 17, among two sisters (Gustavson, Hagberg, Finley and Finley, 1962).

The identity of the extra piece in those instances is difficult to establish, and for the present moment those observations are isolated cases. We must await accumulation of comparable data before new syndromes can be isolated.

In spite of this early stage of the question a few general considerations can be drawn: first, excess of genetic material is generally deleterious, as exemplified by effects of triploidy (Book, 1961; Penrose and Delhanty, 1961; Delhanty, Ellis and Rowley, 1961); second, the bigger the extra element is, the more severe the clinical syndrome — for example chromosome 17 is bigger than 21 and trisomy 17 is much less viable than mongolism. Chromosome (13) is a little bigger than (17) and trisomy for (13) is more severe and the failure to thrive is still more pronounced than in trisomy (17).

If we consider that, by all probability, the genes contained in the extra chromosome are perfectly normal by themselves, it follows that excess of genetic information is harmful by itself and we will come back to this question later.

B. *Rearrangement of Genetic Material*

Most of the rearrangements actually well established concern acrocentric chromosomes, i.e. group 13–15 and group 21–22. In the following paragraphs, symbol (13) means a chromosome of the 13–15 group and (22) a member of 21–22 group.

The overwhelming majority of these structural changes is a fusion of two acrocentric chromosomes which combine to form a new metacentric one, with a minimal, but unavoidable, loss of chromosomal material.

Depending upon the elements involved, we can easily recognize four classes.

Translocation between big and small acrocentrics. The first example known in our species was that of a (22) $\sim$ (13) type found in a retarded child with multiple lesions of the vertebrae (Polydyspondylie) (Turpin, Lejeune, Lafourcade and Gautier, 1959).

This type was found again by Moorhead, Mellmann and Weinar (1961) in a family with speech and mental retardation, and found again in a father and his child (Institut de Progénèse, Obs. No. 293) without phenotypic effect linked to this translocation.

A word must be said about the criteria of recognition of the chromosomes involved in these rearrangements. In fact the diagnosis is not based merely on the abnormal chromosome but also on the normal ones. For instance if two 21 and only one 22 are present the translocated one is supposed to be a 22 and vice versa.

In view of the difficulty of distinction between 21 and 22, the diagnosis remains rather uncertain. Nevertheless, the genetic analysis can in some instances confirm the cytologic inference, as in the family of Moorhead, Mellmann and Weinar, in which the (22) $\sim$ (13) translocated mother had a typical mongolian child with a free 21 trisomy without the translocated chromosome. In such a case, if the translocated acrocentric had been a 21 the mother would have possessed only one 21 free and nondisjunction for one would not have been taking place (at first meiosis at least).

The 21 $\sim$ (13) type seems to be much more frequent and was the first recognized in the determinism of heritable mongolism.

A 21 $\sim$ (13) translocation carrier can produced diplo 21 gametes if the free 21 migrates at the same pole as the translocated chromosome.

The number of instances actually known is great enough to allow an estimate of the occurrence of this event.

Twenty-six translocated mothers are reported in literature to have given birth to 87 children. Of these

22 have 45 chromosomes and exhibit the translocation with a balanced karyotype and a normal phenotype.

21 are entirely normal (phenotype and karyotype)
and 30 are mongols with 46 chromosomes with the translocation.

Fourteen other normal children, non-examined, are probably equally repartited in both categories, translocated ones and nontranslocated.

Taking for granted that the haplo 21 are not viable, the four most likely categories are probably equally distributed, which would lead to the conclusion that nondisjunction of the 21 does occur once in every two divisions in a mother carrier of the translocation.

In the case of translocated father (12 instances recorded), 45 children are born with only one of them being a mongol. The segregation between translocated and nontranslocated being 20 against 14 with 10 other children not tested.

Translocation between two small acrocentrics. This translocation realizes a new element looking like a 19–20 or a 16.

When both elements are 21, the gametes to be formed can be only diplo 21 and nullo 21, i.e. give rise either to abortion or to mongolism.

With the families of Forssman and Lehmann (1962), Hamerton, Briggs, Giannelli and Gartler (1961), Zellweger (1962), Murkherje, Miller and Breg (1962), Dallaire, Fraser and Boyes (1962), a total of 16 children, all mongols, are born from a carrier parent.

On the other hand in the progeny of a mosaic father (Fraccaro, Kaijser, and Lindsten, 1960) there was one mongol and 4 normals, the occurrence of normal children being probably related to the fact that the father was a mosaic for the translocated chromosome.

It is quite likely that in some instances the translocation can be of the 21–22 type, a fact very difficult to establish cytologically, but demonstrable by genetic analysis as in one family reported by Shaw (1962).

Translocation between two big acrocentric chromosomes. Most of these translocations do not have phenotypical consequences. The first case observed was associated with Klinefelter syndrome (Lejeune, Turpin and Decourt, 1960), and another one was a mosaic, half of the cells being 46 and half having the translocations (Institut de Progénèse, Obs. No. 267). The genetic transmission of this type of translocation is examplified in a remarkable family of Walker and Harris (1962) in which there are 9 carriers and 8 normals in the progeny of a carrier ancestor – in this instance, the chromosome cannot be an isochromosome 13∼13 or 14∼14 or 15∼15, but obviously a hybrid because of the lack of trisomy (13) syndome in this extensive pedigree.

Trisomy (13) syndrome by nondisjunction has been observed in a 46 chromosomes boy born from a translocated father (Oikawa, Gromults, Hirschhorn and Novins, 1962), but in most of the other cases of (13)∼(13) translocation (Buhler, Rossier and Vulliet, 1961; Ferguson and Pitt, 1962; Cooper and Hirschhorn, 1961; Makino, Sasaki, Kikuchi and Yoshida, 1962) there are no records of subsequent nondisjunction.

Translocation between acrocentric and nonacrocentric chromosomes.
Another type of translocation involves an acrocentric and another type of
chromosome. So Patau, Therman, Smith, Inhorn and Picken (1961) described
a small extra fragment on a big acrocentric realizing a probable partial
trisomy in a child suffering from Sturge Weber syndrome.

In a child with a clinical picture close to the 17 trisomy, particularly with
the abnormal frequency of arches in digits prints, reported as typical by
Uchida (1962), we observed the presence of an extra segment on the small
arm of a (13) chromosome (Institut de Progénèse, Obs. 491).

Also, a translocation between a 22 and 2 giving rise to a very big acrocentric, has been found in a phenotypically normal mother and her typical
Turner Haplo X daughter (Institut de Progénèse, Obs. No. 420).

Translocations between two nonacrocentric chromosomes have been
involved by Patau, Therman, Inhorn, Smith and Rues (1961), in the Papil-
lon Leage syndrome (insertion on the 1), and Book, Santesson and Zetterqvist (1961), in an apparently normal girl (2 $\sim$ 10 translocation possible).

THE CIRCUMSTANCES OF APPARITION OF AUTOSOMAL DISORDERS

The above review of autosomal disorders makes clear some particularities
in the apparition of these anomalies.

Predisposing Factors

Maternal age. Known since the beginning of this century to play a role
in mongolism (Shuttelworth, 1909) the aging of the mother is also significant in the two other trisomic conditions. In trisomy (17) the mean age of
25 mothers is $35 \cdot 2 \pm 3 \cdot 8$ at the birth of the affected child, and in 13 instances
of trisomy (13) it is $33 \cdot 4 \pm 1 \cdot 7$. Both these means differ significantly from
the mean maternal age in the general population.

Previous Structural Rearrangements

As examplified by the progeny of mother carrying a 21 $\sim$ (13) translocation the risk of abnormal segregation of the normal chromosomes is severely
increased by the presence of the translocated one. Roughly one in every two
meiotic products receive an unbalanced set.

This deleterious effect of structural rearrangement on the meiotic stability
is possibly not restricted to the homologues of the chromosomes involved
in the translocation. It can be remembered that we have encountered the
XXY constitution associated with a (22) $\sim$ (13) translocation in a family

and with a (13) $\sim$ (13) in another case, while a 2 $\sim$ (22) was found in a Turner haplo X case.

Those translocations being very rare by themselves, and sexual aneuploidies being rather uncommon also, it is hard to believe that those combinations of autosomal translocation and sexual aneuploidies are merely coincidental. More precisely these three observations indicate that autosomal changes produce a general impairement of the meiotic stability. This fact is known in *Drosophila* in which Sturtevant (1944) showed that autosomal rearrangement increases the frequency of abnormal segregation of the X chromosome.

Also, an effect of a chromosomal change on other chromosomes is likely to occur: examples are, association of trisomies tri. 21 + XXY (Ford, Jones, Miller, Mittwoch, Penrose, Ridler and Shapiro, 1959), tri. (17) + XXX (Uchida and Bowman, 1961), tri. (17) + tri. 21 (Gagnon, Katyk-Longtin Groot, and Barbeau, 1961), or complex sexual aneuploidies like XXXY, XXXX, XXXXY, XXYY, etc.

Particularities of Chromosomes Themselves

The overwhelming majority of translocations involves acrocentric chromosomes. Even if an observational bias is likely (Turpin and Lejeune, 1961) this type of chromosome seems to have a special risk of undergoing rearrangements.

This risk is probably related to the satellites, because these nucleolus organizers being joined in the resting nucleoli the acrocentrics lie very close together during whole interphase (Ohno, Trujillo, Kaplan, and Kinosita, 1961).

Also, the relative rates of DNA synthesis (Gilbert, Muldal, Lajtha and Rowley, 1962), show after these authors, that 21 and 14 have the same thymidine uptake rhythm, a functional particularity enhancing the possibility of fusion during the synthetic period.

Time of Occurrence of the Aberrations

We know with certainty that in case of constitutional anomalies, the aberration has occurred extremely early, so that the individual is homogeneous for it. Although the meiosis has been generally believed to be the critical period, there is increasing evidence toward a later occurrence.

The observation of mosaicism for trisomy 21, eight cases now reported (Clarke *et al.*, 1961; Fitzgerald *et al.*, 1961; Gustavson *et al.*, 1961; Nicholls, 1961; Warren *et al.*, 1961; Hayashi *et al.*, 1962; Richard *et al.*, 1962; Lindsten *et al.*, 1962), are the proof that the aberration can occur during the first cleavage divisions of the zygote.

More precisely the discovery of monozygotic heterokaryote twins shows that this process can be as precocious as the two blastomeres stage. Of two twins, both nonmosaic, one is normal, the other is a typical trisomic 21 (Lejeune, Lafourcade, Scharer, de Wolff, Salmon, Haines and Turpin, 1962), the monozygosity being nevertheless highly probable.

This type of gemellity previously observed in monozygotic twins one XY the other XO (Turpin, Lejeune, Lafourcade, Chigot and Salmon, 1961; Lejeune and Turpin, 1961) shows that in both types of aberrations, loss of a chromosome or gain of it, can occur in mitotic process so early that instead of a mixed mosaic the result is two twins identical but for the chromosomal abnormalities.

This sensitivity of the early segmentation of the zygote is also found in experiments using X-irradiation in mice (Russell and Saylors, 1960).

These accidents, after meiotic process, can *a priori* occur in a much later stage and remain entirely unnoticed due to the small proportion of abnormal cells.

In some instances, a selective advantage of the mutant cells can lead to the constitution of a "clone" developing inside the host and being related to a neoplastic growth.

Neoplastic Mosaicism

In the case of granulocytic leukaemia a specific deletion of half the long arms of the 21 chromosome realizing the Ph^1 chromosome, was first described by Nowell and Hungerford, 1960, and widely confirmed since.

It is not the place here to discuss the causal relationship between the clinical disease and the chromosomal change (Tough, Court Brown, Baikie, Buckton, Harnden, Jacobs and Williams, 1962) but it is sufficient to say that all observations concord to show that the Ph^1 clone does behave as if it was the stem of the leukaemic cells.

In the same context entire lack of a small acrocentric in acute myeloid leukaemia has been reported (Ruffie and Lejeune, 1962; Atkin and Taylor, 1962) and the parallelism between the two types of lesions is obviously very interesting.

Concerning the other carcinogenic changes, specific chromosome abnormalities are reported in many instances but no clear picture is presently emerging but for macroglobulinaemia with a big extra chromosome (Bottura, Ferrari and Veiga, 1961; German, Bird and Bearn, 1961; Benirschke, Brownhill and Ebaugh, 1961; Pfeiffer, Kosenow and Baumer, 1962). Also in myeloide metaplasia a delection of a medium size was found in three different cases (Lejeune and Salmon, 1961; Grouchy and Lamy, 1962; Solari, Sverdlick and Viola, 1962) but only the Ph[1] chromosome is sufficiently established to be definitely considered as truly related to the disease.

Possible Use of Present Cytogenetic Knowledge

Clinical genetic and counselling. The use of karyotypic analysis in the diagnosis of congenital abnormalities is obvious. If we consider that more than 1/100 of the live births are affected by a sexual or an autosomal aberration, the clinical use of cytogenetics become an outstanding help to the paediatrician and to the obstetrician.

Also the potential danger of occurrence of a disease in a particular family can be measured.

In the common autosomal diseases, particularly in mongolism, the prognosis on the eventual recurrence of the disease in further offspring in an affected sibship can now be reasonably estimated. Translocated mother 21 $\sim$ (13) has 1 chance in 3 of having another mongol, the translocated father having much lower risk. Hence a sound advice can be given and catastrophic families, like in cases of 21 $\sim$ 21 translocation, could be prevented.

This progenetic use imposes the systematical examinations of young mothers of mongols. Also analysis of various other conditions represent an enormous amount of work. This task requires the establishment of a cytogenetic laboratory in every big city of the civilized world.

Research Prospects

The research prospects are still broader and with reason because we need better understanding of things, before trying to act upon them.

The most evident way is the analysis of genetic content of given chromosomes.

Briefly this research can be undertaken on three directions in increasing order of precision:

Clinical manifestation.

Biochemical troubles and antigenic or enzymatic changes.

The clinical analysis is the easiest one in terms of the tools used, which is here medical observation but it is also the less precise.

For example, the dermatoglyphic troubles observed in mongolism (specifically the simian crease) were tentatively related to hypothetical genes of the 21 chromosome after the discovery of the trisomy (Lejeune, 1960) but its existence in various conditions, trisomy (13) for example, or in pseudohypoparathyroidism, seems to show that even a so precise and localized morphological feature can be controlled by quite complex genotypic interaction.

In exceptional instances, heterokaryotic monozygotic twins, localization of genic factors is possibly more practicable. For instance the only phenotypic difference between the normal and trisomic 21 monozygotes previously cited is curled hairs in the normal and flat hairs in the mongol. This difference does not prove that alleles for flat hairs *are* carried by the 21 chromosome, but is an indication that genes in the 21 can do something directly or indirectly on this phenotypical trait.

Also, accumulation of data on partial trisomies or partial delection could become a useful tool in the detection of genes sensitive to genic closage.

The biochemical investigation is more difficult because we have first to find what is to be looked for. Investigations made by Jerome, Lejeune and Turpin (1960) and Jerome (1962) are pointing in the direction of a particular anomaly of tryptophane metabolism in trisomic 21 children.

The main difficulty in these investigations in which negative results cannot be considered as definite, is the absence of a simple biochemical test, like enzymatic reaction with purified extract of tissue. This difficulty can be overcome in some very favorable instances, in which the enzymatic process is easily detectable at the cellular level.

It is known that alkaline phosphatase, cytologically detectable, as well as biochemically, is decreased in granulocytes of chronic myeloid leukaemia (Valentine and Beck, 1951). The deletion of the distal part of the 21 in this disease, and the triplication of the 21 in mongolism lead (Alter, Pourfar and Dorkin, 1962) to tests of the phosphatasic activity of the granulocytes of mongols. The increase of activity, found in 35 mongols, is highly significant and in the proportion of 3 to 2 if compared to normals. Very soon, Trubowitz, Kirman and Masek (1962) confirmed those observations in 22 mongolian girls and Kings, Collins and Baikie (1962) on 32 mongolian boys and 28 mongolian girls and Lennox, White and Campbell (1962) on 39 mongols.

Those observations: diminution when part of the 21 is delected (Ph[1] chromosome) and increase when 21 is in triplicate (mongolism), lead to the conclusion that genes controlling alkaline phosphatase activity of polymorphs could be located on the distal part of the long arm of the 21.

Trying to summarize the data now available on the 21, we can judge that this very small chromosome plays a very important role in the control of polymorphs, which are slightly abnormal in mongols (Turpin and Bernyer, 1947).

	Polymorphs	General phenotype
Normal diplo 21	normal	normal
Constitutional Triplo 21	low segmentation of nuclei excess of alkaline phosphatase	mongolism frequency of acute leukae-mia × 20
Clonal Delection of part of long arm (Ph¹)	diminution of alkaline phosphatase	chronic myeloid leukaemia
Loss of a 21		acute myeloid leukaemia

The heuristic importance of chromosomal research in acquired disease will equal and possibly pass that of the study of congenital chromosomal errors. It is at least likely that many genetic losses or gains, incompatible with embryologic development but compatible with cell survival do occur in neoplastic lines, and this new tool of approaching the general problem of cancerogenesis has just been put in action. Only vanguard battles have been fought, and won.

As the general prospect of medicine remains the fundamental axioma, "divinum est opus sedare dolorem" the ultimate goal of cytogenetics, after the aetiological research on constitutional diesease will be pathogenic study of the consequences of chromosomal aberrations.

So, the next progress to be accomplished is toward palliative therapy. In case of genetic overdosage, for example, there are no theoretical reasons why deviated metabolism (once discovered) could not be adequately controlled by appropriate means.

Even if this goal is very remote it represents the hope that cytogenesis, instead of remaining a chromosomal taxonomy of diseases, will some day become a tool to prevent and even alleviate the errors of the hereditary fatum.

REFERENCES

ALTER A. A., LEE S. L., POURFAR M. and DORKIN G., 1962, Leucocyte alkaline phosphatase in mongolism: a possible chromosome marker. *J. Clin. Invest.* **41**, 1341.

ATKIN N. B. and TAYLOR M. C., 1962, 45 Chromosomes in chronic mycleid leukaemia. *Cytogenetics*, **1**, 97–103.

BENIRSCHKE K., BROWNHILL L. and EBAUGH F. G., 1962, Chromosomal abnormalities in Waldenstrom's macroglobulinaemia. *Lancet*, **ii**, 594.

BIESELE J. J., SCHMIDT W. and LAWLIS M. G., 1962, Mentally retarded schizoid twin girls with 47 chromosomes. *Lancet*, **i**, 403–405.

BOOK J. A., 1961, Clinical cytogenetics. In *De Genetica Medica*, Vol. III, L. Gedda édit. Institut Mendel, Rome.

BOOK J. A., SANTESSON and ZETTERQVIST P., 1961, Translocation heterozygozity in man. *Lancet*, **i**, 167.

BOTTURA C., FERRARI I. and VEIGA A. A., 1961, Chromosome abnormalities in Waldenstrom's Macroglobulinaemia. *Lancet*, **i**, 1170.

BUHLER E., ROSSIER R. and VULLIET V., 1961, 45 Chromosomes in a mentally deficient child with hypogonadism. *Human Chromosome Newsletter*, **5**, 5.

CLARKE C. M., EDWARDS J. H. and SMALLPIECE V., 1961, 21 Trisomy/normal mosaicism in an intelligent child with some mongoloid characters. *Lancet*, **i**, 1028–1030.

COOPER H. L. and HIRSCHHORN K., 1961, Chromosomal anomaly in a phenotypically normal male. *Human Chromosome Newsletter*, **4**, 12.

DELHANTY J. D. A., ELLIS J. R. and ROWLEY P. T., 1961, Triploid cell in a human embryo. *Lancet*, **i**, 1286.

DUNN H. G., FORD D. K., AUSBERG N. and MILLER J. R., 1961, Benign congenital hypotonia with chromosomal anomaly. *Pediatrics*, **28**, 578–591.

FERGUSON J. and PITT D., 1962, Congenital anomalies with chromosome abnormality. *Human Chromosome Newsletter* **7**, 6.

FITZGERALD P. H. and LYCETTE R. R., 1961, Mosaicism involving autosome associated with mongolism. *Lancet*, **ii**, 1961–212.

FORD C. E., JONES K. W., MILLER O. J., MITTWOCH U., PENROSE L. S., RIDLER M. and SHAPIRO A., 1959, The chromosomes in a patient showing both mongolism and the Klinefelter syndrome. *Lancet* **i**, 709–710.

FORSSMAN H. and LEHMANN, O., 1962, Chromosome studies in eleven families with mongolism in more than one member. *Acta Paediatrica (Stockh.)*, **51**, 180–188.

FRACCARO M., KAIJSER K. and LINDSTEN J., 1960, Chromosomal abnormalities in father and mongol child. *Lancet*, **ii**, 724–727.

GAGNON J., KATYK-LONGTIN N., GROOT J. A. DE and BARBEAU A., 1961, Double trisomie autosomique á 48 chromosomes − (21+18). *Union Méd. Canada*, **90**, 1220.

GERMAN J. L., BIRD C. E., and BEARN A. G., 1961, Chromosomal abnormalities in Waldenstroms Macroglobulinaemia.

GILBERT C. W., MULDAL S., LAJTHA L. G. and ROWLEY J., 1962, Time sequence of human chromosome duplication. *Nature*, **195**, 869–873.

GROUCHY, J. DE and LAMY, M., 1962, Délétion partielle d'un chromosome moyen dans une leucémie aigue lymphoblastique. *Rev. Franc. et Clin. Biol.* **7**, 639.

GUSTAVSON K. H., HAGBERG B., FINLEY S. C. and FINLEY W. H., 1962, An apparently identical extra autosome in two severely retarded sisters with multiple malformations. *Cytogenetics*, **1**, 32–41.

GUSTAVSON K. H. and EK J. I., 1961, Triple stem line mosaicism in mongolism. *Lancet*, **ii**, 319.

HAMERTON J. L., BRIGGS S. M., GIANNELLI F. and GARTLER C. O., 1961, Chromosome studies in detection of parents with high risk of second child with Down's syndrome. *Lancet*, **ii**, 788–791.

HAMERTON J. L. and STEINBERG A. G., 1962, Progeny of D/G translocation heterozygote in familial Down's syndrome. *Lancet*, **i**, 1407.

HAYWARD M. D. and BOWER B. D., 1961, The chromosomal constitution of the Sturge-Weber syndrome. *Lancet*, **i**, 558–559.

HAYASHI T., HSU T. C. and CHAO D., 1962, A case of mosaicism in mongolism. *Lancet*, **i**, 218–219.

INSTITUT DE PROGÉNÈSE, Obs. No. 267, Mosaique Trans (13) $\sim$ (13)/normal.

INSTITUT DE PROGÉNÈSE, Obs. No. 293, Translocation 22$\sim$ (13) chez un pére et son fils, ce dernier étant XXY, de surcroit.

INSTITUT DE PROGÉNÈSE, Obs. No. 491, Trisomie partielle probable par translocation (17)$\sim$(13).

INSTITUT DE PROGÉNÈSE, Obs. No. 420, Translocation 2$\sim$22 chez un sujet Haplo X, sa mèreet plusieurs germains.

JEROME H., LEJEUNE J. and TURPIN R., 1960, Étude de l'excrétion urinaire de certains métabolites du tryptophane chez les enfants mongoliens. *C. R. Acad. Sci. Paris*, **251**, 474–476.

JEROME H., 1962, Anomalie du métabolisme du tryptophane dans la maladie mongolienne. *Bull. Mens. Soc. Méd. Hop. Paris*, **113**, 168–172.

KING M. J., GILLIS E. M. and BAIKIE A. G., 1962, The polymorph alkaline phosphatase in mongolism. *Lancet*, **ii**, 661.

LEJEUNE J., GAUTIER M. and TURPIN R., 1959, Les chromosomes humaíns en culture de tissus. *C. R. Acad. Sci. Paris*, **248**, 602–603.

LEJEUNE J., GAUTIER M. and TURPIN R., 1959, Etude des chromosomes somatiques de neuf enfants mongoliens. *C. R. Acad. Sci. Paris*, **248**, 1721–1722.

LEJEUNE J., 1960, Le mongolisme, trisomie dégressive, Thèse Sciences, Paris 1960, in *Ann. de Génétique* **2**, 1–34.

LEJEUNE J., TURPIN R. and DECOURT J., 1960, Aberrations chromosomiques et maladies humaines Syndrome de Klinefelter XXY á 46 chromosomes par fusion centromérique T–T. *C. R. Acad. Sci. Paris*, **250**, 2468–2470.

LEJEUNE J. and TURPIN R., 1961, Detection chromosomique d'une mosaique artificielle humaine. *C. R. Acad. Sci. Paris*, **252**, 3148–3150.

LEJEUNE J., LAFOURCADE J., SCHARER K., DE WOLFF E., SALMON C., HAINES M. and TURPIN R., 1962, Monozygotisme hétérokaryote; jumeau normal et jumeau trisomique 21. *C. R. Acad. Sci. Paris*, **254**, 4404–4406.

LENNOX B., WHITE H. S. C. and CAMPBELL J., 1962, The polymorph alkaline phosphatase in mongolism. *Lancet*, **ii**, 991–992.

LINDSTEN J., ALVIN A., GUSTAVSON K. H. and FRACCARO M., 1962 Chromosomal mosaic in a girl with some features of mongolism. *Cytogenetics*, **1**, 20–31.

MAKINO S., SASAKI M., SASAKI M. S., KIKUCHI Y. and YOSHIDA M., 1961, Further survey of the chromosomes in Japanese. *Human Chromosome Newletter*, **4**, 2.

MOORHEAD P. S., MELLMAN W. J. and WEINAR J., 1961, A familial chromosome translocation with speech and mental retardation. *Am. J. Human Genet.* **13**, 32–46.

NICHOLS W. W., CORIELL L. L., FABRIZIO D. P. A., BISHOP H. C. and BOGGS T. R., 1962, Mongolism with mosaic chromosome pattern. *J. Pediat.* **60**, 69–76.

NOWELL P. C. and HUNGERFORD D. A., 1960, Aetiology of leukemia. *Lancet* i, 113–114.

OHNO S., TRUJILLO J. M., KAPLAN W. D. and KINOSITA R., Nucleolus organisers in the causation of chromosomal anomalies in man. *Lancet*, **ii**, 123.

OIKAWA, GROMULTS J. M., JR., HIRSCHHORN K. and NOVINS J., 1962, 13$\sim$15 trisomy with translocation. *Human Chromosome Newsletter*, **7**, 11.

PATAU K., SMITH D. W., THERMAN E., INHORN S. L. and WAGNER H. P., 1960, Multiple congenital anomaly caused by an extra autosome. *Lancet*, **ii**, 790–793.

PATAU K., THERMAN E., INHORN S., SMITH D. W. and RUES A. L., 1961, Partial trisomy syndromes. An insertion as cause of the O.F.D. syndrome in mother and daughter. *Chromosoma (Berl.)*, **12**, 573–584.

PATAU K., THERMAN E., SMITH D. W., INHORN S. and PICKEN B. F., 1961, Partial trisomy syndromes. I. Sturge-Weber's Disease. *Am. J. Hum. Genet.* **13**, 287–288.

PENROSE L. S. and DELHANTY J. D. A., 1961, Triploid cell cultures from a macerated foetus. *Lancet*, **i**, 1261–1262.

PFEIFFER R. A., KOSENOW N. and BAUMER A., 1962, Chromosomen untersuchungen an Blutzellen eines Patienten mit makroglobulinämie Woldenstrom. *Klin. Wochschrift.* **40**, 342–344.

RICHARD B. W. and STEWART A., 1962, Mosaicism in a mongol. *Lancet*, **i**, 275–276.

RUFFIE J. and LEJEUNE J., 1962, Deux cas de leucose aigue myeloblastique avec cellules sanguines normales et cellules haplo (21 ou 22). *Rev. Franc. et Clin. Biol.* **7**.

RUSSELL L. B. and SAYLORS C. L., 1960, Factors causing a high frequency of mice having the XO sex chromosome. *Science*, **131**, 1321–1322.

RUSSELL L. B. and SAYLORS C. L., 1961, Induction of paternal sex chromosome loss by irradiation of mouse spermatogonia. *Genetics*, **47**, 7–10.

SHAW M. W., 1962, Segregation ratio and linkage studies in a family with sex translocation mongols. *Lancet*, **i**, 1407.

SHAW M. W., 1962, Familial mongolism. *Cytogenetics*, **1**, 141–179.

SCHMIDT W., BIESELE J. J. and LAWLIS M. G., 1962, Mentally retarded schizoid twin girls with 47 chromosomes. *Lancet*, **ii**, 409.

SHUTTELWORTH, 1909, Mongolian imbecility. *Brit. Med. J.* **11**, 661.

SOLARI A. J., SVERDLICK A. B. and VIOLA E. R., 1962, Chromosome abnormality in myeloid metaplasia. *Lancet*, **ii**, 613.

STURTEVANT A. H., 1944, in T. H. MORGAN and A. H. STURTEVANT. *Carnegie Inst. Wash. Year Book*, **43**, 164–165.

TOUGH I. M., COURT BROWN W. M., BAIKIE A. G., BUCKTON K. E., HARNDEN D. G., JACOBS P. A. and WILLIAMS J. A., 1962, Chronic myeloid leukaemia: cytogenetic studies before and after splenic irradiation. *Lancet*, **ii**, 115–120.

TRUBOWITZ S., KIRMAN D. and MASEK B., 1962, The leucocyte alkaline phosphatase in mongolism. *Lancet*, **ii**, 486–487.

TURNER B. and JENNINGS A. N., 1961, Trisomy for chromosome 22. *Lancet*, **ii**, 49–50.

TURPIN R. and BERNYER G., 1947. De l'influence de l'hérédité sur la formule d'Arneth (cas particulier du mongolisme). *Revue d'Hématologie*, **2**, 189.

TURPIN R., LEJEUNE J., LAFOURCADE J. and GAUTIER M., 1959, Aberration chromosomique et maladies humaines. La Polydysspondylie á 45 chromosomes. *C. R. Acad. Sci. Paris*, **248**, 2636–3638.

TURPIN R. and LEJEUNE J., 1961, Chromosome translocations in man. *Lancet*, **i**, 616–617,

TURPIN R., LEJEUNE J., LAFOURCADE J., CHIGOT P. L. and SALMON C., 1961, Présomption de monozygotisme en dépit d'un dimorphisme sexual: sujet masculin XY et sujet neutre, haplo X. *C. R. Acad. Sci.* **252**, 2945–2946.

UCHIDA I. A. and BOWMAN J. M., 1961, XXX 18 Trisomy. *Lancet*, **ii**, 1094.

UCHIDA I. A,, PATAU K. and SMITH D. W., 1962, Dermal patterns of 18 and D_1 Trisomics. *The Am. J. Hum. Genet.* **14**, 345–352.

VALENTINE W. N. and BECKS W. S., 1951, Leucocytes (I) phosphatase activity in health, leucocytosis and myelocitic leukemia. *J. Lab. Clin. Med.* **38**, 39.

VISLE H., WEHN M., GROSSER A. and MOHR J., 1962, Chromosome abnormalities in a mother and two mentally retarded children. *Lancet*, **ii**, 76–78.

WALKER S. and HARRIS R., 1962, Investigation of family showing transmission of a 13–15 chromosomal translocation (Denver classification). *Brit. Med. J.* **ii**, 25–26.

ZELLWEGER M. D., MIKAMO K. and OPITZ J., 1961, Chromosomal aberrations. *Arch. Paediat.* **78**, 85–94.

ZELLWEGER H., 1962, Familial mongolism and eugenic counselling. *Lancet*, **ii**, 455–456.

ZELLWEGER H., 1962, Familial mongolism. *Lancet*, **ii**, 660–661.

TRISOMY OF 13-15 GROUP IN PATIENTS WITH GENERALIZED CONGENITAL ANALGESIA*

W. Beçak, M. L. Beçak, J. D. Andrade and B. J. Schmidt

Laboratório de Genética, Instituto Butantã, São Paulo and Escola
Paulista de Medicina, São Paulo, Brazil

THE "generalized congenital analgesia", also known as "congenital indifference to pain", is a relatively seldom anomaly, being about 40 cases reported until now.[3-8,14] Its characteristic is complete absence of reactions to painful stimula, either superficial or deep, but the affected show normal tactile and thermic sensibility.

In this paper, we present partial results of a cytogenetical study performed in two children with this anomaly, belonging to different families, without any relationship among them. Short-term cultures of leucocytes from peripheral blood were used for this investigation.[1]

The first case is an infant of three years of age, white, male and born at normal birth. The parents are young, apparently normal, not consanguineous, and there was no other case of analgesia in the family. When interned with two years of age, he presented a slight mental retardation, neither spoke, nor walked or stood, sitting only with support. The patient, although being typically white, revealed in the histological examination the presence of a deposit of melanoid substance on the skin, similar to the one found in the melanoderma. Excretion of anomalous substances in the urine was also observed. Skin biopsies performed for the study of sexual chromatin demonstrated that the patient was chromatin-negative. The examination of 162 cells obtained in short-term cultures of blood was performed and a mosaic with 54 per cent of cells with 46, 30 per cent with 47 and 13 per cent with 48 chromosomes was found (Table 1). The cells of 46 chromosomes are apparently normal with sexual chromosomes XY (Fig. 1). The cells of 47 chromosomes presented an additional chromosome, identified as belonging to group

* This work was supported by a grant from the Fundação de Amparo à Pesquisa do Estado de São Paulo.

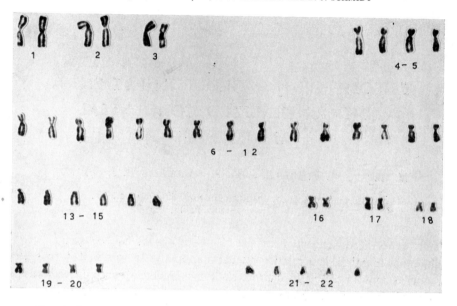

FIG. 1. 1st case. Karyotype with 46 chromosomes, XY. Short-term culture
of blood leucocytes. Orcein.

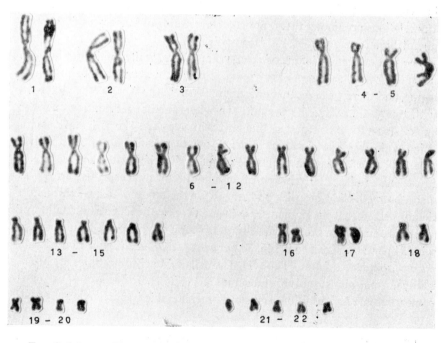

FIG. 2. 1st case. Karyotype with 47 chromosomes, showing trisomy in group
13–15 (Denver system).

TABLE 1.

	Chromosome counts					Total cells
1st case	45	46	47	48	49	162
	2	88	49	22	1	

13–15 (Fig. 2) and the ones of 48 chromosomes have two additional chromosomes also of the group 13–15.

The second case is an infant of seven years of age, white, male, with a slight mental retardation. His parents, apparently normal, are cousins in first degree. They had fourteen children; four died of infectious diseases. He is the fourteenth son and has a brother, the tenth in chronological order, with the same symptoms of the abnormality studied. As in the first case described, the patient presented normal tactile and thermic sensibility, complete absence of sensibility to pain, a large deposit of melanoid substance

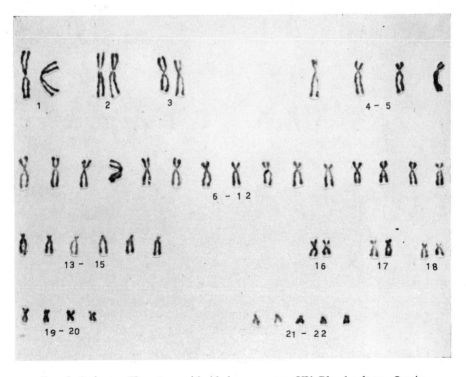

FIG. 3. 2nd case. Karyotype with 46 chromosomes, XY. Blood culture. Orcein.

on skin and excretion of anomalous substances in the urine. In this case, also chromatin-negative, 72 cells of the peripheral blood were studied, showing 66 per cent of cells with 46 chromosomes and 25 per cent with 47 chromosomes (Table 2). The cells of 46 chromosomes are apparently normal

TABLE 2.

	Chromosome counts				Total cells
2nd case	45	46	47	48	72
	2	48	18	4	

with sexual chromosomes XY (Fig. 3) and the ones of 47 chromosomes have an additional chromosome, identified as belonging to group 13–15 (Fig. 4).

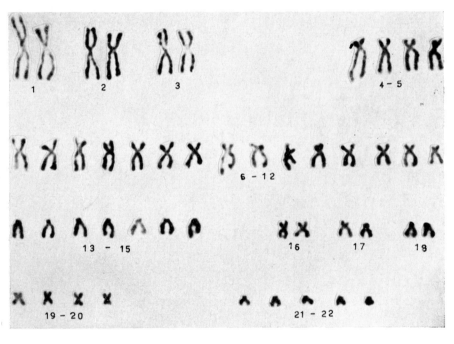

FIG. 4. 2nd case. Karyotype with 47 chromosomes with an additional acrocentric in group 13–15.

In both cases it was observed that in several trisomic cells a 13–15 chromosome was very near or connected to other chromosomes, generally carriers

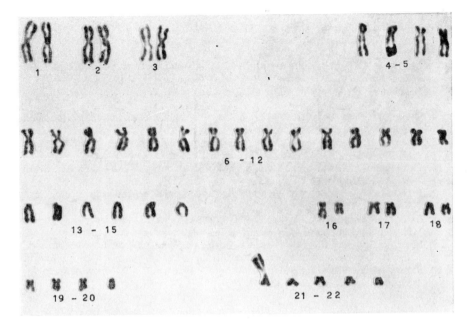

FIG. 5. 1st case. Karyotype showing a 13–15 chromosome connected to a 21–22 chromosome.

of satellites (Fig. 5). A normal sister of this patient was already studied and all the examined cells presented normal karyotypes with 46 chromosomes and constitution XX.

The similarity in the clinical characteristics and in the cytogenetical results obtained in both cases, allows the belief that the generalized congenital analgesia derives from the presence of the additional chromosome 13–15, this chromosome probably being correlated with the mechanism of sensibility to pain.

Patau et al.[10] described the presence of an additional chromosome of group 13–15 in four patients, seriously affected by an anomaly designated as "D_1 trisomy syndrome". The only common characteristic among these cases and the ones described here is mental retardation, which appears slightly in our patients.

The families of the cases described will be studied, as well as another family whose parents, not consanguineous, had seven normal children and three with generalized congenital analgesia, being two male, alive and one female, already dead. This will permit a more detailed interpretation of the etiology of this anomaly, which is also being studied in other aspects.[2,9,11-13]

REFERENCES

1. BEÇAK, W., Human chromosomes in short-term cultures from peripheric blood leucocytes. *Rev. Bras. Riol.* **21**, (3), 281, 1961.
2. CLEMENTE, A. S., SECAF, F., SCHMIDT, B. J., CARVALHO, A. A. and NEVES, J. C., *Rev. Bras. Radiol.* (in press).
3. DEARBORN, G., A case of congenital pure analgesia. *J. Nerv. and Ment. Dis.* **75**, 612, 1931.
4. DURAND, P. and BELLUTI, B. M., Un caso di indifferenza congenita al dolore. *Helv. Paediat. Acta*, **12**, 116, 1957.
5. FANCONI, U. G. and FERRAZINI, F., Kongenital analgesie. *Helv. Paediatr. Acta*, **12**, 79, 1957.
6. FIGUEIREDO, J. A. and MARQUES, J. S., Indiferença congenita universal à dôr. *Seara Médica*, 231, 1955.
7. JULIÂO, D. F. and BROTTO, W., Indiferença congenita generalizada à dôr. *Arq. Neur. Psiq.* **13**, 338, 1955.
8. LAMY, M., GARCIN, R., JAMMET, M. L., AUSSANNAIRE, M., LAMBERT, M., THIRIEZ, H. and GRASSET, A., Analgesie generalisée congenitale. *Sem. Hopit.* **32**, 2823, 1956.
9. LEON, N., SCHMIDT, B. J., OTTENSOOSER, F., BEÇAK, W., BEÇAK, M. L. and SALDANHA, P. H., *Congenital Indifference to Pain. A Genetical Approach* (to be published).
10. PATAU, K., THERMAN, E., SMITH, D. W. and INHORN, S. L., Two new cases of D_I trisomy in man. *Hereditas*, **47**, 239, 1961.
11. RAMOS, A. D. and SCHMIDT, B. J., Neurokinin and PPS on congenital generalized analgesia. *Arch. Neurol.* (in press).
12. SCHMIDT, B. J., MERZEL, J. and KATCHBURIAN, E., Congenital indifference to pain. *Histological Aspects* (to be published).
13. SCHMIDT, B. J., RAW, I., PUDLES, J. and MAIA, F., *Detection of Fluorescent Substance in Urine from Patients with Congenital Indifference to Pain* (to be published).
14. SILVERMAN, F. N. and GILDEN, J. J., Congenital insensivity to pain. *Radiology*, **72**, 176, 1959.

ABNORMALITIES OF SEX CHROMOSOMES

E. H. Y. Chu

Biology Division, Oak Ridge National Laboratory,* Oak Ridge, Tennessee,
U.S.A.

INTRODUCTION

The study of the genetics of sex begins with the discovery of the mechanism of the sex chromosomes (McClung, 1902; Stevens, 1905, 1908; Wilson, 1911), which established that one sex is heterogametic, the other homogametic, in regard to the X chromosome and that, as a consequence, two types of fertilization occur, leading to 50 per cent X and 50 per cent XX individuals — the two sexes. The first discovery of sex chromosomes, however, was made earlier by Henking, who in 1891 found in an insect a "peculiar chromatin element" which in the second spermatocyte division lags behind the separating anaphase chromosomes and then passes undivided to one pole. Because of his uncertainty about its nature he labeled it "X". Even to date a great deal more is to be learned about the sex chromosomes.

De Winiwarter (1912) counted 47 elements in the human testis and 48 in the ovary, concluding that man has an XX–XO sex chromosome constitution. In 1923, Painter concluded that the chromosome number of man is 48 in both sexes and that the sex chromosome constitution is of the XX–XY type. The application of improved techniques of studying human chromosomes in 1956 (Tjio and Levan, Ford and Hamerton) not only established the correct diploid number of man as 46 but also confirmed Painter's observation that the human sex chromosome constitution is XX–XY.

The genetic basis of sex determination has been firmly established by the classic works of Stevens (1905) in several insects, Goldschmidt (1911–1920, see Goldschmidt, 1955) in *Lymantria*, Witschi (1914, see Witschi, 1939) in frogs, Bridges (1961a, b) in *Drosophila*, Blakeslee, Warmke and Westergaard in *Melandrium* (for review, see Westergaard, 1948), and in many other forms. In *Drosophila*, Bridges (1916a, b, 1922) concluded that the Y chromo-

* Operated by Union Carbide Corporation for the United States Atomic Energy Commission.

some is not concerned with sex determination (though essential to male fertility) and that sex phenotype is a function of the balance between male determiners on autosomes and female determiners on the X chromosome. Because of the close parallelism of sex chromosome constitution and transmission of X-linked traits, the mechanism of sex determination in man was presumed to be the same as in *Drosophila*. Not until 1959 did the findings of aneuploidy of the sex chromosomes in the mouse (Welshons and Russell, 1959; Russell *et al.*, 1959) and man (Ford *et al.*, 1959a, b; Jacobs and Strong, 1959) show that the mechanism of sex determination in these mammals is different from *Drosophila*.

Since that time, evidence has been accumulating to indicate that many aberrations of sexual development in man are associated with abnormalities of sex chromosomes. In the light of these cytological observations, meaningful conclusions can be drawn concerning the structure, behavior, and function of human sex chromosomes. It is not my intention to present a complete review and discussion of facts of all human sex anomalies, with or without accompanied chromosomal changes. I propose, rather, to select the salient facts and ideas and draw certain general conclusions regarding the cytogenetics of human sex chromosomes. The topics selected for discussion will be (1) the morphology and behavior of normal sex chromosomes; (2) the type, origin, and frequency of sex chromosome abnormalities; (3) sex determination and sex differentiation; and (4) cytological mapping and evolution of sex chromosomes.

NORMAL SEX CHROMOSOMES

Meiotic metaphase. The behavior of the X and Y chromosomes in sper, matogenesis in man was demonstrated in 1932 by Shiwago and Andres-who found end to end association. This finding was confirmed by studies of many workers (Sachs, 1954; Ford and Hamerton, 1956; Kodani, 1957; Ferguson-Smith, 1961). Koller's (1937) observation of chiasma formation between the X and Y, together with the above-mentioned studies, may provide some support for Haldane's (1936) hypothesis of partial sex linkage.

Kodani (1957) described the structural characteristics of the heteromorphic pair. According to him, the long arm of the X is well condensed, highly "chromatic", and is usually bent twice giving rise to three segments. The short arm of the X that pairs with the Y is often uncondensed, poorly stainable, and varies considerably in length at first metaphase. These characteristics suggest that the short arm of X is largely heterochromatic. The Y also has two arms; the short one pairs with X and is half the length of the long arm. In the fully condensed XY-bivalent, the long arm of the Y is about one half the length of the euchromatic long arm of the X chromosome.

Maclean (1962) suggests, on morphological grounds (see discussion below on structural aberrations), that a portion of the short arm of the human X might be euchromatic. Ohno (1962), however, believes that the human X is not segmented into euchromatic and heterochromatic regions but, rather, has the singular ability to behave on some occasions as though composed entirely of heterochromatin and, on others, as though made entirely of euchromatin. In spermatocytes, both sex chromosomes are precociously condensed. During oögenesis, the XX-bivalent in oöcytes is indistinguishable from the autosomal bivalents (Ohno, Klinger and Atkin, 1962).

Human pachytene chromosomes in spermatogenesis have been studied (Schultz and St. Lawrence, 1949; Yerganian, 1957), but the sex chromosome pair has not been clearly elucidated.

Mitotic metaphase. The mitotic X chromosome is the sixth or the seventh longest chromosome in the complement. The ratio of long to short arm for the X chromosome is estimated to fall within the range of 1·6–2·0. The X chromosome represents between 5·1 and 5·9 per cent of the total haploid female set (Böök *et al.*, Denver report, 1960; Corrigenda, *Ann. Human Genet.*, *Lond.*, **25**, 105, 1961).

The identification of the human X, because of its morphological similarity to autosomes in the 6–12 group, is rather subjective (see Patau, 1960). A large part of the difficulty, however, is probably due to the heterochromatic nature of the X. The relative length of all the chromosomes and their arms, especially the X, can be influenced by cell stage as well as by colchicine, heat, fixative, and other factors in the process of cytological preparation (Boyes, 1961; Ford, 1962). The presence of secondary constrictions on both arms of X which was demonstrated recently (Moorhead, this symposium) should help in its identification.

Sandberg *et al.* (1960b) observed heteropycnosis and allocyclic behavior of the human X of bone marrow cells in culture. Recent autoradiographic studies (Lima-de-Faria *et al.*, 1961; Lima-de-Faria, this symposium; Morishima, Grumbach and Taylor, 1962; Bender and Prescott, 1962; German, 1962a, b) indicated that one of the two X chromosomes in the female synthesizes DNA later than the other X or the autosomes. Patau (1962a) and German (1962b) further showed that the late replicating X, contrary to other studies, corresponds to the eighth or ninth largest chromosome. One possible explanation is unequal metaphase lengths of the two X chromosomes in a female cell, since physiological disparity of the two X chromosomes has already been demonstrated in these labeling experiments.

There have been several reports of presumptive trisomy for large autosomes of the X-6-12 group (Sandberg *et al.*, 1960a; De Carli *et al.*, 1960;
Jacobs *et al.*, 1961). In view of the morphological variability of X chromosomes, these cases might indeed be X-polysomics. In fact, a child with
49 chromosomes as originally described by Fraccaro *et al.* (1960b) turned
out to be XXXXY upon examination of sex chromatin patterns (Fraccaro
and Lindsten, 1960).

The mitotic Y is acrocentric but not telocentric (Chu and Giles, 1959).
It is similar to chromosomes 21 and 22 but is often larger and morphologically distinguishable from them. There is no satellite on the short arm of Y,
but a secondary constriction can be seen on its long arm by certain cytological treatment (Moorhead, this symposium). The centromere region often
assumes a ruffled appearance, making the localization of centromere difficult. The sister chromatids of the long arm frequently appear to be more
tightly paired than other chromosomes. Makino and Sasaki (1961) consider
the allocyclic behavior of the Y helpful in its identification. Autoradiographic experiments indicate that the Y incorporates tritiated thymidine
later than chromosome pairs 21 and 22 (German, 1962a, b).

The relative length of the Y at mitotic metaphase varies from 1·1 to
2·2 per cent of the total haploid length (Denver report, 1960). However, the
length and the morphology of the human Y are highly variable according
to the experience of many workers. For example, unusually long Y chromosomes have been described by Bender and Gooch (1962) in a normal male
and by Jacobs and Harnden (1961, cited by Penrose, 1961b) in a male
mongol. Variable lengths of Y chromosomes have also been observed in
patients with Marfan's syndrome (Källén and Levan, 1962) and with aligo-
spermia or azoospermia (van Wijck, Tijdink and Stolte, 1962). However,
the morphology of the Y does not seem to be related to these abnormal
phenotypes.

TYPE, ORIGIN, AND FREQUENCY OF SEX CHROMOSOME
ABNORMALITIES

Nuclear sexual dimorphism. Before discussing abnormalities of human
sex chromosomes, the phenomenon of nuclear sexual dimorphism must
be briefly described since these properties greatly aid diagnosis of the sex
chromosome abnormalities. The sex chromatin, or Barr body, first observed
by Barr and Bertram (1949), is a Feulgen-positive chromatin mass present
in the intermitotic nuclei of the normal female but absent in those of males.
Another nuclear morphological difference between sexes is found in the

polymorphonuclear leukocytes. In the normal female the nuclei of a small proportion (1–5 per cent) of these cells bear characteristic club-shaped projections usually termed "drumsticks" (Davidson and Smith, 1954). These drumsticks are not found in males.

Variation in number. That chromosomal abnormalities could occur in man was not surprising to geneticists. Haldane (1932) suggested that such abnormalities might explain some aberrations of human sex differentiation. Petterson and Bonnier (1932) and Gowen (1933) also believed that certain types of intersexes might be due to chromosomal abnormalities. Within a period of less than 4 years, numerous reports of human chromosome variations have flooded the genetic and medical literature. No attempt is made here to list every single instance, since a number of excellent recent review papers on human chromosome abnormalities, particularly sex chromosome anomalies, are available (e.g. Ford, 1960; Pappoport and Kaplan, 1961; Sohval, 1961; Hirschhorn and Cooper, 1961; Ferguson-Smith, 1961; Miller, 1961; Harnden, 1961; Harnden and Jacobs, 1961; Hamerton, 1961; Polani, 1961, 1962; Barr and Carr, 1962).

Table 1 shows the demonstrated kinds of number variation of sex chromosomes in man. Since new cases continue to be found, this tabulation is by no means complete and only the first report of each pattern is cited.

The upper part of the table groups cases mostly of phenotypic females. Persons with 45 chromosomes including a single X (or XO constitution) are often short and have low intelligence. The majority have streak gonads, primary amenorrhea, and one or more of the range of congenital anomalies which are usually associated with Turner's syndrome (Ford *et al.*, 1959b; see reviews, Polani, 1961, 1962). Mosaicism involving sex chromosomes commonly exists. In fact, mosaicism cannot be rigorously ruled out in many cases where only limited cells from a single tissue were examined. Ford (1960) reported an XO/XX mosaic; Jacobs *et al.* (1960) found an XO/XXX mosaic. The first case of XO/XX/XXX reported by Ferguson-Smith *et al.* (1960b) was a hermaphrodite. Other cases of the same complex were found to be similar to Turner's syndrome (e.g. Carr *et al.*, 1962).

Certain characteristics of the Turner's syndrome are also known to exist in males. We (Chu *et al.*, 1961), among others, have examined the so-called male Turner's syndrome and found that these individuals have XY sex chromosomes with no apparent chromosome aberrations.

Females with an XXX (Jacobs *et al.*, 1959b) or XXXX (Carr *et al.*, 1961) sex chromosome constitution have no consistent phenotypic abnormalities. Almost all such females, so far described, have been mental defectives, but whether or not mental deficiency is connected with X-polysomy is

TABLE 1. NUMBER VARIATIONS OF SEX CHROMOSOMES IN MAN

Chromosome Number	Sex Chromosomes	Sex Chromatin	Phenotype	First Reference
45	XO	—	Turner's syndrome	Ford et al. (1959b)
45/46*	XO/XX	+	Turner's syndrome	Ford (1960)
45/47	XO/XXX	++	Turner's syndrome	Jacobs et al. (1960)
45/46/47	XO/XX/ XXX	++	Hermaphrodite	Ferguson-Smith et al. (1960b)
46/47	XX/XXX	++	Hermaphrodite	Ferguson-Smith et al. (1960b)
47	XXX	++	Female, variable phenotype	Jacobs et al. (1959b)
48	XXXX	+++	Female, mental retardation	Carr et al. (1960)
47	XXY	+	Klinefelter's syndrome	Jacobs and Strong (1959)
46/47	XX/XXY	+	Klinefelter's syndrome	Ford et al. (1959c)
46/47	XY/XXY	+	Klinefelter's syndrome	Buckton et al. (1961)
48	XXYY	+	Klinefelter's syndrome	Muldal and Ockey (1960)
48	XXXY	++	Klinefelter's syndrome	Ferguson-Smith et al. (1960a)
46/48	XY/XXXY	++	Klinefelter's syndrome	Barr et al. (1962)
49	XXXXY	+++	Klinefelter's syndrome	Fraccaro et al. (1960b)
48/49	XXXY/ XXXXY	+++	Klinefelter's syndrome	Buckton et al. (1961)
45/46	XO/XY	—	Hermaphrodite	Hirschhorn et al. (1960)
45/46	XX/XY	+	Hermaphrodite	Gartler et al. (1962)
45/46	XO/XX/XY	+	Hermaphrodite	Schuster and Motulsky (1962)
46/47/49	XX/XXY/ XXYYY	+	Hermaphrodite	Fraccaro et al. (1962c)
45/46	XO/XY	—	Amenorrhea	Blank et al. (1960)
45/47	XO/XYY	—	Amenorrhea	Jacobs et al. (1961)
47	XYY	—	Male	Sandberg et al. (1961)
45/48	XO/XXXY	++	Male pseudohermaphrodite	Warkany et al. (1962)

* /Separates component karyotypes of a mosaic.

not known because all these cases are found in mental institutions. Some XXX women are fertile (Stewart and Sanderson, 1960; Fraser et al., 1960). The lower half of the table summarizes cases which are mostly phenotypic males or individuals with male gonadal tissues. Jacobs and Strong (1959) showed that XXY is the sex chromosome constitution of the Klinefelter's syndrome which, in a typical case, is a phenotypic male, usually with subnormal intelligence, small sterile testes, and eunuchoid body proportions. Individuals with a further addition of X have more severe forms of the Klinefelter's syndrome, as in the case of XXXY (Ferguson-Smith et al., 1960) and XXXXY (Fraccaro et al., 1960b). The latter may represent a characteristic syndrome (Fraccaro, Klinger and Schutt, 1962b).

Chromosome mosaicism in Klinefelter's syndrome has been demonstrated in a number of instances, such as XX/XXY (Ford et al., 1959c), XY/XXY (Buckton et al., cited by Harnden and Jacobs, 1961), XY/XXXY (Barr et al., 1962) and XXXY/XXXXY (Buckton et al., cited by Harnden and Jacobs, 1961).

Blank, Bishop and Caley (1960) and Jacobs et al. (1961) found two cases of XO/XY mosaic having the symptoms of Turner's syndrome. Hirschhorn et al. (1960) examined an individual who had the same XO/XY sex chromosome mosaicism but developed both testicular and rudimentary ovarian tissues, indicating true hermaphroditism. Schuster and Motulsky (1962) found an XO/XX/XY sex chromosome complex, and, more recently, Fraccaro et al. (1962c) found an XX/XXY/XXYYY combination in cases of true hermaphroditism. Warkany, Chu and Kauder (1962) reported an XO/XXXY male pseudohermaphrodite in whom a single infantile testis and certain female gonodal tissues are found.

Extra Y chromosomes do not seem to modify the phenotype of the individual, as shown in the XXYY (Muldal and Ockey, 1960), XO/XYY (Jacobs et al., 1961), XYY (Sandberg et al., 1961) and XX/XXY/XXYYY (Fraccaro et al., 1962c) combinations.

The maximum number of sex chromatin bodies seen in the interphase nuclei, as a general rule, is one less than the number of X chromosomes. Maclean (1962) has found a similar relationship between the number of drumsticks in polymorphonuclear leukocytes and the number of X chromosomes.

Similar sex chromosome variations have also been found in other mammals. In the mouse, Welshons and Russell (1959) have shown that XO animals are fertile females; XXY mice have been shown by Russell and Chu (1961) and by Cattanach (1961) as sterile males. Thuline and Norby (1961) found a possible XXY sex chromosome constitution in the tortoise-shell male cat.

Origin of numerical variations. Theoretically sex chromosome aneuploidy can result from primary nondisjunction in gametogenesis in either parent and at either of the two stages of meiosis (Table 2). Chromosome loss

TABLE 2. ABNORMAL ZYGOTES RESULTING FROM NONDISJUNCTION AND LOSS
OF SEX CHROMOSOMES IN MEIOSIS

Ovum	Sperm	Normal meiosis		Nondisjunction in meiosis I		Nondisjunction in meiosis II		
		X	Y	XY	O	XX	YY	O
Normal meiosis	X	XX	XY	XXY	XO	XXX	XYY	XO
Nondisjunction in meiosis I or II	XX	XXX	XXY	XXXY	XX	XXXX	XXYY	XX
	O	XO	YO*	XY	OO*	XX	YY*	OO*

* The OO, YO, and YY combinations are probably nonviable.

resulting, for example, from anaphase lagging can also give rise to daughter cells without a sex chromosome.

The origin of more complex sex chromosome aneuploidy is more uncertain. Meiotic nondisjunction in both parents is a possible explanation, although the probability of occurrence is exceedingly low. Repeated meiotic errors in one parent or mitotic error in the zygote appears more likely. The occurrence of several kinds of chromosomal anomalies in the same sibship (Moorhead et al., 1961; Miller et al., 1961) and reports of double trisomy (Ford et al., 1959a; Uchida and Bowman, 1961) suggest that multiple nondisjunctional accidents are likely to occur in the same individual.

In view of the frequent observations of complex number variations of sex chromosomes, we may assume that polysomy, mosaicism, mitotic nondisjunction, and chromosome loss during cleavage probably occur more frequently than previously supposed. Table 3 illustrates some examples of sex chromosome aneuploidy resulting from mitotic nondisjunction. Chromosome loss can yield results similar to those from nondisjunction; during cleavage successive events of either one or both types of errors may lead to the formation of more complex mosaicism not outlined in the table.

Turpin, Lejeune and their co-workers (Turpin et al., 1961; Lejeune and Turpin, 1961) have presented evidence, by means of blood group studies and reciprocal skin transplantation, that a pair of twins with XY and XO sex chromosomes respectively was indeed monozygotic. This is one good example of postzygotic mitotic error. The simplest event would have been the loss of a Y during the first cleavage.

TABLE 3. PATTERNS OF SEX CHROMOSOME ANEUPLOIDY RESULTING FROM MITOTIC NONDISJUNCTION

Zygote	Nondisjunction at First Cleavage Division	Nondisjunction at Second or Subsequent Cleavage Division
XY	XXYY* XXY/XO* XYY/XO*	XY/XXYY XY/XXY/YO* XY/XYY/XO XY/XXY/XO/YO
XX	XXX/XO* XXXX*	XX/XXX/XO* XX/XXXX/OO
XXY	XXXXYY/OO XXXY/XY* XXXX/YY* XXXX/YO* XXYY/XX	XXY/XXXXY/YO XXY/XXXXYY/OO XXY/XXXX/YY XXY/XXXY/XY XXY/XXYY/XX XXY/XYY/XXX
XO	XX/OO*	XX/XO*

* Viable karyotypes have been encountered. The OO, YO, and YY components are probably nonviable and will alter the resultant pattern of mosaicism.

Lenz *et al.* (1959) and Penrose (1961a) suggested that a maternal age effect is present which influences the probability of giving birth to children with Klinefelter's syndrome. Boyer and co-workers (1962), on the other hand, have shown that the probability of giving birth to children with Turner's syndrome is not influenced by either maternal or paternal age or the order of birth. Undoubtedly a considerable proportion of Turner's are the result of postzygotic errors.

Another mechanism of mosaicism is the double fertilization of two maternal gametic nuclei by different sperms, followed by fusion into one individual, as in the remarkable case of an XX/XY true hermaphrodite reported by Gartler, Waxman and Giblett (1962b).

The probable source of distributional errors of sex chromosomes can sometimes be traced by the use of sex-linked mutant genes, such as color blindness (Polani *et al.*, 1956, 1958), glucose-6-phosphate dehydrogenase deficiency (Gartler, Vullo and Gandini, 1962a), and Xg^a blood type (McKusick, 1962). Experimental induction and detection of sex chromosome anomalies in the mouse, employing several sex-linked markers, have already been fully discussed by L. B. Russell in this symposium.

Structural aberrations. Human chromosomes, not unlike those of plants and other animals, are subject to structural alterations, which can either occur spontaneously or be induced. Structural changes are the result of breakage of chromosomes and rejoining of the broken ends in new ways. Four major kinds are found: translocation, inversion, duplication, and deficiency (deletion). Isochromosomes are in a special class of structurally abnormal chromosomes, the two arms being identical morphologically and probably genetically. They arise by misdivision of the centromere, i.e. by transverse division at anaphase instead of the normal longitudinal split.

Human autosomal rearrangements have already been discussed (Lejeune, this symposium). Table 4 summarizes the cases so far reported of morphological abnormalities of human sex chromosomes. Fragmentation of both sex chromosomes has been assumed to occur. The published examples include: (1) deletion of the short arm of the X (Jacobs *et al.*, 1960), (2) deletion of the long arm of the X (Jacobs *et al.*, 1960; de Grouchy *et al.*, 1961; Crawfurd, 1961; Waxman *et al.*, 1962; Miles *et al.*, 1962), and (3) deletion of the major portion, presumably the long arm, of the Y (Ferguson-Smith *et al.*, 1960; Vaharu *et al.*, 1961; Conen *et al.*, 1961; Muldal and Ockey, 1961; Fraccaro *et al.*, 1962a).

Cases of presumed isochromosomes, involving the long arm of the X (Fraccaro *et al.*, 1960a; Jacobs *et al.*, 1961; Bishop, Jagiello, Northfield, Martinez, Villaverde and Polani, cited by Polani, 1962), or of the short arm of the X (Jagiello and Northfield, cited by Polani, 1962) have been reported. Lindsten and Tillinger (1962) found a presumed self-perpetuating ring-X chromosome in a patient with gonadal dysgensies. Elves and Israëls (1962) reported an abnormally large chromosome in a male haemophiliac with sexual infantilism and other congenital abnormalities. The patient had 46 chromosomes including an apparently normal Y and a large abnormal chromosome believed to be an X with duplication. This duplication was interpreted as the result of a translocation between the two maternal X chromosomes during oögenesis. But we see an alternative interpretation: if a translocation between an X and an autosome had occurred, the karyotype may include a normal X and an abnormal autosome (probably a member of the 6–12 group) having a small deficiency but carrying an X chromosome segment.

The interpretation for these presumptive rearrangements of sex chromosomes is based primarily on morphological evidence, which is uncertain

TABLE 4. STRUCTURAL ABERRATIONS AND MOSAICISM OF SEX CHROMOSOMES IN MAN*

Chromosome number	Sex chromosome	Phenotype	Reference
46	Xx	Primary amenorrhea	Jacobs et al. (1960) de Grouchy et al. (1961)
46	XX^a	Primary amenorrhea	Jacobs et al. (1960)
46	XX^b	Primary amenorrhea	Fraccaro et al. (1960a) Jacobs et al. (1961)
45/46	XO/Xx	Primary amenorrhea	Bishop et al. (1962)
46	XX/Xx	Oligomenorrhea	de Grouchy et al. (1961)
47/48	XXY/XXxY	Klinefelter's syndrome	Crawfurd (1961)
46	XX/Xx or XX/XY	True hermaphrodite	Waxman et al. (1962)
45/47	XO/XxY	Male pseudohermaphrodite	Miles et al. (1962)
46	XX^c	Not stated	Jagiello and Northfield (1962)
46/46+f	XX/XX+f	True hermaphrodite	Ferguson-Smith et al. (1960b)
45/46/47	XO/X+X^R/X+ +2X^R	Oligomenorrhea	Lindsten and Tillinger (1962)
46	X^{d}Y	Male haemophiliac with sexual infantilism	Elves and Israëls (1962)
45+f	Xy	Turner's syndrome with rudimentary testicular tissues	Vaharu et al. (1961)
45/45+f	XO/Xy	Amenorrhea; ovarian and testicular tissues	Conen et al. (1961)
45+f	Xy	Hypospadias	Muldal and Ockey (1961)
45/45+ f/47+f	XO/Xy/XXXy	Female with sign of masculinization	Fraccaro et al. (1962a)

* x = presumed deletion of long arm of X.
X^a = presumed deletion of most of short arm of X.
X^b = presumed isochromosome for long arm of X, or duplication of part of short arms.
X^c = presumed isochromosome for short arm of X.

X^d = presumed duplication of X chromosome material.
f = fragment.
y = presumed deletion of long arm of Y, or isochromosome for short arm of Y.
X^R = self-perpetuating presumed ring-X chromosome. Separates component karyotypes of a mosaic.

in many instances. Since the normal human sex chromosomes are known to be variable in morphology, abnormal sex chromosomes are particularly difficult to study. An application of the authoradiographic technique, however, may help to identify materials from both the X and the Y chromosomes that have been involved in rearrangements. Within the present technical limits, small karyotypic changes are often difficult to observe or remain totally undetected. Moreover, the same configuration can be the result of several alternative mechanisms. For example, unequal length of a homologous pair may be due to a simple deletion, reciprocal translocation, or unequal crossing over. Ring chromosomes are unmistakable, but isochromosomes are uncertain. Since there are several isochromosomes of the long arm of X (Jacobs et al., 1960; de Grouchy et al., 1961; Patau, personal communication) and one report of an autosomal isochromosome (Therman et al., 1962), the existence of isochromes in man seems convincing. It must be emphasized, however, that positive identification of isochromosomes or translocations is possible only through the study of synaptic behavior at meiosis (e.g. Hamerton et al., 1961).

The most important criterion for suspecting sex chromosome abnormalities is, of course, the abnormal sexual development of the patient under investigation. Nevertheless, as will be discussed later, sex differentiation can be influenced by factors other than sex chromosomes. Furthermore, the reasoning sometimes becomes circular when abnormal sexual development is interpreted as being caused by the accompanied chromosomal abnormality (which may be entirely unrelated). On the other hand, the observed anatomical and developmental defects are used, in turn, to decide the genetic content or the type of rearrangement of the sex chromosomes.

Another criterion for assuming sex chromosome changes is the variation of the nuclear morphology. Jacobs and co-workers (1961) have shown pictorial correspondence of variation is sex chromatiu morphology to each of the presumptive sex chromosome alterations they studied. This method has theoretical and practical merits because of the unique properties of the nuclear sexual dimorphism. However, the danger of using this criterion is the element of subjectiveness, since the frequency and morphology of sex chromatin bodies vary with the tissue of origin, cell stage, and environmental factors (Sohval and Casselman, 1961).

Similarly, a correlation is assumed to exist between the drumsticks in the polymorphonuclear leukocytes and the heteropycnotic X chromosomes. As mentioned, drumsticks are present in normal females but are absent in normal males. Harnden and Jacobs (1961) have summarized instances of XXX and XXXY individuals in whom two drumsticks were found. From the published preliminary account (Lindsten and Tillinger, 1962), the evidence for the assumption that the self-perpetuating ring chromosome was derived from one of the two X chromosomes seems to be the presence of drumsticks, although other lines of evidence may also be available to these investigators. On the basis of the observations that small drumsticks were present in some polymorphs of a woman with a presumed partial deletion of the short arm of one X, no drumstick in a woman with a presumed partial deletion of the long arm of one X, and unusually large drumsticks in females having one X replaced by a presumed isochromosome for the long arm of the X (Engel and Forbes, 1961; Harnden and Jacobs, 1961), Maclean (1962) suggests that the short arm of the X is, in part, euchromatic. The heterochromatic nature of X chromosomes has already been discussed by Ohno (1962). As a corollary, Maclean seems to infer that the heterochromatic regions of one X, largely its long arm, are directly responsible for the appearance of drumsticks in a certain proportion of polymorphs in the female. The validity of this interesting conclusion and the reliability of using drumstick morphology to distinguish very small changes of the X chromosome must await further investigations.

The time of occurrence of chromosome rearrangements can be either before or during gametogenesis, or during cleavage, as indicated by the experimental data from laboratory animals (Russell, this symposium) and from human materials (Bender, this symposium). The case of XX/XX mosaic reported by de Grouchy et al. (1961) indicates that the chromosome rearrangement occurred during cleavage.

Translocations and deletions have been observed in the mouse (Chu, 1963). There has been no report as yet of X-autosome translocations in man, nor has there been any report of sex chromosome anomalies observed during spermatogenesis or oögenesis because, in many types of abnormal sexual development, gametogenesis is absent. It would be interesting, however, to examine the meiosis of fertile individuals having sex chromosome anomalies, such as some XXX (Stewart and Sanderson, 1960; Fraser et al., 1960), occasional XO (Bahner et al., 1960) and, perhaps, certain other sex chromosome rearrangements. Furthermore, meiotic, especially pachytene, chromosome studies might disclose the presence of inversions or other cryptic structural modifications.

Incidence of sex chromosome abnormalities. Surveys of the frequency of abnormalities of nuclear sex at birth have been made by Moore (1959) in Winnipeg, Canada, by Bergemann (1961) in Berne, Switzerland, and by Maclean et al. (1961) in Edinburgh, Scotland. These surveys yield results in good agreement, and on the average, the frequency of XXY is about 2·65/1000; that of XO, 0·30/1000; and that of XXX, 1·33/1000.

A large number of surveys have been carried out on various groups of mentally subnormal individuals (cf. Maclean et al., 1962). The average frequency of males with a single sex chromatin body (i.e. XXY) is 8·1/1000; the frequency becomes 9·5/1000 if all males with abnormal nuclear sex are included. The frequency of XXX is 4·5/1000, and that of XO is 0·4/1000.

The only other group in which the incidence of sex chromosome abnormalities has been studied is males attending an infertility clinic (Ferguson-Smith et al., 1957) and females with primary amenorrhea attending a gynecological clinic (Jacobs et al., 1961). In the former group, 3 per cent were chromatin positive. Of 32 women with primary amenorrhea in the latter group whose chromosomes were examined, 17 had abnormal sex chromosomes.

In summary, the evidence so far accumulated indicates that abnormalities of the sex chromosomes are relatively common while the abnormalities of autosomes, with the exception of the one associated with Down's syndrome (mongolism), are much less frequently encountered (Harnden and Jacobs, 1961). The incidence of structural abnormalities of sex chromosomes in man appears to be lower than that of numerical variations and cases are as yet too few to make a reliable estimate.

Origin and functional significance of sex chromatin. Based on cytological evidence both in man and in other mammals, Grumbach, Morishima and Chu (1960), Barr and Carr (1960), Ohno and Makino (1961), and many others have come to the conclusion that the sex chromatin mass in somatic interphase nuclei is probably derived from a heteropycnotic segment of a single X chromosome. Recent autoradiographic studies by Morishima, Grumbach and Taylor (1962) further demonstrated that in a normal female there are two types of X chromosomes. One X chromosome continues DNA synthesis for a longer time than the other X or any other chromosomes of the complement. This cytological as well as genetic evidence has led Lyon (1962) to postulate the genetic inactivation of one of the two X chromosomes in the female mammals. The implication of this hypothesis is extremely significant and interesting. Since the problem has been recently reviewed by Hsu (in press), McKusick (1962), Russell (this symposium), and Ohno (this symposium), I shall not go into detail except for pertinent references in the following discussions.

SEX DETERMINATION AND SEX DIFFERENTIATION

Studies of sex chromosome abnormalities suggest that the Y chromosome in mammals is strongly male-determining and is essential for the development of testicular tissues. Whenever a Y chromosome is present in an individual, the individual is more or less a male, irrespective of the number of the X chromosomes. Even when only a small fragment of Y is presumed to be present, masculinization is evident (although masculinization and the presence of male gonadal tissues are taken as evidence for the presence of the Y material). On the other hand, extra Y chromosomes, e.g. XXYY and XYY, do not seem to increase the maleness.

The presence of at least one X chromosome is necessary for survival; one X is also more or less sufficient for femaleness. Since addition of extra X chromosome(s) or deletion of the second X does not grossly alter the female sex phenotype, female determiners are not suspected to be located in the X, but possibly in autosome (L. B. Russell, 1961). Although this possibility cannot presently be ruled out, one can also interpret the above observations by invoking the inactivation hypothesis. According to the latter, all individuals, male or female, normal or pathological, have basically one active X chromosome (Ohno, 1961). The phenotype of a nullo-X individual would have answered the question, but such an individual is almost certainly nonviable.

The second X chromosome, however, is probably not entirely inactivated. Although XO and XXY are not in the direction of intersexuality, human individuals possessing unbalanced sex chromosomes are infertile and more or less phenotypically abnormal. XO female mice, though fertile, are less viable and vigorous. XXY male mice are sterile. This definite developmental effect of the second X chromosome has also been pointed out by Mittwoch (1961).

The study of hermaphroditism in man may also shed some light on the mechanism of sex determination. Human hermaphroditism is clearly different from that in the gypsy moth, *Lymantria dispar*, in which Goldschmidt had demonstrated intersexuality by interbalance of male and female determiners, or from that in *Drosophila*, in which Bridges had shown that unbalanced ratios between autosomal sets and the X chromosomes would result in intersexes (2X : 3A) or supersexes (3X : 2A, 1X : 3A).

In man, XO/XY (Hirschhorn *et al.*, 1960) and XO/XX/XY (Schuster and Motulsky, 1962) and XX/XXY/XXYYY (Fraccaro *et al.*, 1962c) mosaics are found in cases of true hermaphroditism, i.e. individuals having both ovarian and testicular tissues. However, several true hermaphrodites were reported (e.g. Hungerford *et al.*, 1959) as karyotypically normal females. These can be reconciled with a simple hypothesis of undetected mosaicism.

Harnden and Stewart (1959) found a patient with pure gonadal dysgenesis who had female phenotype. The gonadal tissues were similar to those found in Turner's syndrome. The patient, however, did not have many of the other features of this disorder. By chromosome analysis she was shown to be of XY constitution. The patient, while chromosomally a male, developed as a female either because of maternal intrauterine influence or as a result of some rare dominant (or sex-linked recessive) gene mutation.

This case should not be confused with another more commonly occurring type of heteromaphroditism, i.e. male pseudohermaphrodites with testicular feminization. It is characterized by a normal male karyotype (Chu and Giles, 1959; Jacobs et al., 1959a; Lejeune et al., 1960; Puck et al., 1960; Chu, Grumbach and Morishima, 1960), internal testes, and a female phenotype. This type of anomaly is thought to be inherited either as a sex-linked recessive or a sex-limited dominant mutant gene (Puck et al., 1960; Chu et al., 1960).

As Stern (1961) has recently pointed out, in mammals sex determination by a chromosomal mechanism and somatic sexual differentiation are separate events. Cytological evidence supports the hypothesis that mammalian sex chromosomes fundamentally are carriers of sex determiners. The human primordial gonad is bipotential. It is assumed that an actual imbalance in favor of either male or female sex-controlling genes determines the sex of the gonad in placental mammals (cf. Grumbach and Barr, 1958). However, unlike insects, in which soma and germ cells develop separately and hormones are scarce, in mammals the hormonal control and other factors can modify the sexual development (cf. Miller, 1961; Polani, 1962).

CYTOLOGICAL MAPPING AND EVOLUTION OF HUMAN SEX CHROMOSOMES

Cytological evidence, both meiotic synaptic behavior and mitotic metaphase configuration of abnormal chromosomes, has been used to speculate about the alignment of the genetic materials of the X and Y chromosomes. Jacobs and associates (1961) suggested that perhaps it is the loss of all or part of the short arm of the X which is critical to the development of the Turner's syndrome. Supporting evidence comes from the observation that patients with a deletion of part of the long arm have primary amenorrhea or severe oligomenorrhea but have normal stature and none of the stigmata, such as webbed neck, of the Turner's syndrome (Jacobs et al., 1960; de Grouchy et al., 1961). By a similar line of reasoning in conjunction with the fact that women with one normal X and one isochromosome of the long arm of X can exhibit color blindness, it is postulated that this gene may possibly be located on the short arm of the X (Stewart, 1961; Polani and Hamerton, 1961). However, no crucial proof for this conclusion is yet available. Nevertheless, if we assume that the interpretations of the cytological observations are correct, accumulation of further data on structural rearrangements involving the X should eventually lead to a complete mapping of this chromosome.

Linkage relationships of many X-linked genes are well known (see review of McKusick, 1962). It is safe to state that the human X carries important genetic information and that at least one X is indispensable for survival of the organism. We have already seen the variety of X-chromosome abnormalities present in the human population. With the exception of occasional XO and XXX women with proven fertility, the majority of X-chromosome anomalies are associated with phenotypic defects and sterility. The abnormal X chromosome, therefore, appears to have no selective value in human populations (Penrose, 1961).

The Y chromosome, on the other hand, is relatively genetically unknown. Only one gene, "hairy ear", has been demonstrated to be Y-linked (Dronamraju, 1961). In addition, the male-determining properties have been attributed to the Y. Whether there are one or many such factors on the Y is yet uncertain. The fact that a fragmented Y results in incomplete maleness seems to favor the latter possibility. Due to the lack of genetic information and the natural morphologic variability, cytological mapping of the human Y is a formidable, if not impossible, task.

On the basis that there is no proven XO male in mammals, White (1960) concluded that "the Y is an indispensable part of the mammalian sex determining mechanism because it is necessary for the development of the male, and that it has probably not been lost on any occasion in mammalian evolution." What White meant by "loss" of the Y is not an actual loss but a transfer of most of the substance of this chromosome to the X or to an autosome, by translocation, so that females become homozygous for it.

For viviparous mammals, the separation of sexes is of utmost importance. The child-bearing function of the female is one of the many reasons. If sex-determining factors are scattered throughout the X and Y chromosomes, evolution would favor the isolation of the X and Y through a restriction in crossing over between them (Swanson, 1957). The end-to-end XY pairing at first meiotic metaphase can then be explained. In the mouse, Ohno and colleagues (Ohno, Kaplan and Kinosita, 1959; Ohno and Hauschka, 1960) also pointed out that precocious condensation of the sex pair during synaptic stages of meiosis in the heterogametic sex limits the chiasma formation and therefore genetic crossing over. In this connection, the early separation of the X and Y (prereduction) may be assumed to be one of the causes of the production of unbalanced gametes, although the transmission of the latter to form abnormal zygote is another matter.

As a consequence of isolation between the X and Y, large numbers of mutations could have been accumulated on the Y in human evolution. Deleterious gene and chromosome mutations are quickly eliminated. The many reported cases of fragmented Y cannot be transmitted to the progeny and thus have no selective value. On the other hand, neutral or beneficial mutations can be retained and persist in the human karyotypic pool. The observed morphological variability of the Y in human populations is probably the result of such a mechanism. For a British peer who wishes to uphold family tradition, his Y is certainly something to be proud of and is kept within the family. For the ladies who wonder what will happen to the Y in human evolution, I shall say: let us men worry about it!

SUMMARY

An attempt has been made in this paper to summarize the vast amount of literature on the human sex chromosomes. Most of the literature has accumulated within the past few years. Owing to the efforts of many investigators, the morphology and behavior of the normal sex chromosomes, at meiosis and mitosis, have become better understood. It is also clear that variations of sex chromosomes, in both the number and structure, can exist in man. They serve to elucidate the functional significance of sex-linked genes as well as the order of genetic material of the human sex chromosomes. In the light of these studies on abnormal sex chromosomes, the evolution of human sex chromosomes can be visualized and discussed on a solid basis. The conclusions reached are necessarily derived from current information on these subjects; further accumulation of knowledge in this rapidly growing field of human cytogenetics will undoubtedly expand, correct, and modify the views that have been put forth in this review.

REFERENCES

BAHNER, F., SCHWARZ, G., HARNDEN, D. G., JACOBS, P. A., HIENZ, H. A. and WALTER, K. 1960, A fertile female with XO sex chromosome constitution. *Lancet*, ii, 100–101.

BARR, M. L. and BERTRAM, E. G., 1949, A morphological distinction between neurones of the male and female, and the behaviour of the nuclear satellite during accelerated nucleopterin synthesis. *Nature*, **163**, 676–677.

BARR, M. L. and CARR, D. H., 1960, Sex chromatin, sex chromosomes and sex anomalies. *Canad. Med. Assoc. J.* **83**, 979–986.

BARR, M. L., and CARR, D. H., 1962, Correlations between sex chromatin and sex chromosomes. *Acta Cytol.* **6**, 34–45.

BARR, M. L., CARR, D. H., MORISHIMA, A. and GRUMBACH, M. M., 1962, An XY/XXXY sex chromosome mosaicism in a mentally defective male patient. *J. Mental Deficiency Res.* **6**, 65–74.

BENDER, M. A., and GOOCH, P. C., 1961, An unusually long human Y chromosome. *Lancet*, ii, 463–464.

BENDER, M. A., and PRESCOTT, D. M., 1962, DNA synthesis and mitosis in cultures of human peripheral leukocytes. *Exptl. Cell Res.* 27, 221–229.

BERGMANN, E., 1961, Geschlectschromatinbestimmungen am Neugeborenen. *Schweiz. Med. Wochschr.* 91, 292.

BLANK, C. E., BISHOP, A. and CALEY, J. P., 1960, Example of XY/XO mosaicism. *Lancet*, ii, 1450.

BÖÖK, J. A., *et al.*, 1960, A proposed standard system of nomenclature of human mitotic chromosomes (Denver, Colorado), with editorial comment. *Ann. Human Genet., Lond.* 24, 319–325, 1960. Corrigenda (by L. S. Penrose). *Ann. Human Genet., Lond.* 25, 105, 1961.

BOYER, S. H., FERGUSON-SMITH, M. A. and GRUMBACH, M. M., 1961, The lack of influence of parental age and birth order in the aetiology of nuclear sex chromatin-negative Turner's syndrome. *Ann. Human Genet., Lond.* 25, 215–225.

BOYES, J. W., 1961, Human X-chromosome arm ratios and percentages of total complement length. *Am. J. Human Genet.* 13, 104–105.

BRIDGES, C. B., 1922, The origin of variations in sexual and sex-limited characters. *Am. Naturalist*, 56, 51–63.

BRIDGES, C. B., 1916a, Non-disjunction as proof of the chromosome theory of heredity. I. *Genetics*, 1, 1–52.

BRIDGES, C. B., 1916b, Non-disjunction as proof of the chromosome theory of heredity. II. *Genetics*, 1, 107–163.

CARR, D. H., BARR, M. L., and PLUNKETT, E. R., 1961, An XXXX sex chromosome complex in two mentally defective females. *Canad. Med. Assoc. J.* 84, 131–137.

CARR, D. H., MORISHIMA, A., BARR, M. L., GRUMBACH, M. M., LÜERS, T. and BOSCHANN, H. W., 1962, An XO/XX/XXX mosaicism in relationship to gonadal dysgenesis in females. *J. Clin. Endocrinol. Metab.* 22, 671–677.

CATTANACH, B. M., 1961, XXY mice. *Genet. Res.* 2, 156–158.

CHU, E. H. Y., 1963, Mammalian chromosome cytology. *Am. Zoologist*, 3, 3–14.

CHU, E. H. Y. and GILES, N. H., 1959, Human chromosome complements in normal somatic cells in culture. *Am. J. Human Genet.* 11, 63–79.

CHU, E. H. Y., GRUMBACH, M. M. and MORISHIMA, A., 1960, Karyotypic analysis of a male pseudohermaphrodite with the syndrome of feminizing testes. *J. Clin. Endocrinol. Metab.* 20, 1608–1613.

CHU, E. H. Y., WARKANY, J., and ROSENSTEIN, R. B., 1961, Chromosome complement in a case of the "male Turner syndrome". *Lancet*, i, 786–788.

CONEN, P. E., BAILEY, J. D., ALLEMANG, W. H., THOMPSON, D. W. and EZRIN, C., 1961, A probable partial deletion of the Y chromosome in an intersex patient. *Lancet*, ii, 294–295.

CRAWFURD, M. D'A., 1961, Chromosomal mosaicism in a case of Klinefelter's syndrome associated with thalassaemia. *Ann. Human Genet., Lond.* 25, 153–158.

DAVIDSON, W. M. and SMITH, D. R., 1954, A morphological sex difference in the polymorphonuclear neutrophil leukocytes. *Brit. Med. J.* 2, 6.

DE CARLI, L., NUZZO, F., CHIARELLI, B. and POLI, E., 1960, Trisomic condition of a large chromosome in a woman with mongoloid traits. *Lancet*, ii, 130–131.

DE GROUCHY, J., LAMY, M., YANEVA, H., SALOMON, Y. and NETTER, A., 1961, Further abnormalities of the X chromosome in primary amenorrhoea or in severe oligomenorrhea. *Lancet*, ii, 777–778.

DE WINIWARTER, H., 1912, Etudes sur la spermatogenese humaine (I. Cellule de Sertoli. II. Hétérochromosome et mitoses de l'épithélium seminal.) *Archiv. Biol. (Liege)*, 27, 91–190.

DRONAMRAJU, K. R., 1961, Hypertrichosis of the pinna of the human ear, Y-linked pedigrees. *J. Genet.* 57, 230–243.

ELVES, M. W. and ISRAELS, M. C. G., 1962, An abnormal large chromosome in a haemophiliac with congenital abnormalities. *Lancet*, **ii**, 909–911.

ENGEL, E., and FORBES, A. P., 1961, An abnormal medium-sized metacentric chromosome in a woman with primary gonadal failure. *Lancet*, **ii**, 1004–1005.

FERGUSON-SMITH, M. A., 1961, Chromosomes and human disease. In *Progress in Medical Genetics* (A. G. Steinberg, ed.), Vol. 1, pp 229–334, Grune and Stratton, New York.

FERGUSON-SMITH, M. A., JOHNSTON, A. W. and HANDMAKER, S. D., 1960a, Primary amentia and micro-orchidism associated with an XXXY sex-chromosome constitution. *Lancet*, **ii**, 184–187.

FERGUSON-SMITH, M. A., JOHNSTON, A. W. and WEINBERG, A. N., 1960b, The chromosome complement in true hermaphroditism. *Lancet*, **ii**, 126–128.

FERGUSON-SMITH, M. A., LENNOX, B., MACK, W. S. and STEWART, J. S. S., 1957, Klinefelter's syndrome: frequency and testicular morphology in relation to nuclear sex. *Lancet*, **ii**, 167–169.

FORD, C. E., 1960, Human cytogenetics: Its present place and future possibilities. *Am. J. Human Genet.* **12**, 104–117.

FORD, C. E., 1962, Methods in human cytogenetics. In *Methodology in Human Genetics* (W. J. Burdette, ed.) pp. 227–259, Holden-Day, San Francisco.

FORD, C. E. and HAMERTON, J. L., 1956, The chromosomes of man. *Nature*, **178**, 1020–1023.

FORD, C. E., JONES, K. W., MILLER, O. J., MITTWOCH, U., PENROSE, L. S., RIDLER, M. and SHAPIRO, A., 1959a, The chromosomes in a patient showing both mongolism and the Klinefelter syndrome. *Lancet*, **i**, 709–710.

FORD, C. E., JONES, K. W., POLANI, P. E., DE ALMEIDA, J. C. and BRIGGS, J. H., 1959b, A sex-chromosome anomaly in a case of gonadal dysgenesis (Turner's syndrome). *Lancet*, **i**, 711–713.

FORD, C. E., POLANI, P. E., BRIGGS, J. H. and BISHOP, P. M. F., 1959c, A presumptive human XXY/XX mosaic. *Nature*, **183**, 1030–1032.

FRACCARO, M., BOTT, M. G., SALZANO, F. M., RUSSELL, R. W. R. and CRANSTON, W. I., 1962a, Triple chromosomal mosaic in a woman with clinical evidence of masculinization. *Lancet*, **i**, 1379–1381.

FRACCARO, M., KLINGER, H. P. and SCHUTT, W., 1962b, A male with XXXXY sex chromosomes. *Cytogenetics*, **1**, 52–64.

FRACCARO, M., TAYLOR, A. I., BODIAN, M. and NEWNS, G. H., 1962c, A human intersex ("true hermaphrodite") with XX/XXY/XXYYY sex chromosomes. *Cytogenetics*, **1**, 104–112.

FRACCARO, M., IKKOS, D., LINDSTEN, J., LUFT, R. and KAIJSER, K., 1960a, A new type of chromosomal abnormality in gonadal dysgenesis. *Lancet*, **ii**, 1144.

FRACCARO, M., KAIJSER, K. and LINDSTEN, J., 1960b, A child with 49 chromosomes. *Lancet*, **ii**, 899–902.

FRACCARO, M. and LINDSTEN, J., 1960, A child with 49 chromosomes. *Lancet*, **ii**, 1303.

FRASER, J. H., CAMPBELL, J., MACGILLIVRAY, R. C., BOYD, E. and LENNOX, B., 1960, The XXX syndrome frequency among mental defectives and fertility. *Lancet*, **ii**, 626–627.

GARTLER, S. M., VULLO, C. and GANDINI, E., 1962a, Glucose-6-phosphate dehydrogenese deficiency in an XO individual. *Cytogenetics*, **1**, 1–4.

GARTLER, S. M., WAXMAN S. H. and GIBLETT, E., 1962b, An XX/XY human hermaphrodite resulting from double fertilization. *Proc. Natl. Acad. Sci. U.S.* **48**, 332–335.

GERMAN, J. L., III, 1962a, DNA synthesis in human chromosomes. *Trans. N. Y. Acad. Sci.* (Ser. II), **24**, 395–407.

GERMAN, J. L., III, 1962b, Personal communication.

GOLDSCHMIDT, R. B., 1955, *Theoretical Genetics*, University of California Press, Berkeley.

GOWEN, J. W., 1933, Anomalous human sex-linked inheritance of color-blindness in relation to attached sex chromosomes. *Human Biol.* **5**, 130–134.

GRUMBACH, M. M. and BARR, M. L., 1958, Cytologic tests of chromosomal sex in relation to sexual anomalies in man. In *Recent Progress in Hormone Research* (G. Pincus, ed.), Vol. 14, pp. 235–334, Academic Press, New York.

GRUMBACH, M. M., MORISHIMA, A. and CHU, E. H. Y., 1960, On the sex chromatin and he sex chromosomes in sexual anomalies in man; relation to origin of the sex chromatin. *Acta Endocrinol. Suppl.* **51**, 633.

HALDANE, J. B. S., 1932, Genetical evidence for a cytological abnormality in man. *J. Genet.* **26**, 341–344.

HALDENE, J. B. S., 1936, A search for incomplete sex-linkage in man. *Ann. Eugen.* **7**, 28–57.

HAMERTON, J. L., 1961, Sex chromatin and human chromosomes. *Intern. Rev. Cytol.* **12**, 1–68.

HAMERTON, J. L., COWIE, V. A., GIANNELLI, F., BRIGGS, S. M. and POLANI, P. E., 1961, Differential transmission of Down's syndrome (mongolism) through male and female translocation carriers. *Lancet*, **ii**, 956–958.

HARNDEN, D. G., 1961, The chromosomes. In *Recent Advances in Human Genetics* (L. S. Penrose, ed.), pp. 19–38, Little, Brown, Boston.

HARNDEN, D. G. and JACOBS, P. A., 1961, Cytogenetics of abnormal sexual development in man. *Brit. Med. Bull.* **17**, 206–212.

HARNDEN, D. G. and STEWART, J. S. S., 1959, The chromosomes in a case of pure gonadal dysgenesis. *Brit. Med. J.* **2**, 1285–1287.

HIRSCHHORN, K. and COOPER, H. L., 1961, Chromosomal aberrations in human disease. *Am. J. Med.* **31**, 442–470.

HIRSCHHORN, K., DECKER, W. H. and COOPER, H. L., 1960, Human intersex with chromosome mosaicism of type XY/XO: Report of a case. *New Engl. J. Med.* **263**, 1044–1048.

HSU, T. C., (in press), Genetic cytology. In *The Biology of Cells and Tissues in Culture* (E. N. Willmer, ed.), Academic Press, New York.

HUNGERFORD, D. A., DONNELLY, A. J., NOWELL, P. C. and BECK, S., 1959, The chromosome constitution of a human phenotypic intersex. *Am. J. Human Genet.* **11**, 215–236.

JACOBS, P. A., BAIKIE, A. G., COURT BROWN, W. M., FORREST, H., ROY, J. R., STEWART, J. S. S. and LENNOX, B., 1959a, Chromosomal sex in the syndrome of testicular feminization. *Lancet*, **ii**, 591–592.

JACOBS, P. A., BAIKE, A. G., COURT BROWN, W. M., MACGREGOR, T. N., MACLEAN, N. and HARNDEN, D. G., 1959b, Evidence for the existence of the human "super female." *Lancet*, **ii**, 423–425.

JACOBS, P. A. and STRONG, J. A., 1959c, A case of human intersexuality having a possible XXY sex-determining mechanism. *Nature*, **183**, 302–303.

JACOBS, P. A., HARNDEN, D. G., COURT BROWN, W. M., GOLDSTEIN, J. CLOSE, H. G., MACGREGOR, T. N., MACLEAN, N. and STRONG, J. A., 1960, Abnormalities involving the X chromosome in women. *Lancet*, **i**, 1213–1216.

JACOBS, P. A., HARNDEN, D. G., BUCKTON, K. E., COURT BROWN, W. M., KING, M. J., MCBRIDE, J. A., MACGREGOR, T. N. and MACLEAN, N., 1961, Cytogenetic studies in primary amenorrhoea. *Lancet*, **i**, 1183–1189.

KÄLLÉN, B. and LEVAN, A., 1962, Abnormal length of chromosomes 21 and 22 in four patients with Marfan's Syndrome. *Cytogenetics*, **1**, 5–19.

KODANI, M., 1957, The karyotype of man with the diploid chromosome number of 48. *Proc. Intern. Genet. Symp.*, Tokyo and Kyoto, 1956, pp. 103–107.

KOLLER, P. C., 1937, The genetical and mechanical properties of sex chromosomes. III. Man. *Proc. Roy. Soc. Edinburgh*, **57**, 194–214.

LEJEUNE, J. and TURPIN, R., 1961, Détection chromosomique d'une mosaique artificielle humaine. *Compt. Rend.* **252**, 3148–3150.

LEJEUNE, J., TURPIN, R. and GAUTIER, M., 1960, Analyse caryotypique de trois pseudo-hermaphrodites masculins. *Compt. Rend.* **250**, 618–620.

LENZ, VON W., NOWAKOWSKI, H., PRADER, A. and SCHIRREN, C., 1959, Die Atiologie des Klinefelter-Syndromes: Ein Beitrag zur Chromosomenpathologie beim. *Menschen. Schweiz. Med. Wochschr.* **89**, 727.

LIMA-DE-FARIA, A., REITALU, J. and BERGMAN, S., 1961, The pattern of DNA synthesis in the chromosomes of man. *Hereditas*, **47**, 695–704.

LINDSTEN, J., and TILLINGER, K.-G., 1962, Self-perpetuating ring chromosome in a patient with gonadal dysgenesis. *Lancet*, **i**, 593–594.

LYON, M. F., 1962, Sex chromatin and gene action in the mammalian X-chromosome. *Am. J. Human Genet.* **14**, 135–148.

MACLEAN, N., 1962, The drumsticks of polymorphonuclear leucocytes in sex-chromosome abnormalities. *Lancet*, **ii**, 1154–1158.

MACLEAN, N., HARNDEN, D. G. and COURT BROWN, W. M., 1961, Abnormalities of sex chromosome constitution in newborn babies. *Lancet*, **ii**, 406–408.

MAKINO, S. and SASAKI, M., 1961, A study of somatic chromosomes in a Japanese population. *Am. J. Human Genet.* **13**, 47–63.

MACLEAN, N., MITCHELL, J. M., HARNDEN, D. G., WILLIAMS, J., JACOBS, P. A., BUCKTON, K. A., BAIKIE, A. G., COURT BROWN, W. M., McBRIDE, J. A., STRONG, J. A., CLOSE, H. G., and JONES, D. C., 1962, A survey of sex-chromosome abnormalities among 4514 mental defectives. *Lancet*, **i**, 293–296.

McCLUNG, C. E., 1902, The spermatocyte divisions of the Locustidae. *Kans. Univ. Sci. Bull.* **1**, 185–238.

McKUSICK, V. A., 1962, On the X chromosome of man. *Quart. Rev. Biol.* **37**, 69–173.

MILES, C. P., LUZZATTI, L. STOREY S. D. and PETERSON, C. D., 1962, A male pseudo-hermaphrodite with a probable XO/XxY mosaicism. *Lancet*, **ii**, 455.

MILLER, O. J. 1961, Developmental sex abnormalities. In *Recent Advances in Human Genetics* (L. S. Penrose, ed.), pp. 39–55, Little, Brown, Boston.

MILLER, O. J., BREG, W. R., SCHMICKEL, R. D. and TRETTER, W., 1961, A family with an XXXXY male, a leukaemic male and two 21-trisomic mongoloid females. *Lancet*, **ii**, 78–79.

MITTWOCH, U., 1961, Properties of X chromosomes. *Lancet*, **ii**, 880.

MOORE, K. L., 1959, Sex reversal in newborn babies. *Lancet*, **i**, 217–219.

MOORHEAD, P. S., MELLMAN, W. J. and WENAR, C., 1961, A familial chromosome translocation associated with speech and mental retardation. *Am. J. Human. Genet.* **13**, 32–46.

MORISHIMA, A., GRUMBACH, M. M. and TAYLOR, J. H., 1962, Asynchronous duplication of human chromosomes and the origin of sex chromatin. *Proc. Natl. Acad. Sci. U.S.* **48**, 756–763.

MULDAL, S. and OCKEY, C. H., 1960, The "double male": a new chromosome constitution in Klinefelter's syndrome. *Lancet*, **ii**, 492–493.

MULDAL, S. and OCKEY, C. H., 1961, Muscular dystophy and deletion of Y chromosome. *Lancet*, **ii**, 601.

OHNO, S., 1961, Properties of X chromosomes. *Lancet*, **ii**, 723–724.

OHNO, S., 1962, More about the mammalian X chromosome. *Lancet*, **ii**, 152–153.

OHNO, S. and HAUSCHKA, T. S., 1960, Allocycly of the X-chromosome in tumors and normal tissues. *Cancer Res.* **20**, 541–545.

OHNO, S., KAPLAN, W. D. and KINOSITA, R., 1959, On the end-to-end association of the X and Y chromosomes of *Mus musculus. Exptl. Cell Res.* **18**, 282–290.

OHNO, S., KLINGER, H. P. and ATKIN, N. B., 1962, Human oogenesis. *Cytogenetics*, **1**, 42–51.

OHNO, S. and MAKINO, S., 1961, The single-X nature of sex chromatin in man. *Lancet*, **i**, 78–79.

PAINTER, T. S. 1923, Studies in mammalian spermatogenesis. II. The spermatogenesis of man. *J. Exptl. Zool.* **37**, 291–336.

PATAU, K., 1960, The identification of individual chromosomes, expecially in man. *Am. J. Human Genet.* **12**, 250–276.

PATAU, K., 1962a, The sex chromosomes of man — some unresolved problems. Presented at a Joint Symposium of the American Society of Human Genetics, Genetics Society of America and American Society of Zoologists, AIBS, Oregon State Univ., Corvallis.

PATAU, K., 1962b, Personal communication.

PENROSE, L. S., 1961a, Parental age and non-disjunction. In *Human Chromosomal Abnormalities*. Proceedings of a Conference held at King's College Hospital Medical School (W. M. Davidson and D.K. Smith, eds.), pp. 116–122, Staples Press, London.

PENROSE, L. S., 1961b, Mongolism. *Brit. Med. Bull.* **17**, 184–189.

PENPOSE, L. S., 1961c, Human chromosomal aberrations and natural selection. In *Proc. Second International Conference of Human Genetics*, pp. E71–E72, Excerpta Medica Foundation, Amsterdam.

PETTERSON, G. and BONNIER, G., 1937, Inherited sex-mosaic in man. *Hereditas*, **23**, 49–69.

POLANI, P. E., 1961, Turner's syndrome and allied conditions. *Brit. Med. Bull.* **17**, 200–205.

POLANI, P. E., 1962, Sex chromosome anomalies in man. In *Chromosomes in Medicine* (J. L. Hamerton, ed.), pp. 73–139, Little Club Clinics in Medicine, No. 5, W. Heinemann Books, London.

POLANI, P. E., BISHOP, P. M. F., LENNOX, B., FERGUSON-SMITH, M. A., STEWART, J. S. S. and PRADER, A., 1958, Colour vision studies and the X-chromosome constitution of patients with Klinefelter's syndrome. *Nature*, **182**, 1092–1093.

POLANI, P. E. and HAMERTON, J. L., 1961, Genetic factors on the X chromosome. *Lancet*, **ii**, 262–263 and 317.

POLANI, P. E., LESSOF, M. H. and BISHOP, P. M. F., 1956, Color-blindess in "ovarian agenesis" (gonadal dysplasia). *Lancet*, **ii**, 118–120.

PUCK, T. T., ROBINSON, A. and TJIO, J. H., 1960, Familial primary amenorrhea due to testicular feminization: a human gene affecting sex differentiation. *Proc. Soc. Exptl. Biol. Med.* **103**, 192–196.

RAPPOPORT, S. and KAPLAN, W. D., 1961, Chromosomal aberrations in man. *J. Pediat.* **59**, 415–438.

RUSSELL, L. B., 1961, Genetics of mammalian sex chromosomes. *Science*, **133**, 1795–1803.

RUSSELL, L. B., and CHU, E. H. Y., 1961, An XXY male in the mouse. *Proc. Natl. Acad. Sci. U.S.* **47**, 571–575.

RUSSELL, W. L., RUSSELL, L. B. and GOWER, J. S., 1959, Exceptional inheritance of a sex-linked gene in the mouse explained on the basis that the X/O sex-chromosome constitution is female. *Proc. Natl. Acad. Sci. U.S.* **45**, 554–560.

SACHS, LEO, 1954, Sex-linkage and the sex chromosomes in man. *Ann. Eugen.* **18**, 255–261.

SANDBERG, A. A., CROSSWHITE, L. H. and GORDY, E., 1960a, Trisomy of a large chromosome. Association with mental retardation. *J. Am. Med. Assoc.* **174**, 221–225.

SANDBERG, A. A., KOEPF. G. F., CROSSWHITE, L. H. and HAUSCHKA, T. S., 1960b, The chromosome constitution of human marrow in various developmental and blood disorders *Am. J. Human Genet.* **12**, 231–249.

SANDBERG, A. A., KOEPF, G. F., ISHIHARA, T. and HAUSCHKA, T. S., 1961, An XYY human male. *Lancet*, **ii**, 488–489.

SCHULTZ, J. and ST. LAWRENCE, P., 1949, A cytological basis for a map of the nucleolar chromosome in man. *J. Heredity*, **40**, 31–38.

SCHUSTER, J. and MOTULSKY, A. G., 1962, Exceptional sex-chromatin pattern in male pseudohermaphroditism with XX/XY/XO mosaicism. *Lancet*, **i**, 1074–1075.

SHIWAGO, P. I. and ANDRES, A. H., 1932, Die Geschlechtschromosomen in der Spermatogenese des Menschen. *Z. Zellforsch. Mikroskop. Anat. Abt. Histochem.* **16**, 413–431.

SOHVAL, A. R., 1961, Recent progress in human chromosome analysis and its relation to sex chromatin. *Am. J. Med.* **31**, 397–441.

SOHVAL, A. R. and CASSELMAN, W. G. B., 1961, Alteration in size of nuclear sex-chromatin mass (Barr Body) induced by antibiotics. *Lancet*, **ii**, 1386–1388.

STERN, C., 1961, The genetics of sex-determination in man. In *Proceedings Second International Conference of Human Genetics*, p. E94, Excerpta Medica Foundation, Amsterdam.

STEVENS, N. M., 1905, Studies in spermatogenesis with special reference to the accessory chromosome. *Publ. Carneg. Inst.* **36**, 3–32.

STEVENS, N. M., 1908, A study of the germ cells of certain Diptera, with reference to the heterochromosomes and the phenomena of synapsis. *J. Exptl. Zool.* **5**, 359–374.

STEWART, J. S. S., 1961, Genetic factors on the X-chromosome. *Lancet*, **ii**, 104 and 317.

STEWART, J. S. S. and SANDERSON, A. R., 1960, Fertility and oligophrenia in an apparent triplo-X female. *Lancet*, **ii**, 21–23.

SWANSON, C. P., 1957, *Cytology and Cytogenetics*. Prentice-Hall, Englewood Cliffs, New Jersey.

THERMAN, E., PATAU, K., DE MARS, R. I. and SMITH, D. W., 1962, Mosaicism for a presumed D_1 isochromosome. (Presented at the American Society of Human Genetics Meeting, Oregon State Univ., Corvallis, Oregon, August 29–31, 1962.)

THULINE, H. C. and NORBY, D. E., 1961, Spontaneous occurrence of chromosome abnormality in cats. *Science*, **134**, 554–555.

TJIO, J. H. and LEVAN, A., 1956, The chromosome number of man. *Hereditas*, **42**, 1–6.

TURPIN, R., LEJEUNE, J., LAFOURCADE, J., CHIGOT P.-L. and SALMON, C., 1961, Présomption de monozygotisme en dépit d'un dimorphisme sexuel: sujet masculin XY et sujet neutre Haplo X. *Compt. Rend.* **252**, 2945–2946.

UCHIDA, I. A. and BOWMAN, J. M., 1961, XXX 18-Trisomy. *Lancet*, **ii**, 1094.

VAHARU, T., PATTON, R. G., VOORHESS, M. L. and GARDNER, L. I., 1961, Gonadal dysplasia and enlarged phallus in a girl with 45 chromosomes plus "fragment." *Lancet*, **i**, 1351.

VAN WIJCK, J. A. M., TIJDINK, G. A. J. and STOLTE, L. A. M., 1962, Anomalies in the Y chromosome. *Lancet*, **i**, 218.

WARKANY, J., CHU, E. H. Y. and KAUDER, E., 1962, Male pseudohermaphroditism and chromosomal mosaicism. *Am. J. Diseases Children*, **104**, 172–179.

WAXMAN, S. H., KELLEY, V. C., GARTLER, S. M., and BURT, B., 1962, Chromosome complement in a true hermaphrodite. *Lancet*, **i**, 161.

WELSHONS, W. J. and RUSSELL, L. B., 1959, The Y-chromosome as the bearer of male determining factors in the mouse. *Proc. Natal. Acad. Sci. U.S.* **45**, 560–566.

WESTERGAARD, M., 1948, The relation between chromosome constitution and sex in the offspring of triploid *Melandrium*. *Hereditas*, **34**, 257–279.

WHITE, M. J. D., 1960, Are there no mammal species with XO males — and if not, why not? *American Naturalist*, **94**, 301–304.

WILSON, E. B., 1911, Studies on chromosomes. VII. A review of the chromosomes of *Nezara;* with same more general considerations. *J. Morphol.* **22**, 71–110.

WITSCHI, E., 1939, Modification of the development of sex in lower vertebrates and in mammals. In *Sex and Internal Secretions*, 2nd ed. (E. Allen. ed.), pp. 145–226, The Williams and Wilkins, Baltimore.

YERGANIAN, G., 1957, Cytologic maps of some isolated human pachytene chromosomes. *Am. J. Human Genet.* **9**, 42–54.

DETECTION AND USE OF CYTOLOGICAL ANOMALIES IN THE MOUSE

W. J. WELSHONS

Biology Division, Oak Ridge National Laboratory,* Oak Ridge, Tennessee, U. S. A.

INTRODUCTION

In the general sense, the mouse is not a particularly good organism for genetic research, but in a more restricted sense, it is the best available mammal for this type of investigation. Its use will undoubtedly continue to increase since genetic and cytogenetic information obtained from mouse experiments are more easily and validly extended to humans. One need only consult the papers at this and the sister symposium in Rio de Janeiro to discern this.

The value of the mouse for cytogenetic studies is restricted by both its genetic and cytological potentialities. Unfortunately, the somatic chromosomes leave much to be desired since the diploid number equals 40 and the haploid complement consists, grossly, of a series of rods varying from long to short with relatively little existing chromosome difference, other than length, to aid in the recognition of specific members. While it is true that the interpretation of some genetic data can be substantiated by a procedure as simple as an accurate chromosome count, it is obvious that the lack of clear-cut differences between somatic chromosomes will soon become a formidable limitation to some cytogenetic experiments. With this impending limitation in mind, the decision was made to turn to the cytology of synaptically paired meiotic chromosomes of the mouse in order to evaluate their potentiality for gathering pertinent cytological data when somatic chromosomes would not suffice.

Since there is a litter size criterion normally used for the detection of reciprocal translocations, we decided to produce a number of these chromosomal rearrangements and compare the reliability and merits of the breeding and cytological criteria. The production and cytological investigation of

* Operated by Union Carbide Corporation for the United States Atomic Energy Commission.

translocations was undertaken for another purpose — events leading to their production can cause such extreme changes in chromosome morphology that the difference can be easily detected in a somatic cell. When this happens, the resultant "cell marker" translocation is useful for immunogenetic experiments, as will be demonstrated shortly.

PRODUCTION AND DETECTION OF RECIPROCAL TRANSLOCATIONS

For the production of translocations, a group of males were irradiated with 600 r of X-rays administered to the testes. They were then supplied with females until it was obvious that the irradiated animals had entered their period of temporary sterility. With this dose of irradiation and breeding procedure one can expect about 20 per cent of the progeny to be heterozygous for a translocation (Russell, 1952). The F_1 male progeny were then mated with vigorous females in order to estimate the productivity of each of these male animals, for if the male parent is heterozygous for a translocation, one can expect the ensuing litters to be approximately one-half normal size. This criterion of a reduced litter size is based on the fact that an animal heterozygous for a reciprocal translocation can be expected to produce various types of gametes; one will carry the translocation, another will be completely normal, and the remaining gametes will generally be duplicated for one piece of chromosome and simultaneously deficient for another. Fertilization by the aneuploid gametes results in the formation of lethal zygotes and a consequent reduction in litter size.

When this phase of the experiment was completed, we had six males that were definitely semisterile and 30 that had normal or near-normal fertility. The next step was a cytological one, for we wished to examine the meiotic figures to see how well litter size and cytological criteria would agree.

Because homologous chromosomes pair during meiosis, it is possible to detect reciprocal translocations as an abnormal pairing configuration in the form of a ring or chain of four chromosomes. Actually, Koller (1944) had already used metaphase and late prophase stages of the first meiotic division to obtain critical confirmation for the existence of reciprocal translocations in the mouse, but the techniques that had to be used at the time would normally not be used for routine examinations. Recently, it has been found that by employing a technique that incorporates the use of hypotonic treatment of testis tubules followed by a routine for rapid screening of the fixed and stained material, one can find large numbers of meiotic division I figures suitable for chromosome analysis (Welshons, Gibson, and Scandlyn, 1962).

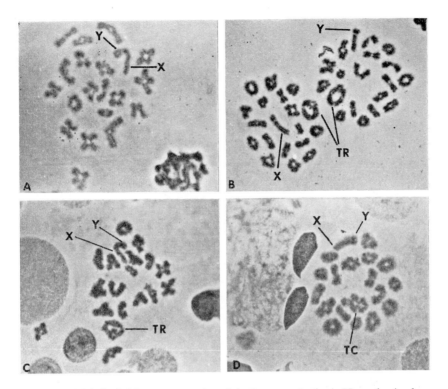

FIG. 1. Meiotic divisions, premetaphase I, in the mouse testis. A, Normal animal; B, two cells each showing a translocation ring; C and D, a reciprocal translocation of different origin than B, showing the ring (C) and chain (D). X and Y, sex chromosomes; TR, ring; TC, chain.

When this technique was used, it was found that in one of six semisterile males the examination of 53 meiotic figures failed to provide cytological confirmation for the presumed presence of a translocation. In the remaining five animals that were semisterile, a translocation configuration in the form of a ring or chain was rapidly and easily discerned (Fig. 1), although it is by no means true that an association of four chromosomes will occur in every meiotic cell of a translocation heterozygote. One of the five animals had produced exceptionally small litters and was found to be heterozygous for two independent translocations. No cytological abnormalities could be detected in the 30 remaining males.

In addition to these 36 F_1 males from which litter size data were procured, there were four males that proved to be completely sterile. One had testes of normal size, and upon cytological examination it was apparent the animal had a translocation. The three remaining males all had testes that were obviously reduced in size, and in two of them the germ cells proceeded at least as far as meiotic division I, but no evidence for a translocation could be found. The germ cells of the third animal did not progress to meiosis.

Besides the translocations produced in this experiment, some 15 different mutant stocks were obtained from W. L. Russell. Of these, seven were semisterile and cytological confirmation for a reciprocal translocation was obtained with little or no difficulty. In eight remaining cases there was neither cytological nor litter size indications favoring the presence of a translocation.

Apparently, translocations can be detected cytologically in the mouse with about the same accuracy as when a litter size criterion is used, and with surprisingly little effort. It is reasonable to suppose that by incorporating some sensible variations in technique, the meiotic chromosomes of many mammals can be made available for cytological purposes. For human cytogenetic studies, a satisfactory technique, even if limited to the male sex, could reveal the presence of a translocation in cases where a karyotype analysis of somatic chromosomes would certainly fail.

DETECTION AND USE OF CELL MARKER TRANSLOCATION

Since reciprocal translocations result from the interchange of two non-homologous chromosomes, it is sometimes possible to exchange pieces of such unequal lengths that one chromosome becomes noticeably longes or shorter than any chromosome ordinarily present. When this happens in the mouse the somatic karyotype becomes visibly different from that of a normal animal and the so-called "cell-marker" translocation is then a valuable tool for certain types of transplantation work. To appreciate their usefulness, it is only necessary to note that in cases where cells from such an animal are transplanted into a normal recipient, the donor cells can be visibly identified in the host at a subsequent mitotic division (Ford, Hamerton, Barnes and Loutit, 1956).

One of our translocations, produced and maintained in animals of the inbred $C3H/R_1$ strain, was a cell marker type in which one of the somatic chromoomes had been greatly reduced in size and was noticeably smaller than the smallest chromosome normally present (Fig. 2). It has been used in experiments which we were stimulated to do upon seeing some recent published results of Till and McCulloch (1961).

These investigators found that the intravenous injection of appropriate numbers of bose marrow cells into supralethally irradiated animals led

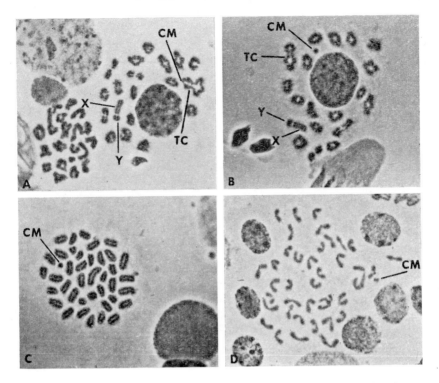

FIG. 2. The meiotic and mitotic appearance of the cell marker translocation. A, chain of four chromosomes (meiotic); B, a chain of three and the free cell marker chromosome (meiotic); C, mitotically dividing cell of the testis; D, female bone marrow, treated with colchicine. X and Y, sex chromosomes; TC, chain; CM, cell marker chromosome.

to the formation of proliferating cell colonies grossly observed as splenic nodules in the irradiated recipients. Additional observations and considerations made it seem likely that each nodule was derived from either a single cell or a very small number of cells.

In order to obtain additional information concerning the initial composition of these splenic nodules, supralethally irradiated recipients were injected intravenously with a mixed suspension of spleen cells from normal and cell marker animals. If, upon cytological examination of the mitotically dividing cells of a given nodule, one finds cells with the somatic chromosome constitution of the normal and cell marker type, it is obvious that these nodules are derived from more than one cell. On the other hand, if a given splenic nodule has the somatic karyotype of either the normal or cell-marker variety but never has both types of cells present simultaneously, the proliferating cells could be of clonal origin.

We have, to date, examined 27 splenic nodules. Of these the mitotically dividing cells in nine nodules had the normal chromosome constitution, and 18 had that of the cell marker. No nodules of mixed origin were observed. While these data are meager and cannot be accepted without certain reservations, they are, so far, consistent with the hypothesis that nodules are of clonal origin.

It should be noted, however, that even if the data were satisfactorily voluminous, they could not prove nodular origin from a single cell, although to find mixed types would certainly prove a multiple origin. This is so for the following reason: The spleen cells injected into irradiated recipients are in a mixed suspension, but it does not follow that the suspension consists only of single isolated cells. The injected suspension could have in it clumps of two or more that have maintained their original association. If these clumps that never have existed as isolated cells are primarily responsible for nodule formation, the proliferating cells later examined cytologically would still be all of one type or the other, never both.

Following a suggestion by D. L. Lindsley in this laboratory, a similar experiment can be designed which should neatly overcome the difficulty. One first produces a chimera whose hematopoietic tissues consist of cells originally derived from a mixture of normal and cell marker-bearing cells, and the chimera is subsequently used as the source of injected spleen or bone marrow. If nodules in irradiated recipients are derived from two or more cells that have not been isolated in suspension, the unit of proliferating cells will be composed both of normal and cell marker types in a proportion of cases; if the origin is from a single cell, a nodule will always be of one or the other type.

THE MALE-DETERMINING CAPACITY OF THE Y CHROMOSOME

The discovery of the male-determining capacity of the Y was virtually simultaneous in man and mouse. It is interesting to note, however, that while the conclusion concerning the Y chromosome is identical for both species, the initial, pertinent observations and subsequent paths of investigation were interestingly different in the two species.

Events culminating in the proof of the male-determining capacity of the Y chromosome in man began with the discovery of sex chromatin in the motor neurons of the cat (Barr and Bertram, 1949), and the subsequent demonstration of its presence in human tissues. The normal human male is sex chromatin-negative while the female is positive; however, some striking exceptions to this rule were soon discovered. For example, aberrant males having a series of abnormalities referred to as Klinefelter's syndrome were frequently found to be sex chromatin-positive, and some abnormal females having the manifestations of Turner's syndrome were shown to be sex chromatin-negative.

About the same time, significant advances in tissue culture and cytological technique led to the discovery that the somatic chromosome number in man was 46, instead of 48 (Tjio and Levan, 1956). With the superior techniques and additional knowledge subsequently obtained, it was soon discovered that the sex chromatin-positive Klinefelter's male had a total of 47 chromosomes. The chromosome complement included a Y, and an additional chromosome in the size range of the X (Jacobs and Strong, 1959). The Turner's female, sex chromatin-negative, had only 45 chromosomes, and the missing element was apparently an X (Ford, Jones, Polani, de Almeida and Briggs, 1959). Hence, from the cytological information, one could conclude that the Y chromosome was male-determining — the addition of a Y to the chromosome complement of the XO Turner's female with 45 would yield a normal male with 46, the identical addition to a normal female with 46 in an XXY Klinefelter's male having 47.

While the male-determining capacity of the Y chromosome in man could be demonstrated by cytological observations alone, it was genetic evidence in mice that first suggested the Y had this capacity. Two differences between man and mouse were primarily responsible for the genetic approach. First of all, the XO female mouse is fertile, whereas the human counterpart is sterile like the XXY in both species. Secondly, the XO and XXY equivalents of Turner's and Klinefelter's syndrome in mice are not so abnormal in appearance as to attract attention.

Since, as ultimately shown, the XO mouse is fertile, the clue to their hemizygous condition was obtained from genetic experiments in which it was noted that some females bred as if they had but one X chromosome (Russell, Russell and Gower, 1959; Welshons and Russell, 1959). Furthermore, the use of sex-linked markers in appropriate crosses made it possible to pick out the specific animals that were XO since, otherwise, XO and XX are grossly indistinguishable. All that remained was to verify the genetic evidence by a somatic chromosome count, for if the females were truly XO, they were deficient for an X chromosome, and the total count would be one less than the normal number of 40. When the cytology was completed, their XO nature was confirmed (Welshons and Russell, 1959).

A combination of genetics and cytology was also required to discover the XXY mouse, which was needed to make the man-to-mouse comparison more nearly perfect. Detection was based on the fact that some sex-linked mutants and translocations involving the X and an autosome have a phenotype that is normally seen only in a heterozygous female. If one were to obtain a male animal having the heterozygous phenotype, it would suggest the presence of two X chromosomes instead of the normal complement of one. Since the two-X condition is female, one would assume that "maleness" was due to the addition of a Y, and, cytologically, this animal should have an extra chromosome yielding a count of 41, rather than 40. Almost simultaneously two exceptional males were detected by genetic means in different laboratories and proved cytologically to be XXY (Cattanach, 1961; Russell and Chu, 1961). This completed the man-to-mouse comparison.

THE MALE ANTIGEN IN MICE

It is quite impossible to consider the strong male-determining capacity of the Y chromosome and not become at least a little bit curious about the male antigen in mice. It has been discovered within relatively recent times that female mice of certain inbred strains will reject skin transplants from isologous males (Eichwald and Silmser, 1955; Eichwald, Silmser and Wheeler, 1957). However, there is considerable strain differences in this response of female anti-male. In the extreme cases females of some strains virtually never reject, while in other strains the female regularly rejects the male transplants. Between these extremes, some strains of females reject in an unpredictable manner.

In the normal situation, the inheritance of maleness, i.e. Y chromosome, exactly parallels that of the male antigen; consequently, one is tempted to conclude at first that the male antigen is, in fact, a Y-chromosome antigen. Males certainly differ from females in that they possess a Y, but they also differ by having one X chromosome rather than two (Fox, 1958). This latter difference could be responsible for the appearance of antigen in the male sex. For example, the antigenic locus could be autosomal, always present homozygously in both sexes, but functionally suppressed in the presence of the two X chromosomes of the female.

The problem of whether or not the male antigen is a Y antigen can be resolved by using animals with abnormal chromosome constitutions. If the determination of male antigen depends upon the presence of a Y chromosome rather than the hemizygous X condition, XO females, similar to a male in that they have a single X but differing in that they lack a Y, will not posses the antigen. On the other hand, if the male antigen is the Y antigen, it presumably could be detected in an XXY male having both a Y and the two X chromosomes of the normal female.

Experiments utilizing mice with exceptional chromosome constitution were performed, but a spleen cell transfer method was utilized instead of the familiar skin transplantation technique. This method was described earlier by Celada and Makinodan (1961) and subsequently applied to the investigation of a hybrid anti-parent immunological reaction (Celada and Welshons, 1962). The technique was well-suited to these experiments since it allowed the accumulation of maximum data from a minimum number of XO and XXY noninbred mice.

The results can be briefly stated: XX and XXY animals differ antigenically, whereas XX and XO do not. It can be inferred that the male antigen is a Y antigen, i.e. the presence of a Y chromosome rather than the single-X condition is required for antigen production (Celada and Welshons, 1963).

Since there is no antigenic difference between XO and XX animals, our experiments imply that an XO female will reject the skin graft of a male, although the data were not obtained in this way. It is interesting to note that in the human species such an experiment has been performed and the skin graft was accepted. Turpin, Lejeune, Lafourcade, Chigot and Salmon (1961) discovered a case of monozygotic twins in which one individual was an XO female (Turner's syndrome), the other a normal male. Reciprocal transplants between the "isologous" individuals were successful (Turpin et al., 1961; Lejeune and Turpin, 1961). Several interpretations of what appears to be a discordant finding can be made at the moment. Two that come to mind immediately are as follows: (1) as in some strains of mice, the human female will not reject the isologous male tissue, (2) the human XO female twin failed to reject the male because a state of tolerance had been induced.

As is often the case, the successful culmination of one problem simply suggests another. For example, we found that the XX animal does not reject the XO, but both are females; the XX rejects the XXY but the recipient is female while the donor is male. In short, if we knew absolutely nothing about the chromosomal constitutions of the exceptional animals, we would have obtained an expected result; hence, one wonders if the determination of male or Y antigen is dependent upon the prior differentiation of male sex. Theoretically, the male sex-determining factor(s) and factor(s) reponsible for antigen production could be identical. Antigen production could be a pleiotropic effect of genetic loci responsible for male sexual differentiation.

A very simple but impossible experiment to perform at the moment could provide the answer. We ask the question, will a normal XX female reject the tissues of an XY "female"? If it does, antigen determination is independent of sexual differentiation since both are females. But since an XY "female" represents an unknown combination of sex and sex chromosomes in mice, the answer must be obtained in some alternative way.

Hauschka, Grinnell, Meagher and Amos (1959) have obtained data indicating that in nonreactive strains, the female mice possess the antigen, hence, cannot reject the male tissue because of the consequent loss of antigenic difference between the sexes. They postulate that this has come about by the insertion of an appropriate piece of the Y chromosome into one of the autosomes (Hauschka, Meagher and Holdridge, 1962). If female mice can have the "male" antigen, it must follow that antigen determination is independent of sexual differentiation. However, other data, just as convincing, indicate that the results of Hauschka *et al.* (1962) cannot be generalized. Billingham and Silvers (1960), showed that in their nonreactive strain, the males possessed the antigen although the females failed to reject the transplant. Then, using the same experimental criterion (induction of tolerance), they found it impossible to demonstrate the presence of antigen in the nonreactive females. Evidently, the final answer to this question must await further experimentation.

It is apparent from the foregoing discussion that even though, by many criteria, the mouse is not a particularly good organism for genetic research, the interest in mammalian genetics will cause an expansion of its use. Already the classical habit of combining cytology and genetics has enabled investigators to gain information that would be difficult, if not impossible, to obtain by direct genetic means. As demonstrated here, the immunological discipline combined with cytogenetics can be expected to play an increasingly important role in the endeavor to obtain more complete information from the mouse.

ACKNOWLEDGEMENTS

The author would like to thank W. L. and L. B. Russell for the mouse stocks used in these experiments. The able assistance of Miss B. J. Scandlyn was greatly appreciated.

REFERENCES

BARR, M. L. and BERTRAM, E. G., 1949, A morphological distinction between neurones of the male and female, and the behavior of the nucleolar satellite during accelerated nucleoprotein synthesis. *Nature*, **163**, 676–677.

BILLINGHAM, R. E. and SILVERS, W. K., 1960, Studies on the tolerance of the Y chromosome antigen in mice. *J. Immunol.* **85**, 14–26.

CATTANACH, B. M., 1961, XXY mice. *Genet. Res.* **2**, 156–158.

CELADA, F. and MAKINODAN, T., 1961, A new model to study hematopoietic transplantation antigens. *J. Immunol.* **86**, 638–645.

CELADA, F. and WELSHONS, W. J., 1962, Demonstration of F_1 hybrid anti-parent immunological reaction. *Proc. Natl. Acad. Sci. U.S.* **48**, 326–331.

CELADA, F. and WELSHONS, W. J., 1963, An immunogenetic analysis of the male antigen in mice utilizing animals with an exceptional chromosome constitution. *Genetics*, **48**, (in press).

EICHWALD, E. J. and SILMSER, C. R., 1955, *Skin Transplant. Bull.* **2**, 148–149.

EICHWALD, E. J., SILMSER, C. R. and WHEELER, N., 1957, The genetics of skin grafting. *Ann. N. Y. Acad. Sci.* **64**, 737–740.

FORD, C. E., HAMERTON, J. L., BARNES, D. W. H. and LOUTIT, J. F., 1956, Cytological identification of radiation-chimeras. *Nature*, **177**, 452–454.

FORD, C. E., JONES, K. W., POLANI, P. E., DE ALMEIDA, J. C. and BRIGGS, J. H., 1959, A sex-chromosome anomaly in a case of gonadal dysgenesis (Turner's syndrome). *Lancet*, **I**, 711–713.

FOX, A. S., 1958, Genetics of tissue specificity. *Ann. N. Y. Acad. Sci.* **73**, 611–634.

HAUSCHKA, T. S., GRINNELL, S. T., MEAGHER, M. and AMOS, D. B., 1959, Sex-linked incompatability of male skin and primary tumors transplanted to isologous female mice. In *13th Annual Symposium on Fundamental Cancer Research*, pp. 271–294, The University of Texas M. D. Anderson Hospital and Tumor Institute, Houston.

HAUSCHKA, T. S., MEAGHER, S. T., and HOLDRIDGE, B. A., 1962, Autosomal translocation of the "male antigen" of mice and immunoselection against the Y-chromosome. In *Proceedings of the International Symposium on Tissue Transplantation*, pp. 25–36, University of Chile Press, Santiago.

JACOBS, P. A. and STRONG, J. A., 1959, A case of human intersexuality having a possible XXY sex-determining mechanism. *Nature*, **183**, 302–303.

KOLLER, P. C., 1944, Segmental interchange in mice. *Genetics*, **29**, 247–263.

LEJEUNE, J. and TURPIN, R., 1961, Détection chromosomique d'une mosäique artificielle humaine. *Compt. Rend.* **252**, 3148–3150.

RUSSELL, L. B. and CHU, E. H. Y., 1961, An XXY male in the mouse. *Proc. Natl. Acad. Sci. U.S.* **47**, 571–575.

RUSSELL, W. L., 1952, Mammalian radiation genetics. In *Symposium on Radiobiology*. (James L. Nickson, ed.), pp. 427–440. Sponsored by the National Research Council of the National Academy of Sciences, John Wiley and Sons.

RUSSELL, W. L., RUSSELL, L. B. and GOWER, J. S., 1959, Exceptional inheritance of sex-linked gene in the mouse explained in the basis that the X/O sex-chromosome constitution is female. *Proc. Natl. Acad. Sci. U. S.* **45**, 554–560.

TILL, J. E. and McCULLOCH, E. A., 1961, A direct measurement of the radiation sensitivity of normal mouse bone marrow cells. *Radiation Res.* **14**, 213–222.

TJIO, J. H., and LEVAN, A., 1956, The chromosome number of man. *Hereditas* **42**, 1–6.

TURPIN, R., LEJEUNE, J., LAFOURCADE, J., CHIGOT, P. L. and SALMON, C., 1961, Présomption de monozygotisme en dépit d'un dimorphisme sexuel: sujet masculin XY et sujet neutre haplo X. *Compt. Rend.* **252**, 2945–2946.

WELSHONS, W. J., GIBSON, B. H. and SCANDLYN, B. J., 1962, Slide processing for the examination of male mammalian meiotic chromosomes. *Stain Technol.* **37**, 1–5.

WELSHONS, W. J. and RUSSELL, L. B., 1959, The Y-chromosome as the bearer of male-determining factors in the mouse. *Proc. Natl. Acad. Sci. U. S.* **45**, 560–566.

CHROMOSOME STUDIES IN HEMOPOIETIC DISEASES AND IN ANOMALIES OF SEX DEVELOPMENT

C. BOTTURA

Medical School of Ribeirão Prêto, São Paulo, Brazil

IT IS THE purpose of this communication to report the results of cyto-genetic studies, performed in our laboratory, in patients with abnormal sex development and in cases of leukemia and multiple myeloma.

In all cases the chromosome analysis was carried out on bone marrow cells using a direct method.[5] A colchicine derivative (Colcemid–Ciba) was injected intravenously and bone marrow collected two hours after-wards.

The first case is a 9-year-old coloured girl who was referred to us because of abnormal sex development.[6] The physical examination was entirely negative except for the external genitals. They consisted of an enlarged phallus measuring about 4·5 cm in length without urethral meatus. It was bent downward by a web. Two skin folds with scrotal rugae concealed a vestibulum and when parted they disclosed a single orifice about 8 mm in diameter. Pubic hair was absent. Following the introduction of radio-opaque material through the perineal orifice, X-ray examination disclosed a small vagina, a rudimentary uterus and permeable tubes. The urethra opened at the roof of the vagina.

Exploratory laparotomy showed a rudimentary uterus and filiform Fallopian tubes. No gonad was found on the left side of the pelvis. On the right side, at a position normally occupied by the ovary, there was a white structure, approximately 1 cm long, which was removed for examination. Its histological appearance was that of an immature testis, in which no later phases than spermatogonia could be identified.

The sex chromatin was negative in cells from oral smears, abdominal and phallus skin, smooth muscle and in cells within the seminiferous tubules. No drumsticks were seen in 600 neutrophil leukocytes. The chromosomes of 55 cells were counted. Of these, 51 contained 45 chromosomes and 4 small acrocentrics were present. In the 6-12-X group there were only

15 chromosomes. One cell with 47 and 3 cells with 46 chromosomes which did not show a constant pattern were considered as being the result of technical error. The karyotype of this patient was thought to be of the 45/XO type.

The second patient, a 25-year-old girl, came to the clinic complaining of lack of menses. She had always been slow in growing. At school she was slow and completed elementary studies at 19.

On physical examination, a number of nevi were visible on the face. Lack of breast development. Hypotrophic nipples widely separated. Kyphosis of the spine. External genitals examination showed an enlarged clitoris, about 1·5 cm in length. Infantile labia minora and separated hymenal and urethral openings.

Bucal smear chromatin was negative. In peripheral blood no drumsticks were seen in 800 neutrophil leukocytes. Urinary gonadotropin: 80 M. U. in 24 hr. 17 KS: 8·91 mg in 24 hr. Bone age: 15 years.

On laparotomy, a small uterus was found and the tubes were thin and long. The gonads, protruding slightly into the abdominal cavity, lay parallel to the mesosalpinx. On the gonadal surface, small pinhead-sized yellow points were seen. Microscopic examination showed that these yellow points were large Leydig cells nests bulging on the surface of the left gonad and immediately under the cortical ovary-like stroma in the right gonad. Mesonephric tubular structures were seen in the left gonad.

The chromosomes of 30 metaphases were counted. 27 showed 45 chromosomes and only four small acrocentrics were seen. Three cells had less than 44 chromosomes and were interpreted as artefacts. The karyotype of this patient was considered as being of the 45/XO type.

The third patient is a 15-year-old girl showing short stature, mental retardation, amenorrhoea, lack of breast development, without any other somatic anomalies. The external genitalia were infantile. Cells of bucal mucosa and skin were chromatin-negative. No drumsticks were seen in 800 neutrophil leukocytes. Urinary gonadotropin: 320 M.U. in 24 hr. 17 KS: 1·4 mg in 24 hr.

Laparotomy revealed infantile uterus and tubes, and the gonads were similar to those seen in Turner's syndrome. At microscopic examination they were composed of wavy connective tissue and clusters of epithelial cells which were interpreted as Leydig cells. 45 metaphases were analysed and all showed 45 chromosomes and XO-sex chromosome complement.

According to the type of gonad present, these 3 cases are variants of male pseudohermaphroditism.[14] All of them showed 45 chromosomes and XO-sex chromosome constitution on bone marrow cells. These findings suggest that male pseudohermaphrodites may show different karyotype from that expected.[1]

In fact, a few patients with gonads containing medullary structures and without a demonstrable Y chromosome have been described. These include several cases of true hermaphroditism and a male pseudohermaphrodite,[11] all showing a female sex-chromosome constitution. Two very similar cases of male pseudohermaphroditism disclosed an XO sex-chromosome complement.[2,4] Two other examples of this syndrome showed 45 chromosomes plus a fragment which might be a deleted Y.[9,13] However, in all these cases, a mosaic could not be excluded since only one or two tissues were examined.

In the three cases reported the chromosome studies were carried out only on bone marrow cells. Thus, mosaic states of the types XO/XY[3,10] or XO/XY/XX[12] cannot be discarded. Furthermore, a possible translocation of the whole or part of the Y on to another chromosome would be very difficult to detect cytologically.

Further chromosome studies in more than one tissue, specially in testis, in similar cases may clarify the role played by the Y chromosome in the differentiation of the male gonad.

Concerning the hemopoietic diseases, we have studied the chromosomes of bone marrow cells in 8 cases of leukemia and in four cases of multiple myeloma. Of the leukemia patients, 1 was of the chronic myeloid type and 7 were acute cases.

In 40 cells counted in the patient with chronic myeloid leukemia, 46 chromosomes were present, and one minute small acrocentric, the Ph^1, could be distinguished in 87·5 per cent of the cells (Fig. 1).

All 7 acute cases were studied before treatment and no abnormalities were seen in 6. In the only patient who showed an abnormal karyotype before treatment, the chromosome study was made just before death.[8] He showed a high degree of hyperdiploidism. The chromosome number ranged from 45 to 54, with a modal number of 53. However, we could not detect any structural abnormalities. The chromosomes in excess belonged to the well-known groups (long, medium length and short) and each cell contained variable numbers of them. Polyploid cells were seen and they contained chromosome numbers different from multiples of the normal haploid complement. We considered these chromosome alterations as secondary in nature and not of etiological significance.

In one patient, the chromosomes were studied twice during the evolution of the disease.[7] Before treatment, the analysis of 20 cells showed the normal number of 46 without structural abnormalities. However, important alterations of the karyotype were seen in a second analysis while the patient was under treatment with 6-mercaptopurine. From a total of 67 cells counted, 27 had 46 chromosomes without structural abnormalities and they were considered as normal bone marrow cells in mitosis. Of the remaining cells,

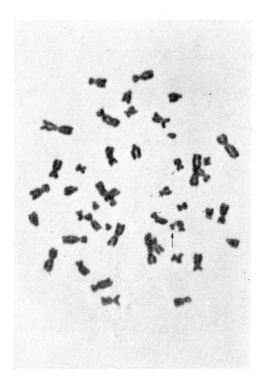

FIG. 1. Metaphase of bone-marrow cell from a case of chronic myeloid leukemia. Ph[1] chromosome arrowed.

32 had 44 and 8 had 43 chromosomes. The majority of these aneuploid cells showed in addition a small fragment and a few had two fragments. In view of the number of leukemic cells in mitosis present in bone marrow smears, this abnormal karyotype was considered as belonging to the leukemic cells. Two possibilities must be considered to account for this abnormal karyotype. Firstly, as they were not present at an early stage of the disease, the abnormalities could have arisen during the course of the leukemic process. Secondly, the chromosome abnormalities observed could be the result of the damaging effects of 6-mercaptopurine and it would suggest that the leukemic cells are more sensitive to the effects of the antimetabolite. In both

circumstances, the chromosome abnormalities would be of secondary nature and not of primary etiological significance.

The other striking finding in this case was the high incidence of cells showing the feature of endoreduplication. During these studies, 61 hypo-

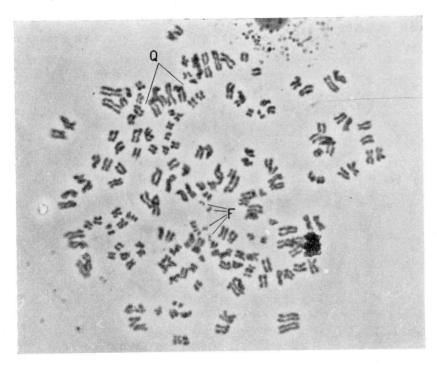

FIG. 2. Metaphase of a hypo-octoploid cell showing the feature of repeated endore-duplication. Q — Quadruplo-chromosome. F — Fragments.

tetraploid cells were seen which showed 44 diplochromosomes and in some two fragments could be seen. Noteworthy was the observation of a hypo-octoploid cell with 176 chromosomes plus 4 fragments (Fig. 2). The presence of quartets (quadruplo-chromosomes) was obvious and the figure was inter-preted as an example of repeated endoreduplication.

In this case, the endoreduplication seems to be restricted to the leukemic cells. However, we cannot predict whether the phenomenon has any rela-tion to the leukemic process or is an occurrence brought about by 6-merc-aptopurine therapy. In skin cultures, the phenomenon tends to increase with transfers. Since our observations were performed *in vivo* by a direct method, culture conditions were excluded.

We have also studied four cases of multiple myeloma. No chromosome abnormalities were detected in three cases showing the electrophoretic patterns of the types beta, gamma and M (abnormal fraction with mobility between beta and gamma). Of course, we had no evidence that the metaphases analysed represented actually mitotic myeloma cells. They might well be normal bone-marrow cells in mitosis.

The fourth case was a 61-year-old male with serum electrophoretic pattern of the alpha-2 type. The clinical and laboratorial diagnosis of multiple myeloma was later confirmed at postmortem examination. 70 metaphases were counted, 23 having 46 chromosomes and 47 having 45. The cells with 46 chromosomes had apparently normal karyotype and were considered as normal erythroblasts in mitosis. In all cells with 45 chromosomes, one small acrocentric chromosome was missing which, after careful analysis, was identified as a small acrocentric autosome. However, because of overcontraction due to an excess of colchicine effect, it was impossible to establish whether the missing chromosome belonged either to pair 21 or 22. There was also no evidence towards a translocation involving the small autosome or part of it with another chromosome.

The abnormality observed may be secondary to the evolution of the disease. However, if detected in other cases of the disease, our finding would be of interest on several points. Firstly, it suggests the genetic nature of multiple myeloma. Secondly, it would be another hemopoietic disease in which a small acrocentric autosome is involved, the other one being chronic myeloid leukemia. Finally, there seems to be an increased tendency towards acute leukemia in mongolism, which is a trisomic state for one small acrocentric autosome. These observations suggest that a pathogenetic interrelation may occur in these apparently so different diseases.

REFERENCES

1. ALEXANDER, D. S. and FERGUSON-SMITH, M. A., Chromosomal studies in some variants of male pseudohermaphroditism. *Pediatrics*, **28**, 758–763, 1961.
2. ATKINS, L. and ENGEL, E., Absence of the Y chromosome (XO sex-chromosome constitution) in a human intersex with an extra-abdominal testis. *Lancet*, **2**, 20–23, 1962.
3. BERGADA, C., CLEVELAND, W. W., JONES, H. W. JR. and WILKINS, L., Gonadal histology in patients with male pseudohermaphroditism and atypical gonadal dysgenesis: relation to theories of sex differentiation. *Acta Endocr.* **40**, 493–520, 1962.
4. BLOISE, W., ASSIS, L. M. DE, BOTTURA, C. and FERRARI, I., Gonadal dysgenesis (Turner's syndrome) with male phenotype and XO chromosomal constitution. *Lancet*, **2**, 1059–1060, 1960.
5. BOTTURA, C. and FERRARI, I., A simplified method for the study of chromosomes in man. *Nature*, **186**, 904–905, 1960.
6. BOTTURA, C. and FERRARI, I., Male pseudohermaphroditism with XO chromosomal constitution on bone marrow cells. *Brit. Med. J.*, in press.

7. BOTTURA, C. and FERRARI, I., Endoreduplication in acute leukemia. *Blood*, in press.
8. BOTTURA, C., FERRARI, I. and VEIGA, A. A., Caryotype anormal dans la leucémie aigue. *Acta Haematol.* **26**, 44–49, 1961.
9. CONEN, P. E., BAILEY, J. D., ALLEMANG, W. H., THOMPSON, D. W. and EZRIN, C., A probable partial deletion of the Y chromosome in an intersex patient. *Lancet*, **2**, 294–295, 1961.
10. FERRIER, P., GARTLER, S. M., WAXMAN, S. H. and SHEPARD, T., Abnormal sexual development associated with sex chromosome mosaicism. *Pediatrics*, **29**, 703–713, 1962.
11. SHAH, P. N., NAIK, S. N., MAHAJAN, D. K., PAYMASTER, J. C., DAVE, M. J. and TIWARI, R., Male pseudohermaphroditism with female chromosomal complement. *J. Clin. Endocrinol. and Metab.* **21**, 727–731, 1961; *Brit. Med. J.* **2**, 474–477, 1961.
12. SCHUSTER, J. and MOTULSKY, A. G., Exceptional sex-chromatin in male pseudo-hermaphroditism with XX/XY/XO mosaicism. *Lancet*, **1**, 1074–1075, 1962.
13. VAHARU, T., PATTON, R. G., VOORHESS, M. L. and GARDNER, L. I., Gonadal dysplasia and enlarged phallus in a girl with 45 chromosomes plus "fragment". *Lancet*, **1**, 1351, 1961.
14. WILKINS, L., Abnormalities of sex differentiation. Classification, diagnosis, selection of rearing and treatment. *Pediatrics*, **26**, 846–857, 1960.

THE SEX CHROMATIN: ITS ORIGIN
AND NATURE*

S. Ohno†

Department of Biology, City of Hope Medical Center, Duarte, California, U.S.A.

Since 1949 when Barr and Bertram first reported the presence of a female-specific chromocenter in the nerve cell nuclei of the cat, sexual dimorphism of somatic interphase nuclei has been found in many mammalian species, including man. Identification of nuclear sex by the presence or absence of the sex chromatin body in certain cells soon found wide clinical application and stimulated a vast amount of research in the field of human sexual anomalies.

The origin and nature of the sex chromatin body itself, however, remained obscure until 1959 when our study on mitotic figures of regenerating rat liver revealed that it represents one entire condensed X-chromosome (Ohno et al., 1959). Thus was uncovered the unique ambivalent nature of the mammalian X-chromosome.

For many years, the mammalian X was thought to be similar to the X-chromosome of *Drosophila melanogaster*, which is composed of two distinct areas: a genetically-active euchromatic region, and a heterochromatic region which invariably forms a chromocenter (Heitz, 1933; Kaufmann, 1934). That the situation in many mammalian species is quite different was shown by a series of studies in our laboratory.

We were able to conclude that the mammalian X is not divided into heterochromatic and euchromatic regions, but rather that each X has the inherent capacity to perform in two distinctly different ways. In the somatic cells of the normal XY male, the X is indistinguishable from the euchromatic autosomes, remaining elongated from telophase to the next prophase. In the female diploid nucleus, however, the two X-chromosomes act oppo-

* This work was supported in part by grant C-5138 from the National Cancer Institute, U.S. Public Health Service, and grant C-17601 from the National Science Foundation.

†The author gratefully acknowledges a travel grant from the National Science Foundation which permitted him to present this paper before the International Symposium on Mammalian Tissue Culture and Cytology held in São Paulo, Brazil, in 1962. The author also wishes to express appreciation for the editorial assistance of Patricia A. Ray.

sitely to each other: one always behaves as do the autosomes (or the X in male cells), while the other always behaves as though made entirely of heterochromatin, condensing precociously and conspicuously to form the interphase chromocenter known as the Barr sex chromatin body.

Ordinarily, two homologues within the same nucleus are considered to function synchronously. When it became obvious that the two X-chromosomes in female somatic cells are exceptions to this rule, we devoted considerable attention to learning what we could of this phenomenon. The behavior pattern of the mammalian X-chromosome as seen under the microscope will be described in some detail.

1. *Behavior of the Sex Chromosomes in Germ Cells*

In spermatocytes, the entire X as well as the Y appears heavily condensed from leptotene of first meiosis to the end of second meiosis (Ohno *et al.* 1958). This contrasts sharply with the situation in oöcytes, in which both of the two X-chromosomes remain fine and elongated, and behave much like the autosomes (Ohno *et al.*, 1961). Figure 1 shows a pachytene nucleus from a spermatocyte of the rat, *Rattus norvegicus*, with an arrow indicating the condensed form assumed by the XY bivalent. The autosomal bivalents demonstrate the fine banding pattern characteristic of this stage. In Fig. 2, an oöcyte at the same stage from the same species contains an XX bivalent quite similar in appearance to the 20 autosomal bivalents in the same nucleus.

Precocious condensation of the sex chromosomes throughout meiosis in male germ cells appears to preclude pairing between the female-determining X and the male-determining Y. If interstitial chiasmata were to form between the X and the Y, the resulting linkage in most species would be disastrous to the XY-XX sex-determining mechanism (Ohno and Weiler, 1961). At diplotene in most mammalian species, including the mouse (Fig. 3) and man (Fig. 4), the X and Y are invariably joined end-to-end. Such a form of association preserves the individual integrity of both the X and the Y, while assuring their unfailing segregation from each other at first meiotic anaphase.

In the homogametic female, however, the two homologous sex chromosomes do pair, and the unrestricted exchange of genetic materials between them leaves unaltered the female-determining capacity of either X. Only in the heterogametic male did there exist the phylogenic need to prevent linkage between the two sex-determining elements during meiosis. This need can be regarded as an underlying cause of the acquisition by the X of its unique ambivalent nature.

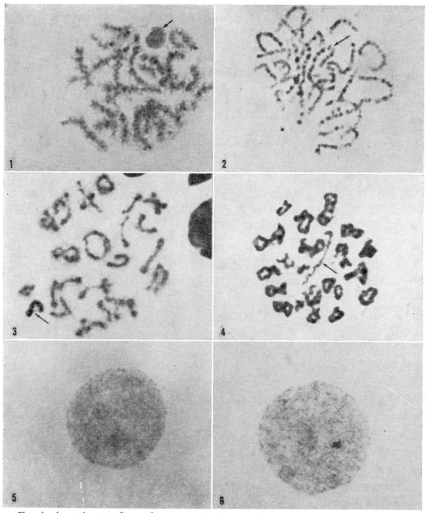

FIG. 1. A pachytene figure from a spermatocyte of a male rat, *Rattus norvegicus*. An arrow indicates the sex vesicle containing the XY bivalent.

FIG. 2. A pachytene figure from an oöcyte of a newborn female rat. An arrow indicates the isopycnotic XX bivalent.

FIG. 3. A late diplotene figure from a mouse spermatocyte. The X and Y in characteristic end-to-end association stand out from the autosomal bivalents by virtue of positive heteropycnosis. The XY bivalent is indicated by an arrow.

FIG. 4. A diakinesis metaphase figure from a human spermatocyte. The X and Y in end-to-end association is indicated by an arrow

FIG. 5. A male interphase nucleus from a liver parenchymal cell of the rat.

FIG. 6. The sex chromatin body is conspicuous in a female interphase nucleus from a liver parenchymal cell of the rat.

All the photomicrographs were taken by Leitz Panphoto (lenses used: 90 × 10).

2. The Single-chromosome Derivation of the Barr Sex Chromatin Body

Adult liver parenchymal cells in *Rattus norvegicus* were investigated cyto-logically, with partial hepatectomy used to induce mitotic activity.

A diploid interphase nucleus of the male is shown in Fig. 5. In the female interphase nucleus shown in Fig. 6, the sex chromatin body is conspicuous. In the male prophase figures examined, all 42 chromosomes in each nucleus were in a fine, thread-like state (Fig. 7), while each female prophase figure contained one medium-sized chromosome heavily condensed along its entire length (Fig. 8).

Obviously in male somatic cells the X and great portions of all the auto-somes remain extremely extended from telophase to next prophase, forming at interphase a fine network of chromatin. This is not the case in female somatic cells. In view of the fact that the X of this species condenses preco-ciously during male meiosis, the similarly condensed chromosome seen in female somatic prophase figures was interpreted to be one of the two Xs. Thus it became quite clear that the Barr sex chromatin body actually repre-sents the entire length of a single chromosome, presumably the X (Ohno *et al.*, 1959).

Subsequent studies were made of male and female somatic prophase figures of many other mammalian species, including man (Ohno and Makino, 1961). The exclusive occurrence in the female of a single condensed chromosome was noted in every instance.

It was of interest to find that the condensed X was as readily demonstrable in female prophase figures of the mouse (Tjio and Ostergren, 1958; Ohno and Hauschka, 1960) as in other mammals studied. In *Mus musculus*, sexual dimorphism of somatic interphase nuclei is obscured by the occurrence of several coarse chromocenters in both sexes (Moore and Barr, 1953). Since each autosome of the mouse carries a small block of heterochromatin adjacent to its kinetochore (Ohno *et al.*, 1957) and these tend to aggregate, chromocenters are formed which closely approximate in size the Barr sex chromatin body.

At this point, the behavior pattern of the Y-chromosome deserves brief mention. While in most mammalian species the Y appears to manifest positive heteropycnosis in somatic cells, a Y-chromocenter as such is usually unrecognizable because of its extreme smallness. Only in the opossum has the condensed Y been identified as the male sex chromatin body (Graham and Barr, 1959; Ohno *et al.*, 1960).

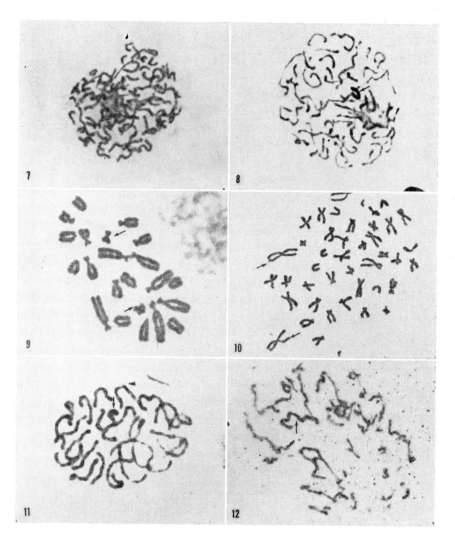

FIG. 7. Male somatic prophase figure recovered from regenerating rat liver.
FIG. 8. An arrow indicates the heteropycnotic X of the female somatic prophase nucleus from regenerating rat liver.
FIG. 9. Somatic metaphase figure of the female opossum, *Didelphys virginiana* (2n=22). Two X-chromosomes, indicated by arrows, constitute the smallest pair.
FIG. 10. Somatic metaphase figure of the female golden hamster, *Mesocricetus auratus* (2n = 44). The largest two chromosomes are labeled with arrows, and are the pair of X-chromosomes.
FIG. 11. Female prophase figure of the opossum recovered from an ovarian follicle. The condensed X is indicated.
FIG. 12. Prophase figure of the female golden hamster recovered from regenerating liver. An arrow indicates the X precociously condensed along its entire length.

3. *Positive Identification of the Condensed Chromosome seen at Female Somatic Prophase as an X*

In most of the well-studied mammalian species such as man, rats, and mice, the X-chromosome is one of a group of medium-sized elements which are similar morphologically.Thus it can only be inferred that the single condensed chromosome seen in female somatic prophase figures is an X-chromosome.

Fortunately, the chromosome complements of the opossum and the golden hamster lend themselves more readily to the task of identifying the elements in question. As shown in Fig. 9, the X-chromosome of *Didelphys virginiana* of the order *Marsupialia* is smaller than the smallest autosome (Shaver, 1962). As shown in Fig. 10, the X-chromosome of *Mesocricetus auratus* of the order *Rodentia* is by far the largest element in the complement (Awa *et al.*, 1959). The situation at somatic prophase in the females of these two species is shown in Figs. 11 and 12. The condensed chromosome in Fig. 11 is unmistakably one of the smallest in the complement while that in Fig. 12 is equally certain to be one of the largest. Thus our observations on *Didelphys virginiana* (Ohno *et al.* 1960) and *Mesocricetus auratus* (Ohno and Weiler, 1961) confirmed beyond a reasonable doubt our assumption that the condensed chromosome seen in female somatic cells is a single X-chromosome in its entirety. We reached the general conclusion that in mammalian female somatic cells, one of the two X's behaves as though made completely of euchromatin, remaining extremely extended during interphase, while the other X manifests positive heteropycnosis along its entire length, forming a chromocenter at interphase.

4. *Ontogeny of X-chromosome Behavior*

Sex chromatin studies on mammalian embryos at various stages of gestation have shown that female nuclei become sex-chromatin-positive at the onset of somatic differentiation. Austin and Amoroso (1957) studied 70 cat embryos ranging from the 2-cell stage to 20 days gestation. No sex chromatin was found in any of 26 morulae nor in three embryos of an earlier stage. But the imprint of sex was plain in the cell nuclei of 29 implanted embryos (15−20 days): 15 had the female chromatin pattern, 14 the male pattern. Similar findings on human embryos were reported by Parks (1957).

Over the years, we have made squash preparations from early embryos of mice, rats, and golden hamsters whenever the occasion presented itself. To date, not one of approximately 50 embryos recovered from Fallopian tubules was found to contain a condensed X-chromosome in its prophase

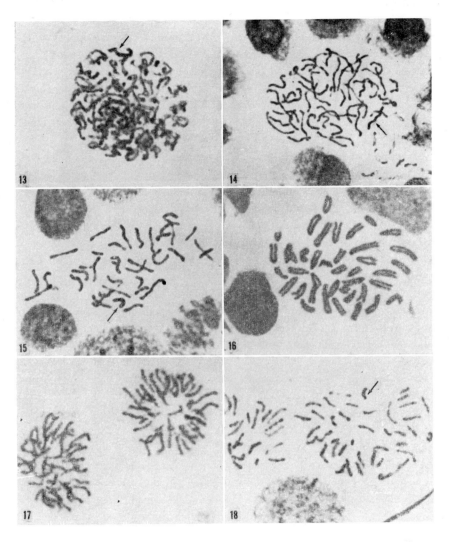

FIGS. 13 to 18 are from a female embryo of the mouse, *Mus musculus*. The arrow in Figs. 13, 14, 15, and 18 indicates the positively heteropycnotic X.

FIG. 13. An early prophase figure.

FIG. 14. A middle prophase figure.

FIG. 15. A late prophase figure.

FIG. 16. A full metaphase figure, in which all 40 chromosomes are equally condensed.

FIG. 17. An anaphase figure.

FIG. 18. One daughter nucleus of telophase and part of the other daughter nucleus.

nuclei. Conversely, all of the implanted embryos with an XX constitution, numbering perhaps 100, invariably contained a single condensed X in every prophase as well as telophase nucleus. Mitotic figures from such an XX mouse embryo are shown in Figs. 13–18. The condensed X is conspicuous in early prophase (Fig. 13) and midprophase (Fig. 14), as well as late prophase (Fig. 15). At metaphase (Fig. 16) and anaphase (Fig. 17), all 40 chromosomes appear equally condensed. However, at telophase (Fig. 18), the X-chromosome again becomes recognizable in each of the two daughter nuclei because of its heavy condensation.

Apparently the mammalian XX-zygote begins development with both X-chromosomes fully extended during interphase, but about the time of implantation, the decision is made quite suddenly that one of the two X's in every cell in the female embryo will manifest positive heteropycnosis.

Of particular interest here is the fact that female germ cells found in the ovary remained sex-chromatin-negative. Oögonial prophase figures of rats (Ohno et al., 1961) and man (Ohno et al., 1961, 1962) did not contain a heteropycnotic X, while follicular cell nuclei from the same fetal ovary invariably exhibited a condensed X. Since Witschi (1957) reported that primordial germ cells seen in the yolk sac of female human embryos were sex-chromatin-positive, germ cells may revert to the chromatin-negative state only after they complete migration to the cortex of the indifferent gonad.

5. *Autosomal Control over the Behavior of Individual X-chromosomes*

Recent studies of humans with abnormal sex chromosome constitutions such as XO, XXY, XXX, and even XXXY (Lancet editorial 1960) have shown that the autosomes exert some control over the behavior of individual X-chromosomes. The presence of a diploid set of autosomes (2A) in the complement apparently requires one X to behave as though composed of euchromatin, and remain isopycnotic while any number of additional X's become heteropycnotic. Thus two sex chromatin bodies are seen in somatic interphase nuclei of 2A-XXX individuals.

However, autosomal control appears to operate only at the time of embryo implantation, when the decision is made for an X to remain isopycnotic or become heteropycnotic. Once decided, this characteristic becomes fixed and irreversible.

Exhaustive studies on aneuploid male human tumors have been conducted by N. B. Atkin (personal communication). He found that while many such tumors were either hyperdiploid or hypotetraploid, the X-chromosomes never formed sex chromatin bodies. Since the X in the somatic cells of the normal male always elects at the time of implantation to behave like an auto-some, all three X's in the 2A-XXXY male tumor cell were incapable of forming a sex chromatin body since all were derived from a single isopycnotic X.

It seems likely that once the autosomes have provoked the X-chromosomes into differentiation very early in embryonic development, their control ends. Later changes in the ratio of autosomes to X-chromosomes have no effect on X-chromosome behavior.

6. *Dynamics of the Sex Chromatin Body during Interphase*

A condensed X-chromosome is seen in virtually every prophase as well as telophase figure of well-prepared squash preparations of female somatic cells, whether from early embryos or from adult ovaries and regenerating liver. Obviously every female somatic cell enters into and emerges from every interphase with one X-chromosome heavily condensed. It follows then that in a multiplying female cell population, two classes of sex chromatin bodies should be found in interphase nuclei. Before chromosome replica-tion, the mass would correspond to the heteropycnotic X of telophase; afterward, to the condensed X of prophase.

There are indications that only after the autosomes and the isopycnotic X have replicated themselves does the heteropycnotic X do so, usually just before the end of interphase (Lima-de-Faria, 1959; Taylor, 1960; German, 1962). Thus even in a rapidly growing cell population, only a small portion of interphase nuclei are likely to contain sex chromatin bodies similar in mass to the condensed X at prophase. In a static population, such as adult neurons, all sex chromatin bodies should be uniformly equivalent in mass to the condensed X at telophase.

While at H. P. Klinger's laboratory at the University of Basel in the sum-mer of 1961, I had the good fortune to study his excellent Feulgen-stained preparations of male and female human embryonic cells grown in a single layer on a coverslip. Even in preparations of such superior quality, none of the male interphase nuclei contained a sex chromatin body. In the female cells, however, the presence of the sex chromatin body was unmistakable in no less than 90 per cent of the interphase nuclei, often in as many as 97 per cent, even though the cells were dividing about every 48 hr. Since from 3 to 10 per cent of the female nuclei were genuinely sex-chromatin-negative, it is tempting to speculate that the condensed X might be extend-ing itself briefly during replication, despite the lack of any evidence to support this notion. This speculation raises in turn the question of whether every female nucleus in a static cell population contains a sex chromatin body. So far as I know, a 100 per cent frequency of the sex chromatin body has not been found in any type of somatic cells from any mammalian species, which of course may indicate no more than the limitations of our present techniques.

7. *Nucleolus-organizing Activity of the Condensed X*

On the basis of the series of cytological studies from this laboratory, Lyon (1961) and Beutler (1962) independently formulated the hypothesis which postulates that the condensed X in female somatic cells cannot exert its genetic influence during interphase. Thus both the normal male and the normal female of the mammalian species actually have only one functional X in their somatic cells. While supporting evidence is rapidly accumulating (Lyon, 1962; Grumbach *et al.*, 1962; Motulsky *et al.*, 1962), it should be mentioned that the condensed X is known to be capable of at least one important function during interphase, namely participation in nucleolus-organization.

When Barr and Bertram (1949) first reported the presence of a female-specific chromocenter in nerve cell nuclei of the cat, they remarked that the body was most frequently found adjacent to the nucleolus. While the X-chromosome of the rat and man does not seem to carry a nucleolus-organizer, the X of the mouse most definitely does (Ohno *et al.*, 1957). In order to estimate the frequency with which the condensed X participates in nucleolus-organization, we re-examined 300 female prophase figures from our collection of squash preparations of regenerating liver cells from various strains of mice. The positively heteropycnotic X was associated with a nucleolus in 30 per cent of the early prophase figures (Fig. 19). It is possible that certain other X-linked genetic activities may also remain unhampered by the extreme condensation assumed by an X.

8. *The Consequences of X-autosome Translocation*

Recently X-autosome translocations have been shown to cause somatic variegation in *Mus musculus*, an effect manifested only when two X-chromosomes, one normal (X^n) and one translocation-bearing (X^t), are present, never when the X^t exists alone (Russell and Bangham, 1959, 1960; Cattanach, 1961).

A cytological study of Cattanach's stock of translocation-bearing mice has revealed the mechanism which produces the variegation (Ohno and Cattanach, 1962). In these mice, a piece of the autosome known as Linkage group I carrying dominant wild-type alleles of *pink-eye* and *chinchilla* has been transposed to the X. When germ cells of the X^tY were examined,

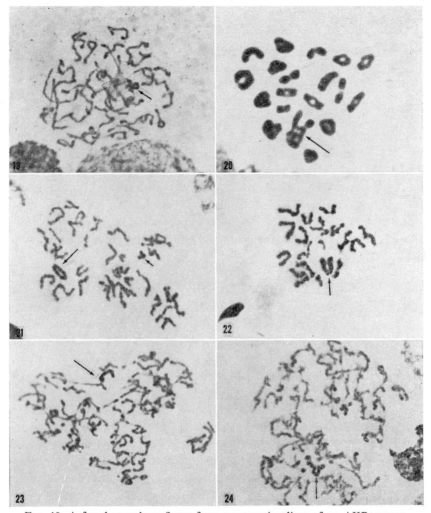

FIG. 19. A female prophase figure from regenerating liver of an AKR mouse. The condensed X (indicated by an arrow) is in association with the nucleolus (encircled by a dotted line).

FIGS. 20–24 are from Cattanach's stock of mice carrying an X-autosome translocation.

FIG. 20. A male first meiotic metaphase figure with 18 autosomal bivalents and the XY-autosomal quadrivalent (indicated by an arrow).

FIG. 21. A male first meiotic anaphase figure in which both the translocation-bearing X and the Y stand out by virtue of their complete positive heteropycnosis. Both are indicated by arrows.

FIG. 22. A male second meiotic prometaphase figure with the translocation-bearing X condensed along its entire length.

FIGS. 23 and 24. The two types of prophase figures recovered from regenerating liver of an X^tX^n female. In Fig. 23, an arrow indicates the normal X in a condensed state. In Fig. 24, an arrow indicates the considerably larger translocation-bearing X in a condensed state.

XY-autosome quadrivalents were found in about 10 per cent of the first meiotic figures (Fig. 20). Study of the configuration of such a quadrivalent, and of the autosomal bivalent of Linkage group I, led to three conclusions: (1) The autosomal piece had been inserted into the long arm of the acrocentric X. (2) The insertion represented at least one third of the Linkage group I autosome. (3) The translocation was non-reciprocal since the X lost little or nothing. Thus the X^t was 20 per cent longer than the X^n.

Of significance was the fact that throughout first and second meiosis of the X^tY male, the X^t appeared heavily condensed along its entire length. This is illustrated in the first meiotic anaphase shown in Fig. 21 and the second meiotic prometaphase shown in Fig. 22. Since the autosomal insertion was behaving as an integral part of the X, it had obviously acquired the ambivalent nature of the X. This ability to completely integrate a transposed autosomal piece may be regarded as another unique property of the mammalian X.

9. *Natural Mosaicism of the Mammalian Female*

Both Lyon (1961) and Beutler (1962) postulated that the mammalian female is a natural mosaic with two populations of somatic cells: in one the paternally-derived X is condensed and inactive; in the other, the maternally-derived X is the condensed inactive one.

While this postulate cannot be tested cytologically in ordinary females, the X^tX^n females of Cattanach's stock of mice were singularly well suited for just such a determination, since the condensed X^n should be distinctly smaller than the condensed X^t in prophase figures.

Figures 23 and 24 show the two types of prophase figures that were indeed recovered from regenerating liver cells of these females. The condensed chromosome seen in Fig. 23 is well within the size range of similar elements seen in the ordinary female. Prophase figures of this type represented cells in which the X^n was positively heteropycnotic while the X^t remained indistinguishable from the autosomes. The condensed chromosome seen in Fig. 24, on the other hand, considerably exceeds the uppermost size limits shown by the condensed X^n. Thus cells of this group contained a heteropycnotic X^t while the X^n remained isopycnotic. We found that by and large, the regenerating liver cells of these females contained as many condensed X^t as X^n cells; the distribution was roughly 50:50.

Direct cytological studies of skin cells from patches showing different coat colors further confirmed the natural mosaicism of the female. Since somatic variegation caused by an X-autosome translocation is, in essence, regional suppression of dominant autosomal genes translocated to the X, recessive genes allelic to them will find phenotypic expression in parts of the heterozygote's body.

In Cattanach's mice, the X^tY males and X^tO females are uniformly wild-type. Since the X^t with its autosomal insertion behaved like euchromatin in the somatic cells, the wild-type alleles were still completely dominant over the genes for *pink-eye* and *chinchilla*. On the other hand, studies of white patches and wild-type patches from the X^tX^n females and an X^tX^nY male showed that in the white patches where the recessive genes were finding phenotypic expression, the X^t with its autosomal insertion was heavily condensed while the wild-type patches were populated with cells containing a condensed X^n.

Thus cytological studies on Cattanach's X^tX^n female mice not only upheld the contention of Lyon and Beutler that the mammalian female is a natural mosaic, but showed as well that the functional suppression of the translocated autosomal genes is due to the positively heteropycnotic state assumed by the entire X^t.

SUMMARY

Once the single-X nature of the Barr sex chromatin body had been revealed, the unique ambivalent nature of the mammalian X-chromosome was explored.

1. In most mammalian species, man and mouse included, the X-chromosome is not divided into euchromatic and heterochromatic regions as it is in *Drosophila melanogaster*. Rather the entire length of an individual X is capable of behaving in either of two opposite ways; as though composed entirely of euchromatin or entirely of heterochromatin.

2. In male germ cells, the entire X behaves throughout first and second meiosis as though made only of heterochromatin, while in female germ cells, the XX bivalent demonstrates the intricate pachytene banding pattern characteristic of the euchromatic autosomes.

3. When the X-chromosome exists singly in somatic cells, as in XY males and XO females, it behaves exactly the same as the euchromatic autosomes.

4. The XX zygote begins development with both X-chromosomes elongated during interphase. At the time of implantation, however, one X in every cell suddenly becomes positively heteropycnotic. Beyond that moment, all female somatic cells have one condensed X and are therefore sex-chromatin-positive.

5. A euchromatic autosomal piece translocated into the X becomes an integral part of the X, acquiring its unique nature. This appears to be the cause of the somatic variegation seen in mice carrying the X-autosome translocation. In somatic cells of XY males as well as XO females, the X carrying the autosomal insertion remains extended during interphase, and no variegation occurs. When the translocation-bearing X is accompanied by a normal X, as in XX females and XXY males, certain parts of the body are populated with cells in which the entire length of the translocation-bearing X remains condensed from telophase to the following prophase. The translocated autosomal genes are thus suppressed and somatic variegation does occur.

6. Since her body contains two populations of cells, one with an inactive maternally-derived X, the other with an inactive paternally-derived X, the mammalian female does indeed appear to be a natural mosaic.

REFERENCES

Austin, C. R. and Amoroso, E. C., 1957, *Exptl. Cell Res.* **13**, 419.

Awa, A., Sasaki, M. and Takayama, S., 1959, *Jap. J. Zool.* **12**, 257.

Barr, M. L. and Bertram, L. F., 1949, *Nature*, **163**, 676.

Beutler, E., Yeh, M. and Fairbanks, V. F., 1962, *Proc. Natl. Acad. Sci., Wash.* **48**, 9.

Cattanach, B. M., 1961, *Z. Vererbungslehre*, **92**, 165.

German, J. L., 1962, *Trans. N. Y. Acad. Sci.* **24**, 395.

Graham, M. A. and Barr, M. L., 1959, *Arch. Anat. Micr. Morph. Exp.* **48**, 111.

Grumbach, M. M., Marks, P. A. and Morishima, A., 1962, *Lancet*, i, 1330.

Heitz, E., 1933, *Z. Zellforsch.* **20**, 237.

Kaufmann, B. P., 1934, *J. Morphol.* **56**, 125.

Lancet editorial, 1960, ii, 191.

Lima-de-Faria, A., 1959, *Science*, **130**, 503.

Lyon, M. F., 1961, *Nature*, **190**, 372.

Lyon, M. F., 1962, *Am. J. Human Genet.* **14**, 135.

Moore, K. L. and Barr, M. L., 1953, *J. Comp. Neurol.* **98**, 213.

Motulsky, A., Nyegaard, H., Schultz, A., Critchlow, J., and Buettner, K., *Am. Soc. Human Genet.* Corvallis, Oregon, 1962

Ohno, S. and Cattanach, B. M., 1962, *Cytogenetics*, **1**, 129.

Ohno, S. and Hauschka, T. S., 1960, *Cancer Res.* **20**, 541.

Ohno, S., Kaplan, W. D. and Kinosita, R., 1957, *Exptl. Cell Res.* **13**, 358.

Ohno, S., Kaplan, W. D. and Kinosita, R., 1958, *Cytologia*, **23**, 422.

Ohno, S., Kaplan, W. D. and Kinosita, R., 1959, *Exptl. Cell Res.* **18**, 415.

Ohno, S., Kaplan, W. D. and Kinosita, R., 1960, *Exptl. Cell Res.* **19**, 417.

Ohno, S., Kaplan, W. D. and Kinosita, R., 1961, *Exptl. Cell Res.* **22**, 535.

Ohno, S., Klinger, H. P. and Atkin, N. B., 1962, *Cytogenetics*, **1**, 42.

Ohno, S. and Makino, S., 1961, *Lancet*, i, 78.

Ohno, S., Makino, S., Kaplan, W. D. and Kinosita, R., 1961, *Exptl. Cell Res.* **24**, 106.

Ohno, S. and Weiler, C., 1961, *Chromosoma (Berl.)* **12**, 362.

Parks, W. W., 1957, *J. Anat. (Lond.)* **91**, 369.

RUSSELL, L. B. and BANGHAM, J. W., 1959, *Genetics*, **44**, 532.
RUSSELL, L. B. and BANGHAM, J. W., 1960, *Genetics*, **45**, 1008.
SHAVER, E. L., 1962, *Canad. J. Genet. Cytol.* **4**, 62.
TAYLOR, J. HERBERT, 1960, *Cell Physiology of Neoplasia*, pp. 547–575, University of Texas Press, Austin.
TJIO, H. J. and ÖSTERGREN, G., 1958, *Hereditas*, **44**, 451.
WITSCHI, E., 1957, *Science*, **126**, 1288.

ROUND TABLE ON FUTURE
DEVELOPMENT OF RESEARCH

CHAIRMAN (W. L. RUSSELL): As you probably know, when Alfred Hitchcock makes a movie, he likes to "sign" it by appearing in one of the crowd scenes. Similarly, whenever there is a symposium in which Dr. Hollaender is concerned, you can count on there being a round table in it. I do not know whether he was responsible for this one, but I suspect so. I have been to many of these round tables and never was there any lack of discussion. I hope that we can have worthwhile discussion this afternoon, so please feel free to interrupt, interfere, scream or do anything you wish during the discussion period.

I suppose the original round table, at least the oldest one I know about, was King Arthur's. The table is still said to be in the City of Winchester in England and, as you may know, King Arthur had trouble with his Knights — they were all fighting for priority — and to avoid difficulties he constructed a round table in which no one was "top knight". To carry out this idea now I suppose the twelve knights I have selected should stand up and talk at once, but that would not be very practical.

I do not know exactly why I picked these twelve people for the first part of the discussion — anybody left out should not feel insulted, perhaps rather grateful. (I left my wife out because I feel very kindly toward her!) The people included have attempted many things — they are not only people closely engaged in one specific piece of research, but also some who have had an overall look at research programs throughout countries or on an international basis and perhaps in their position can see some of the gaps in our present knowledge with a little more breadth of vision than those of us in specific research projects. Speakers may talk about anything they think might interest the group. I have asked each one to take not more than 3–4 min, so that they will be popping up and down, throwing out, I hope, ideas that will stimulate discussion in the second part of the program.

M. A. BENDER: As these formal talks will be fairly brief and we have been left to pick our own topics, I would like to tell you about what we have been doing in the area of human somatic chromosome aberrations, and then present some of my ideas about what still needs to be done in this field. I hope that later in the discussion we will have criticism or comment on this type of approach.

For a number of years I have been interested in the production of chromosomal aberrations in human somatic cells by radiation. There are several reasons for my interest, and these have a direct bearing on what I feel should be done in the field. I am interested in aberration types and rates because of their connection with specific problems in genetics and cell survival. There are more practical reasons, however. An obvious one is the bearing of such measurements on the issue of radiation hazards to man and other mammals. In this respect, work with cells *in vitro* must be taken with a great deal of caution, because these cells are in an obviously abnormal environment, and what we really need to know is what happens in the normal environment in the body of the mammal. Another reason for interest in these measurements is the hope that they will enable us to use the somatic chromosomes as a "biological dosimeter" — a crude one, perhaps, but nevertheless useful — for estimating the effective dose received by people involved in radiation accidents. In these cases, the effective whole body dose is frequently not known, and I believe that the cytologist could give the physicians in charge of the care of the irradiated persons enough information to enable them to make the necessary decisions about treatment.

We have studied human chromosome aberration types and rates both in tissue cultured cells *in vitro* and in leukocytes irradiated *in vitro* as freshly drawn blood. In addition to our X-ray studies, we are now making studies of aberrations induced by neutrons and by protons of various energies. We have begun fairly extensive studies which parallel the human studies but use the South American Spider Monkey (chosen largely because of its very low diploid chromosome number of 2n = 34) as the experimental animal. Since we cannot irradiate humans for our experiments, we are using the monkey in the hope of extrapolating the results to the case of irradiation of humans. The monkey experiments provide a way of making an experimental comparison between aberrations induced *in vitro* and *in vivo*. Ultimately we hope to establish accurate coefficients of aberration production and fission neutron RBE values for use in dose estimation. One might call this work the experimental "calibration" of our biological dosimeter.

Recently we have been able to make direct measurements of aberration production in accidentally irradiated men. Such measurements not only help in estimating radiation hazards and in evaluating the dosimetric use of aberration measurements, but they also provide a means for learning more about the kinetics of loss and production of the circulating leukocytes which possess the ability to divide in culture.

It seems obvious to me that such studies should continue in the future. Everything that has been done so far, or that is planned for the future, however, is restricted to somatic cells. So far as I am aware, no one is investigating the production of chromosomal aberrations in germ line cells. The need to do this is very real. Studies of aberration induction in the germ line, of the transmission of aberrant chromosomes to the offspring, and of the effect of the aberrations on the phenotype would be of inestimable value as a direct measure of the genetic hazard of radiation to man. The techniques for the preparation of mammalian testicular material which were described earlier in this symposium should make the first type of investigation possible. The peripheral leukocyte technique for somatic chromosomes makes the other investigations possible. Suitable material already exists in the irradiated human populations from Hiroshima and Nagasaki, in persons irradiated in accidents or for therapeutic reasons, and in populations living in high natural radiation areas. It seems impossible that use will not be made of this material in the near future.

H. EAGLE: I don't have the temerity to predict the development of research; but the three areas which I will have the greatest personal interest in following are the fields of virus replication, cancer and differentiation. In the virus problem, it will be interesting to follow the elucidation of the chemical mechanisms by which cells make viruses, and the biochemical effects of virus infection on the cell. In the cancer problem, I will be interested in studies relating to the biochemical differences between normal and malignant cells. The very fact that two cells which are indistinguishable in culture behave so differently when they are injected into the proper host, and in the proper biological environment, necessarily means that there is a biochemical difference between these two cells, a difference which we have so far not been able to determine. The transformation effected in normal cells by tumor viruses is of obvious relevance. Finally, in the problem of differentiation, it is my hope that the art of cell culture will be developed to the point that such cultures will in fact become, as they are not at the present time, a useful tool in the exploration of the process of differentiation. Finally, to cast a net very widely, I submit for your consideration the possibility that all three of these broad areas of biological exploration are really tangential, in that all three may involve the same basic mechanisms of cellular metabolic control.

S. M. GARTLER: I can add little more than was given in the conclusion of my talk. Our major interest is to try and utilize cell culture techniques for studies in human genetics. One of the major problems is an adequate supply of useable markers for normal cell cultures. We are also extremely interested to see whether the mechanisms of hereditary information transfer between cells in culture which now seem to be effective in established cell lines will apply to normal cultures. Many of the problems which Dr. Eagle referred to in his paper are of great concern to us. The fact that normal cell lines appear to have a finite life span is at the same time a depressing and stimulating problem. For the fertile mind, this may be one of the best materials to explore the question of longevity, but to the geneticist interested in cell culture work, this feature of normal cells is at present a serious limitation. Another critical technique problem also mentioned by Dr. Eagle is that of cloning normal cell lines. Effective cloning is essential to most genetic studies planned for cell culture work. Selecting mutant cells, the detection of rare recombinants or any number of rare genetic events requires that the investigator be able to generate a measurable population from a single cell. The alternative to this, and unfortunately a most difficult one, is to work only with single cells. However, the difficulty of cloning normal cultures is one that will certainly be overcome, although a certain amount of time will be involved in the solution of this problem. In conclusion, I believe that in the first five years of heavy activity in this specialized area a reasonable amount of progress has been made and that we can certainly expect many exciting developments in the near future.

A. HOLLAENDER: Of course my interest is in the radiation field. Having hardly any opportunity to get into the laboratory any more, I will not discuss these points although I would like to see them developed very much.

What we fear to see in a discussion on radiation effects on chromosomes is the lack of understanding of the literature already published in the microbiology field. There is a tremendous amount of basic information available and it is not being applied to the study of effects of radiation on chromosomes. This is unfortunate. These two fields which are so very similar in many aspects must be more closely coordinated. We have hundreds or thousands of publications in the microbiology field, bacteria, fungi, paramecium, which are hard to read — I'm sure — but there are good summaries available. It would save us a lot of time and a lot of effort if the cytologists and cytogeneticists would take advantage of these.

From the radiation point of view, we are still very much puzzled about what are the initial effects of radiation because what we observe usually is something which has taken place many steps after the absorption of radiation. We are along way from understanding the initiation, the first step in radiation damage.

Another field in which we would like to see more effort, and probably it is not too easy, experimentally, is the study of effects of very low radiation. This is, of course, closely connected with the initiation of radiation effects. What are the smallest quantities of radiation which would produce damage in living cells? Are they really so low that they could reach what we get in background radiation? There is a good chance that there are means of finding this if we develop appropriate tools.

One field which I feel has not been developing too much and in which I think cytogenetics will have a very good future is getting much more biochemical approaches to human cytology. Here, of course, many of us in the laboratories get stuck on the difficulties of experimental techniques.

Other rapidly developing fields are protein synthesis, nucleic acid synthesis, transfer of information. The final analysis must go back to the chromosome to see what the chromosome does to be able to tell the cytoplasm what to do and how to develop. This of course leads to the problems that Dr. Eagle has already mentioned. These are many and most interesting fields and I visualize that the next ten years will see a vast expansion of the biochemical and biophysical approaches to cytogenetics.

L. D. HAMILTON: I would like to drive your attention from the chromosome level to the molecular level. I think it's fair to say that in the past 9–10 years we have seen an enormous revolution in the molecular level. One could almost say without exaggerating the situation, that we are now rapidly approaching the end of the beginning of the phase of molecular biology in so far as it affects the storage and transfer of information.

Certain developments, such as improvement in the techniques of X-ray diffraction, lead us to believe that with the ability to resolve by X-ray diffraction distances between atoms it will be possible to improve still further our knowledge of the fine structure, of, for example, the DNA molecule. It will never be possible, probably, because of the size of this molecule, to get any idea from X-ray diffraction of the sequence of the base pairs in the long chain. On the other hand it has recently been shown by Wilkins and his colleagues that there is a very good chance of this being done for transfer RNA. Transfer RNA has a much smaller molecule and it should be possible by securing pure samples of transfer RNA and crystallizing these actually to work out the base sequence, that is, the code with which the biochemists have been struggling with some success recently. This should give us the most definitive evidence for the individual coding.

I think another physical development very soon to appear is the improvement of electronic microscopy. It has been possible recently to resolve biological materials to 10 Å and I am sure that very shortly it will be possible to do the same kind of work down to 2 Å. This, of course, would enable us actually to analyze long sequences in the DNA molecule and in fact study the relationship of the DNA to the messenger RNA molecule and of this to the transfer RNA molecule.

Now how does all this apply to mammalian cells? Most of our knowledge about DNA, messenger RNA, transfer RNA and the relationship to the genetic coding has been worked out very beautifully in simple organisms, in model systems, such as phage-bacteria, about which we have a great deal of information. In the mammalian system, of course, we have a different problem. First of all we are dealing in the human species with 46 chromosomes. The general mechanism is very similar but it is obviously somewhat more specialized. It has to be because in mammalian systems we are dealing with large masses of dependent cells. This problem has been alluded to already by Dr. Eagle and I think it is the problem of differentiation. Essentially the genetic message is probably the same in all cells. Probably it remains the same, but for some reason a liver cell is a liver cell and an eye cell is an eye cell and they are putting out different messages, or different messages are being repressed in different cells. It is very interesting to take all these cells out of the body. The genetic information is the same in all of them. Yet when they are placed in tissue culture, the genetic message does not function apparently for a large number of specialized functions, so that some information making these cells function is apparently lacking. An immediate approach to this problem is to try to do something more about the actual molecular arrangement in parts of the chromosome. It is possible that this would give us a clue as to how in these quite complicated mammalian chromosomes the information is stored and how this may differ from the general arrangement in the microorganisms. I have thrown out a number of wild speculations in some order, but I hope we have some discussion on how these mechanisms may function on the mammalian cell.

R. S. CALDECOTT: I am not sure most of you know just what my capacity is; sometimes I wonder myself, so perhaps it would be desirable to provide a word of explanation. In the Division of Biology and Medicine of the U. S. Atomic Energy Commission a number of specialists in different fields are hired with the understanding that they will remain for two or three years before returning to the laboratory, thus assuring that a maximum number of members of the scientific community have an opportunity to have some input into the Nation's science programs at the administrative level. I moved to Washington a two years ago to handle the genetics research program in general and, specifically, to appraise critically the program in plant genetics and cytogenetics. In this capacity, as a geneticist, it is, of course, necessary to scrutinize the entire field of genetics and try to make some reasonable judgment as to where support should be put in research programs. One of the reasons I travel around to the laboratories and meetings such as this one is to enable me to take home facts which will help determine directions in which the program might profitably be shifted.

It has often been demonstrated that one cannot take care of the applied missions, such as confront the Atomic Energy Commission, without developing a sound back-up program in basic research. This has been beautifully emphasized at this meeting where the medical cytogeneticists have discussed techniques and described anomalies in human cells that were first catalogued in plant systems and other lower forms over 30 years ago. Indeed, today I strongly suspect that the best basic training a young man could obtain in preparation for his becoming a medical cytogeneticist would be with a competent corn cytogeneticist. In this regard, witness the beautiful pachytene preparations shown to us by Dr. Valencia. Even a specialist would have difficulty stating with conviction that they were from a mammal rather than a corn plant.

Because of the apparent similarity of chromosome behavior in lower forms and mammals, one is tempted to consider the following question. Would it not be desirable to concentrate research on the lower forms, that are less expensive to use than mammals, and then only trouble-shoot with the higher organisms to be certain that the phenomena under consideration are common to all forms? I would welcome your views on this matter.

In looking at the entire program of this meeting, and in considering the mammalian genetics and cytogenetics that the USAEC supports at the present time, one of the things that troubles me a good deal is that we have devoted the bulk of our attention to the effects of ionizing radiations on gene mutations. Clearly, the real problems in human genetics, those that you have examined at this meeting at least, are not associated with gene mutation; rather, they are associated with chromosome assortment. As we know that ionizing radiations cause translocations and other chromosome changes, which affect disjunction, I wonder if more emphasis should be given to those aspects of our program that look at the relation between dose and the frequency of 2-hit events. I would enjoy hearing some discussion of this matter.

Finally, I appreciate having the opportunity to participate in your symposium and would like to congratulate the organizers for a splendid effort as well as to thank those among you who have been such gracious hosts and hostesses.

CHAIRMAN: Thank you Dr. Caldecott. I am sure we can go back at least to some of these points. Our next speaker, I am told, is known as "the great Pavan". I think that this is the first time that he has appeared formally in the program and I am very delighted to have the honor to introduce him.

C. PAVAN: Let me thank you very much for these very friendly words. Dr. Russell was kind enough to include me on the round table and I am happy to be here to try to help my friends from below the Equator on the work they are doing. Many people from outside Latin America do not know how hard it is to work here even doing simple work on account of a series of bureaucratic difficulties and other factors that we can not easily avoid. Everyone who comes here and stays with us for some time does understand this. We are very happy to help these visitors because they also can help us very much.

I would like to comment upon three points in this round table on the future development of research on human cytology. First, to us here in South America, publications like the *Human Chromosome Newsletter* are very important because they bring us fresh news and techniques much more quickly than the normal publications do. For this reason we are very grateful to Dr. Harnden and Dr. Jacobs for organizing this Newsletter and to Dr. Hsu for distributing the *Mammalian Chromosomes.* Likewise we appreciate, among others, Dr. Demerec for starting the DIS *(Drosophila* Information Service), Dr. E. Witkin with her *Microbiological News* and Dr. A. Sokolov with his *Tribolium* Information Bulletin. This type of publication helps us very much because we would not know about similar work to ours being done elsewhere until several months after, or several years.

Another point is the importance for us of a symposium such as this one. You cannot imagine how important it is for us here in Brazil and in all South America to bring people here to describe in a few words things that we would have to spend months learning from books or magazines. First, we have the difficulty of the language — we have always to read from a foreign language. Second, we are almost completely isolated. Here in Brazil, for instance, each of us who achieves do something in science is the greatest, the most important and the only one who works in his field! There is no competition at all, so it is easy to be the best. This isolation really makes the advancement of science difficult in our countries where there are too few scientists. In this type of meeting we learn a lot about what is going on in the world. We are very grateful to Dr. Hollaender who made possible the organization of this symposium.

The third point which I think is important for the development of human cytology is to have more work on wild mammals. Human chromosomes are not the best for a number of studies which could be done in mammals. Some species are disappearing from the earth now, with the spreading out of human populations, and maybe some of these are specially favorrable for some types of work. We must try to get better and varied material so that we can see if something that we find in one species has general significance. We should also try to construct a general picture of cytology, which I think we still do not have.

J. I. VALENCIA: Most of what I was planning to say appears to have been said. When this morning Dr. Russell asked me to say something here I planned to ask to be the first so that I could say everything. Now, I am the last! Nevertheless, I have some points that I would like to mention here. First of all I would like to say something about what Dr. Eagle has said before. I would like to emphasize the importance of tissue culture. Karyotype studies are always very important, but we should endeavor to emphasize their use on the study of fundamental problems rather than do a mere cataloging of new cases. I also agree with Dr. Pavan that we should be very careful in not becoming too enthusiastic with the studies of human cytogenetics and forget to maintain fundamental research with experimental organisms like *Drosophila*, microorganisms and plants. Concerning human chromosomes I would like to say a word in favor of the pachytene stage. If a good technique could be developed — and we think we are on the way to doing it — it is very important to develop a good cytological chromomeric map. It would be very useful for complementing the work which is being done on karyotype analysis specially with respect to small deficiencies, small inversions and translocations. Perhaps this will explain some of the problems mentioned here, as well as some of the phenomena of nondisjunction which Dr. Lejeune mentioned yesterday when speaking about inter-chromosomal effects. There is a point I would like to complement in what Dr. Pavan just said. It is very important to exchange scientists. Perhaps a way will be found in which this exchange could be made easier and more frequent. We are working on many of the problems that you mentioned here, but we are quite a bit behind. Dr. Hollaender mentioned the biochemical approach. We are trying to do something in that line but many times we begin an original research only to find that it was done by somebody else. We do not have enough information and enough contact with scientists from other parts of the world.

F. A. SAEZ: I would like to express my agreement with Drs. Pavan and Valencia concerning the isolation in which we, investigators of Latin America and specially this Southern part, have fallen. Brazil is not a particular case because it is nearer the Northern part of the Continent, but Uruguay can be an example. When I started research on cytogenetics in South America, 35 years ago, I was the first and only one to isolate species of this kind! Fortunately, things have changed and now it is really flattering the way in which genetic research has progressed.

Brazil can be an example of this fast growth, as in the works on *Drosophila* of Pavan, Da Cunha, Cordeiro, Freire-Maia, Cavalcanti, Salzano and many other distinguished investigators. The same can be said about Chile where a pattern of progress showed in genetic disciplines as in Argentina.

The work on *Drosophila* is perhaps a good example in South America of what can be done in mammalian cytogenetics. Among the lines of research in our Department of Cytogenetics one is the investigation of the wild mammalian fauna of the South Continent. I think it will be necessary, for instance, to intensify the research on rodents. We must remember that the greater part of our knowledge in the mechanisms of sex chromosomes came from rodents and this is why we have to look all over the Continent and try to clarify with new materials some problems still unsolved.

We must also reinvestigate, with the aid of the tissue culture techniques, the karyotypes and behaviour of the mammals' chromosomes of this part of America.

We all know that general work is very important, and that in any part of the world we must work with general views. Human cytogenetics interests everybody all over the world, but, as I said before, in the case of South America we must intensify the study of all mammalian animals, many of them living in our lands, which are yet unknown.

This work must be done in each one of our countries without losing contact among researchers of other parts, if we are to avoid overlapping in the literature.

Here in Uruguay we have to wait three months or more for a journal to arrive and I think it is the same for Argentina and Chile. With such a delay we are slowed down and we lose track of what is being done in the Northern Hemisphere, whether in Europe or in the United States; and cannot take into account the recent publications of authors working on similar subjects. This delay in the publications is undoubtedly one of our most difficult problems and it is hoped it will be solved in a profitable way.

J. LEJEUNE: As far as I can see this round table is a mixture of confession and of profession of faith. My confession is that I am a specialist of human genetics. Being a specialist is to know many things about a very small thing. Nevertheless we try to know a lot more things about many other things. That is why we are interested in any aspect of biology if it can give us a clue to understanding what is occurring in congenital disorders. It has been supposed repeatedly that the study of syndromes, provoked by chromosomal aberration, was steadily declining because the easiest discoveries were already made. I do not think this is true. The most obvious and most frequent may have been found, but possibly there are many other interesting ones. For example, the systematic study of rare translocations, which possibly have no phenotypical expressions, is very important. They can help us to map chromosomes, and even if this research does not seem immediately rewarding, it is possible that with international co-operation it will help towards the understanding of human cytogenetics. To confess everything, I would say that I feel there are two big failures in the way we approach cytogenetics. First is a possible error regarding the interpretation of the karyotype. This is forgivable at present because nobody is very sure of anything! The other pitfall is that clinical reports of cases having a special chromosomal change are unsatisfactory. Most people are very happy to describe some extraordinary chromosome, but do not bother to give an accurate medical report of the case, which makes the comparison of cases extremely difficult and for the moment impossible even.

This is what we hope to do and what we hope others will do if we are not able to do it ourselves. We are not only interested in inborn chromosomal errors, but also — and possibly much more — in acquired chromosomal errors. The study of leukaemia is a promising field and has yielded wonderful successes, but I do not think it is the only one. The study of chromosomes in cancer was considered very interesting twenty or thirty years ago and has been in relative discredit ever since. I suppose this was mainly because people were counting the bodies inside the nuclei and could not go further than that. Now we are in a position to build a real karyotype even if there are many chromosomal changes. Some day a picture will emerge to show that this apparently random variegation of chromosomes in cancer is not a random process. Surely a careful analysis of the karyotype could tell us many things about the partial differentiation of the cells in the neoplastic process. Also related to cancer, the study of virus could throw a bridge between the viral theory of cancer and the chromosomal theory. It has been reported for example that the virus SV40 was acting on diploid strains by knocking out some chromosomes. The frequency of the loss of chromosome number 21 and the chromosome 13 was definitely much higher than for any other pair. If we consider that acrocentrics are related to nucleolus and, on the other hand, suppose that the virus is going in the nucleolus, then we understand why possibly by just mechanical reasons some particular chromosomes are at risk when viral infection of the cell occurs this preliminary observation may not give us the final explanation of cancerous transformation by some viruses but possibly other mechanisms will be discovered to bridge the gap between the theories of the virus lovers and of the chromosome lovers.

Now the third thing could be to study biochemistry. One laboratory has little chance of a major achievement in the field of a given chromosomal aberration and it is why I would like to stress that point. With inborn chromosomal error we are dealing with an entire population of abnormal cells consituting an individual. We can get from him substances like the blood or other fluid of the body. We can study them chemically and in my opinion it is not very wise to do chemistry only in tissue culture. At the moment we have with a grown-up individual a pure culture of a given chromosomal aberration Now that we are in the science fiction field, I would briefly say a word about what Dr. Lima de Faria said about the use of the fecundation *in vitro* and recognition of XO and other abnormalities. I would say that this "hurt" two principles: the first is the Heisenberg principle of uncertainty. An accurate observation of a very small event changes the event itself, so that uncertainty of the event remains. To know whether a fertilized egg contains one X or an X and Y it is necessary to fix it to look at its chromosomes. Then it never develops to give an individual. The other principle which hurts me here is the principle of love itself. I would maintain firmly that the old fashion was the good one.

CHAIRMAN: The informal part of the discussion is open now.

A. HOLLAENDER: About the question raised by Dr. Pavan on the failure of journals to reach Latin American centers speedily enough to prove useful in research. I think you can take a good lesson from Soviet Russia where distances are much greater than in many areas and there is much more isolation than in Latin America. They have overcome this by setting up a scientific news center, where science journals are reproduced and sent to the individual laboratories by air. I wonder if such a center could not be developed in Latin America probably under the auspices of the Organization of American States. I think this would be worth trying and if it is worked out carefully and systematically I am sure it could be efficient. Some of the International Foundations would probably be willing to support this. To make this possible the scientists of Latin America must get together and chose a reasonably small number of journals to start with. These could be brought to you by air, reproduced here and sent on to individual laboratories by air. With the close cooperation of individual scientists, this need not be expensive.

J. I. VALENCIA: A few years ago such an idea was presented to an international agency but unfortunately was not considered reasonable at the time.

A. HOLLAENDER: This kind of proposition should not be made by one individual. I think you ought to get together as many scientists as possible and show in definite form how you want to do it. Reproducing all journals would be impossible. You must choose the ones you think are more important, and work out how many individual copies should be made available. I think it is better to do this now than it was three or four years ago.

C. PAVAN: I am very glad you brought out this point, because it is something that we are very much interested in. Although I was complaining about the situation in South America, some efficient steps have been taken to compensate it. Here in Brazil we organized in the Society of Genetics, under the sponsorship of the Rockefeller Foundation, what we call the Committee on Human Genetics, composed of seven geneticists from different parts of Brazil. The Committee has enough funds to provide for meetings three or four times a year. Every research plan of some size on human genetics in Brazil is discussed by the Committee, assisted by other scientists when necessary. The Committee also studies the difficulties which hinders development in particular laboratories and in Brazil in general and takes steps to counteract them, for instance by using its prestige to obtain grants and fellowships. It develops a number of other activities aiming at the divulging of genetics to students, training of new researchers, etc. After three years of activities the results of this policy were so good that recently similar committees have been established for Animal Genetics and Plant Genetics.

M. A. BENDER: May I take this opportunity to make one plea which falls, I think, into the subject matter of both of these round tables. In South and Central America there is a large group of primates. I am particularly interested in their cytology, particularly in the cytotaxonomy of the group. Some of these animals are extremely difficult to obtain; they are really available only to those of our South American colleagues who happen to enjoy the proper location for their "isolation". Certainly research on these animals would be valuable, and it is certain that it could not be duplicated by workers in North America or in Europe, due to the difficulty workers in other areas have in obtaining specimens. I can think of a number of primate species for which I would be extremely interested in having karyotypic information available. Undoubtedly there are many other cytologists who feel the same way about unique South American species belonging to other groups of mammals. Just as certainly there are other fields of investigation which could profit from studies of unique South American species. I can only hope that more South American scientists will take advantage of the special opportunities offered by their isolated location in the future.

CHAIRMAN: I see that Dr. Bender two years from now can take up the journal and find somebody else in South America did it two years before him. Now, please, Dr. Bender and Dr. Lejeune, would you summarize?

M. A. BENDER: As you can see from the program, Dr. Jack Schultz was originally scheduled to sum up this symposium. Unfortunately, he could not be here. Dr. Pavan has prevailed on myself and Dr. Lejeune to try to take his place. We are in a somewhat difficult position in trying to sum up this Symposium, for several reasons. First, we have not had very much time to prepare to do it, and second, it is a rather difficult job for two people to do. Our solution to the latter problem is to try to split up the subject material into two natural segments. We have come to the conclusion that the best we could do would be to separate work on the cellular level from work which deals mainly with the whole organism. I shall try to review the cellular material.

I think that the material presented during the past four days falls naturally into three major areas. The first is what we might call the behavior of mammalian somatic cells placed in an *in vitro* environment, the response of cells to the unnatural environment of a tissue or cell culture, and the effects of specific environmental factors on the cell. We have heard Dr. Eagle's excellent presentation on the nutritional biochemistry of cultured cells. In his paper he raised several extremely interesting and important questions. One is the explanation for the often observed failure of cells from specific organs to maintain their specific functions for very long *in vitro*. Another is the often observed failure of diploid cells to continue to grow as vigorous cell lines for long periods in culture. While there are occasional reports that the latter observation is not always true, it is certainly at least the general rule. I cannot help but think that this phenomenon might well be due, as I believe that Dr. Eagle implied, to the inability of such cells to synthesize certain compounds as rapidly as they are lost from the cell to the unusually large volume of liquid medium surrounding them in tissue cultures. In any case, this is obviously an area of great interest to human cytogenetics, and even more particularly to those interested in the development of a science we might call human genetics *in vitro*.

A number of authors at this symposium have reported on topics very directly related to this new field of human genetics, which actually constitutes the second broad area of research on the cellular level reported here.

Dr. Moorhead has pointed out that phytohaemagglutinin, an extract from beans, has a rather mysterious ability to promote mitosis in cultures of peripheral leukocytes. Perhaps future studies of the phenomenon will provide some answers to the question of why some particular types of cells refuse to divide *in vitro*. Another topic which has been discussed here is the use of what we might call environmental factors to make it easier for the cytologist to differentiate certain chromosomes, particularly in the human set. These are certainly very important studies. In addition, the use of the differential DNA synthesis of certain chromosomes of the human complement, as observed by tritium-labeled thymidine autoradiographs, offers further hope in this direction. The possibility that cells grown in culture might be made to fuse, and perhaps exchange genetic information, as well as the fact that cultured mammalian cells can take up foreign DNA, offer the hope of achieving a sort of "mating" of cells *in vitro*, and thus of developing a real genetics of cells *in vitro*. Reports of the transformation of cells *in vitro* by means of a transforming principle are particularly encouraging, as are the observations of association and possibly even somatic pairing of mammalian chromosomes *in vitro* reported by Dr. Gartler.

A major area which has been discussed at this symposium is mutation, both on the gene and the chromosome levels, in individiual cultured cells. Work has been mentioned with single genetic characters, the nature of which is known in the whole mammal, and which would seem to be scorable in single cells *in vitro*. When such techniques are developed to the point that they can be used routinely, they will become a powerful tool for the new field of mammalian cell genetics. They will also make possible something in which I am personally very interested, namely the measurement of gene mutation rates in single mammalian cells in culture. Earlier I discussed chromosomal mutations in cultured cells. I should here re-emphasize a point that was made by Dr. Caldecott. Most of the phenomena which we have studied in cultured cells are exactly the same as were described many years ago for plant material. Nevertheless, I think the recent studies on mammalian cells are necessary, if only to provide a check on our prediction that mammalian cells would behave no differently from plant cells, at least with respect to chromosomal aberrations. In addition, some of the observations which have been reported here would not have been predicted. Dr. Moorhead's observations on the ability of the virus SV–40 to induce aberrations in mammalian chromosomes in particularly exciting. Perhaps we will be able to find out more about the process of chromosomal breakage and reunion from such studies, as well as from specific studies such as those described by Drs. Lozzio and Valencia on the effect of a specific modifier of radiaton-induced chromosomal aberrations in mammalian cells.

A third major area which has been discussed is that of mammalian cell survival. This area is certainly related to mutation and chromosome aberration, although not in a simple or obvious way. Studies such as Dr. Barendsen reported, of the influence of various factors on the kinetics of mammalian cell survival kinetics, will certainly help us to understand the way in which irradiated cells die, and thus to understand the roles of mutation and chromosomal aberrations in the killing process.

To sum up, as it were, this half of the Summation, I should like to point to the amazing strides which have been made in the field of mammalian tissue culture in the last few years. We now have ways to culture mammalian cells routinely which enable us to use them in much the same ways that bacteria are used for all sorts of quantitative studies. We have seen methods developed which enable us to use such cells for cytological and now even genetic studies. These techniques are particularly interesting, although not unique, in that they have actually enabled us to learn things about mammals which we could not learn from direct study of the whole animal. One needs only to point to the fact that we learned the correct human chromosome number only recently, and then from the study of cells in culture, in order to demonstrate the importance of tissue culture techniques. The recent bloom of human cytogenetics would not, indeed, have occurred without tissue culture techniques. On this note I should like to turn the Summation over to Dr. Lejeune, who will doubtless mention many of the ways in which our knowledge of whole mammals has been advanced by the use of tissue culture techniques.

J. Lejeune: As you can see I am the second mouth of the bicephalic representation of Dr. Schultz. As I have not taken any notes, I cannot summarize what has been said, but must rely on memory and apologise if I forget something important. Dr. Bender spoke of the cell and I would like to speak of the individual considered as a population of cells. First we have learned about the recognition of the cell with the special problem of chromosomal taxonomy. We have heard about the opossum, about the dasypus about the bull, about the pig and about other animals, some of which I did not know even existed. I was extremely glad to get acquainted with them. It will be important to use this taxonomic tool with the possibility in view of the Robertsonian type of evolution. This could lead to some pertinent inferences at least in the primates and possibly in all mammals. Let's come now nearer to my personal field. We have been told many things about what chromosomes do or look like. We have been told that acrocentric chromosomes could be extremely unstable in certain genotypic environments and that would not be surprising if what is true with the SV40 virus story holds true for other genic components. We have also realized that sexual chromosome disorders are important in our species. Of course we know these to be very interesting, but I was much impressed by the work of Dr. Ohno and by the discussion of Dr. Chu. The X chromosome is an extremely polymorph, changing and troubling thing. That is not so unexpected if we remember that it has something to do with the work of Eros.

About the understanding of all those things, I remember the question asked by the father of my assistant as he came one day in the laboratory to see our work.

We showed him exactly what was in progress and he was extremely interested in the mongolian trisomy and other abnormal karyotypes. After a while, he just asked "What is the use of all of that?" I must confess that this naive question is the very question that we should always keep in our minds: "What is the use of what we are doing?" That question I would like to try to answer in the light of what has been said in this symposium. What we are doing is not only collecting stamps as Dr. Hamilton told me a few minutes ago. We try to understand what they represent and for that we need first an improvement of our techniques and specially an improvement of the recognition of chromosomes and more precisely of the rearranged chromosome. As far as I can see the pachytene stage as shown by Dr. Slizhinsky and Dr. Valencia and also of a later stage as shown by Dr. Welshons are both extremely important. This can become a very powerful tool in recognizing that chromosomes are really involved in a given translocation. This tool, not yet entirely dependable, has some restrictions. First it is restricted to the male sex and secondly it cannot be used in some very interesting syndromes. In sexual disorders, for example, because there are no spermatogenes in the people who have two X and one Y, three X and one Y and so on. This tool is probably usable for autosomal translocation and we can get much information this way.

We are also confronted with another problem: the understanding of the action of chromosomal abnormalities. It seems obvious that if something occurs in the patrimony of the cell which gives rise to an individual, the individual should be abnormal. But it is not because when this occurs the phenomenon is always explained. I would stress two points in this respect. The first is the possibility of observing biochemical troubles in relation to specific changes. That is known in the Philadelphia chromosome, for example, and with the alkaline phosphatase. It is a minor thing, but it is this kind of thing that we must get in all chromosomal disorders. Instead of having one sign, we need to discover a hundred, or a thousand of them, because there are probably more than a thousand genes in the 21 chromosome. I would make a point here on the fact that we are still gambling about the interest in what we do. Let us suppose the mental deficiency of mongols, for example, is due to the additive action of genes and that a thousand genes are involved. Even if we can correct the action of one gene (and this will be very difficult), we will only improve the intellectual quotient by one thousandth. Such a result will not be very benefical.

The contrary supposition is: there is no additivity. That means that some genes are much more important than others. If this is the case, and if we can detect some important genes, then the correction of the biochemical trouble could be of real significance for the individual. We have no reason to believe that one or other hypothesis is true, but the answer to that problem is very old and was given by Pascal. On one side, you are sure to lose if you gamble; on the other side, possibly you can get a result. So we have no choice, and we are forced to suppose that the genes are not strictly additive. We have also to study the acquired chromosomal abnormalities and the study of the very abnormal chromosome, karyotypes as shown by Prof. Bottura, seems to me very important. I do not believe that these karyotypic changes can be a purely random shift. There is probably some law underlying them.

On the other hand some changes can occur in somatic cells which are surely not viable at the individual level, but which can possibly be recognized. This would be another way of using chromosomal changes to map human chromosome.

I am afraid I have not summarized what has been said in this symposium. I have tried to summarize what I have learned myself, for we have in this research, as in any other discipline, to follow three steps. The first is to learn, the second to understand what we learn and the third is to try to use it. I think that the real goal of human cytogenetics is to produce new knowledge which will enable us to help suffering people.

To conclude, I would like to try to be a representative sample of the whole Assembly. All the participants are very grateful to the organizers of this symposium which was extremely rewarding for all of us. Also I would extend to the organizers our deep appreciation of the Brazilian way of barbecuing meat, of cutting stones and of receiving foreigners, without forgetting also the kindness of the two X bearing members of his staff.

The friendship and the courtesy of our scientific debates prove that chromosome lovers are members of a worldwide family. It is well known that the greater pleasure for members of a family is to meet together. We have enjoyed this meeting very much and it is the hope of all of us to experience this pleasure again. The best concluding remark I can think of is a simple French phrase which synthesizes our wishes: *A bientôt.*

Selected Topics in Radiobiology

MOLECULAR CHANGES RESPONSIBLE
FOR ULTRAVIOLET INACTIVATION
OF THE BIOLOGICAL ACTIVITY OF DNA

R. B. SETLOW

Biology Division, Oak Ridge National Laboratory,* Oak Ridge, Tennessee,
U.S.A.

INTRODUCTION

Biological systems depend particularly on the properties and organization of large molecules. Therefore it is reasonable to suppose that the effects of radiation on such systems can be interpreted in terms of the effects of radiation on these large molecules. The present coding dogma states that DNA specifies RNA which in turn specifies the properties of proteins. The mechanisms by which these specificities are transferred from one molecular species to another are beginning to be understood, and because DNA is at the beginning of this series we expect that the key to the understanding of the effects of radiation is an understanding of their action on DNA. The first identification of nucleic acids as critical elements in cellular mutation as well as in cellular radiobiology came with the identification of the action spectrum for killing and mutation of cells with the absorption spectrum of nucleic acids.[15]

The macroscopically observable effects produced by X-rays and ultraviolet radiation are often similar, but at the molecular level the effects are very different. For example, X-rays produce many chain breaks in DNA whereas ultraviolet does not, but ultraviolet drastically affects the ability of DNA to act as a primer[7] for further synthesis, but no such effects are observed with X-irradiated DNA[4] at similar biological inactivation levels. It is possible to isolate from ultraviolet irradiated DNA a specific photochemical product and to show that this product is largely responsible for the effects of ultraviolet on simple biological and biochemical systems. This particular photochemical change — the production of dimers between ad-

* Operated by Union Carbide Corporation for the United States Atomic Energy Commission.

adjacent thymines   thymine dimer

jacent thymine residues[2] in the same DNA chain — is the only one that has been correlated with the biological inactivation of DNA. We shall, therefore, be concerned almost entirely with the proof that thymine dimers lead to inactivation, and with a possible mechanism by which they produce their effects. More general reviews of nucleic acid photochemistry will be found elsewhere.[20,25,29]

Photochemical Products in Irradiated DNA's

Ultraviolet produces a variety of photochemical changes in DNA and in nucleoproteins. If these changes are to have appreciable biological importance they must be numerous enough so that, for a dose that on the average inactivates all cells or molecules, there is at least one-tenth such photochemical alteration per cell or per molecule. However, the existence of a large number of photochemical changes does not prove that these changes affect the biological system. For example, the irradiation of DNA in its disorganized state results in the photohydration of cytidine residues. However, at 37°C the photohydration product reverses rapidly to normal cytidine.[29] Therefore, it is not pertinent to our discussion. The four known changes that are pertinent (and there may be many more undiscovered ones) are listed in Table 1. The possible importance of each of these photochemical changes in the inactivation of three systems — transforming principle, T2 bacteriophage, and E. coli — can be calculated in the following way. The approximate mean lethal dose for inactivation of each of the biological systems is known, as is the total molecular weight of the DNA in each (Table 2). One may use the data in Table 1 to estimate the numbers of each type of photochemical event that are formed by this mean lethal dose by extrapolating data obtained at high doses to the low doses that correspond to the biological inactivation. Table 3 shows the estimates of the numbers of photochemical events per mean lethal dose for each of the three biological systems. The only known change that occurs in sufficient numbers to affect transforming DNA and T2 phage is thymine dimerization. All of the photochemical mechanisms may be effective in bacterial inactivation because of the large amount of bacterial DNA.

TABLE 1. PHOTOCHEMICAL PRODUCTS THAT MAY BE RESPONSIBLE FOR THE INACTIVATION OF DNA

	1/e dose at 280 mμ (erg/mm^2)	Reference
1. Dimers between adjacent thymine residues	10^5	9, 17, 27
2. Cross-links between complementary strands	$\sim$ 10^5 for M.W. = 6 $\times$ 10^6	11
3. Chainbreaks	$\sim$ 2 $\times$ 10^{5*} for M.W. = 6 $\times$ 10^6	20
4. Protein-DNA links†	$\sim$ 10^4	1, 31

* This value may be too large because the authors give the 1/e dose for T4 phage as $\sim$ 800 erg/mm^2. Much lower values are found by other workers.[22]
† The molecular processes and sizes involved are not understood. The linking is not found with all types of extraction procedures.

TABLE 2. THREE PHOTOBIOLOGICAL SYSTEMS

	M. W. of DNA	Number of TT sequences	m.l.d. at 280 mμ (erg/mm^2)	Ref.
Transforming principle (H. influenzae)	6 $\times$ 10^6	2 $\times$ 10^3	700	28
T2 bacteriophage	1·6 $\times$ 10^8	5 $\times$ 10^4	20	22
E. coli 15 T$^-$A$^-$U$^-$	1·6 $\times$ 10^{10}	3 $\times$ 10^6	50	8

TABLE 3. NUMBERS OF PHOTOCHEMICAL EVENTS PER MEAN LETHAL DOSE FOR THREE BIOLOGICAL SYSTEMS

	Thymine-dimers	Cross-links	Chain breaks	Protein-DNA links %
Transforming principle	7	7 $\times$ 10^{-3}	3 $\times$ 10^{-3}	—
T2 bacteriophage	6	5 $\times$ 10^{-3}	2 $\times$ 10^{-3}	—
E. coli	800	1·3	0·4	0·2

The numerological evidence indicates that thymine dimerization is almost sufficient to account for the observed ultraviolet inactivation of DNA systems and that none of the other known photochemical changes is sufficient. There are five other lines of evidence that indicate that thymines, and most probably dimerization of adjacent thymines, are the crucial elements in ultraviolet inactivation of biological activity.

(1) The action spectrum for the production of reverse mutations in two T4 bacteriophage mutants (irradiated while the DNA was supposedly in a disorganized state) is very similar to the absorption spectrum of thymidine and bears no resemblance to any of the other bases.[23] This result indicates that a photochemical alteration of thymine leads to mutation.

(2) The ultraviolet sensitivity of bacteria increases with the amount of thymine in their DNA.[14,19] The sensitivity is defined in terms of the ultimate slope of the survival curve and is not related to the shoulder because the shoulder may reflect the existence of an intracellular reactivating or repair system.[13,16,35]

(3) Many biological systems are photoreactivable by wavelengths > 300 mμ. It has been shown that an enzyme preparation from yeast capable of photoreactivating transforming DNA also splits thymine pimers.[21,36] We shall elaborate on this point below. None of the other photochemical changes have been enzymatically photoreactivated, nor does cross linking show the peculiar photochemical properties of thymine dimers described below.[10]

(4) Replacement of thymine by 5-bromouracil results in a loss of photoreactivability.[32]

(5) More dimers per incident dose are found in denatured DNA than in native DNA.[34] In synchronized E. coli cultures, both dimer production and inactivation depend on the stage in the division cycle when the irradiation is given. Irradiation at times that produce more dimers also give rise to more inactivation.[34] This argument implicating thymine dimers as the inactivating events is not too definitive because many other photochemical processes may also depend upon the state of organization of DNA. For example, just before the onset of temperature denaturation the amount of cross linking between individual DNA strands increases markedly.[11]

Direct Evidence that Thymine Dimers Inactivate DNA

The above evidence indicates that thymines, and probably adjacent pairs of thymine residues, are important from a photobiological point of view. However, it does not indicate definitively that it is the dimerization of thymines that is responsible for a large fraction of the inactivation, and it does not indicate how much of the inactivation is attributable to thymine dimers. The conceptual difficulty in identifying dimers with ultraviolet-lesions is that increasing doses of ultraviolet − doses that lead to increasing amounts of inactivation − yield increasing amounts of *all* types of photochemical products. In order to ascertain the importance of one particular type of product as compared to others one must have a way of varying the amount of that particular product without changing the others. Such a way is available. It depends upon the peculiar photochemical properties of thymine dimers. These dimers are not only formed by ultraviolet but they are also split by ultraviolet to yield the original residues unchanged.[9,17]

$$————pTpT———— \underset{\longleftarrow}{\overset{h\nu}{\longrightarrow}} ————p\hat{T}pT————$$

The quantum yield for the forward reaction is approximately 0·02 whereas the reverse reaction has a quantum yield of approximately 1. Despite the large quantum yield for the reverse reaction, many dimers are still formed by ultraviolet-irradiation because the dimer itself has very little absorption at longer wavelengths in the ultraviolet as a result of saturation of the 5, 6 double bond. At any given irradiating wavelength a steady state exists at high doses (Table 4) such that the rate of formation of dimers equals the

TABLE 4. STEADY STATE FRACTION OF THYMINE DIMERS IN POLY-T FOR SEVERAL INCIDENT WAVELENGTHS[9]

Wavelength (mμ)	Relative number of dimers	Dose of 280 mμ to yield the same fraction (10^4erg/mm^2)
239	0·14	1·1
248	0·32	2·6
265	0·82	12
280	0·98	∞
290	1·0	—

rate of breakage. It is apparent that long wavelength irradiation yields a steady state value in which almost all the thymine residues are dimerized whereas short wavelength irradiation yields a steady state with very few dimers. Therefore it is possible to shift from one equilibrium value of dimers to another by changing the incident wavelength. For example, if one irradiates with a large dose of 290 mμ and makes a large number of dimers, subsequent irradiation by shorter wavelengths will break some of these dimers and yield an equilibrium value characteristic of the last wavelength used. Figure 1 shows the shift in dimer equilibrium in native DNA as observed by the decrease in absorbance of the DNA.[27] (The existence of thymine dimers in irradiated DNA may be inferred not only from the absorbance measurements shown in Fig. 1 but also from the direct isolation and chemical characterization[2] of the dimers by acid[33] or enzymatic hydrolysis[6] of irradiated DNA.) The reactivating effect of short wavelengths has not been found

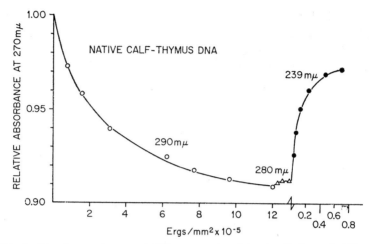

FIG. 1. Absorbance changes at 270 mμ produced by irradiations of different wavelengths. Absorbance decreases correspond to the formation of thymine dimers. Increases represent the splitting of dimers.[27]

for any other photochemically produced system of DNA except thymine dimers, and is experimentally different from the enzymatic photoreactivation that utilizes wavelengths > 300 mμ.

The implication of reversibility of thymine dimerization is clear. The transforming ability of DNA irradiated with a large dose of 280 mμ (large enough to make more dimers than would be produced by short wavelength irradiation) should be reactivated by subsequent irradiation at a shorter wavelength.[28] Such is found to be the case as is indicated in Fig. 2. These data supply conclusive evidence that the breakage of thymine dimers restores the transforming activity of inactivated DNA. The reactivation shown in Fig. 2 depends on the order in which the two wavelengths are given. If the shorter wavelength had been given first, no reactivation would have been observed. The reactivation by wavelengths other than 239 mμ has been shown to follow the expected wavelength dependence of dimer splitting. Moreover the splitting of thymine dimers is quantitatively related to the increase in biological activity (Fig. 3).[28] The reactivation by 239 mμ does not bring the biological activity back to 100 per cent because (a) 239 itself does not split all the thymine dimers, and (b) there exist other photochemical products (at present unidentified) which are responsible for inactivation.[28] At the high doses shown in Fig. 2 thymine dimers account for between 50 and 70 per cent of the inactivation of biological activity and a mean lethal dose corresponds to one dimer every 200 nucleotides. Because of the one to one correspondence of the ordinates of Fig. 3, one may extend them

FIG. 2. Effects of irradiations with two wavelengths on the transforming activity of DNA of *H. influenzae*. Several doses of 280 mμ (— — —)followed by 239 mμ (——). The doses are plotted as the sum of the initial dose at 280 mμ and that 239 mμ.[28]

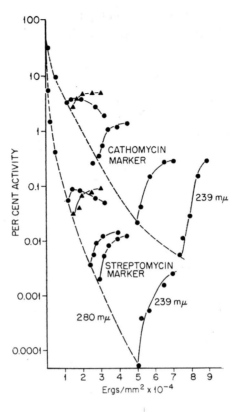

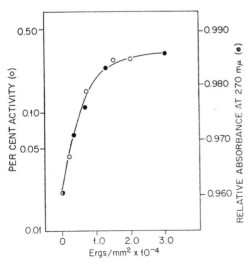

FIG. 3. Reactivation by 239 mμ following inactivation by 280 mμ. The quantitative agreement between dimer splitting (measured by the absorbance increase of DNA on the right scale) and reactivation of biological activity (measured by the ability to transform to cathomycin resistance, left scale).[28]

to obtain the survival level (2 per cent) which would correspond to all the dimers split (relative absorbance at 270 mμ equals 1·000).

Photoreactivation and Thymine Dimers

If an irradiated transforming DNA is treated with a photoreactivating enzyme from yeast[21] in the presence of light, the DNA is partially reactivated and no further reactivation by 239 mμ can be demonstrated.[24] Moreover, the level of activity reached after maximum enzymatic photoreactivation corresponds to the level, calculated above, for all the thymine dimers broken. It is concluded that (a) the production of thymine dimers is responsible for the biological inactivation of transforming principle DNA, and (b) the photoreactivating enzyme from yeast does nothing but split thymine dimers.[24] If this last statement can be proven for other photoreactivating systems one might have a rapid method of ascertaining the fraction of ultraviolet damage that arises from the formation of thymine dimers.

Three additional remarks are pertinent: (1) At low doses of radiation the dose reduction factor produced by use of the photoreactivating enzyme is about 9[21], implying that ~90 per cent of the ultraviolet damage results from thymine dimers. (2) The DNA's used for these studies *(H. influenzae)* are rich in TT sequences.[18] DNA's which contain relatively fewer TT sequences either may be more radioresistant or may be inactivated by other mechanisms. (3) RNA containing viruses can be photoreactivated (see Ref. 25 for a review). At this stage of our knowledge it is tempting to guess that such reactivation proceeds by reversal of dimers between the adjacent uracil residues that have been observed in irradiated polynucleotides.[30]

Molecular Mechanisms by which Thymine Dimers Affect DNA

We have presented extensive evidence that ultraviolet affects the biological activity of DNA by the production of thymine dimers. The reaction of enzymes with irradiated DNA suggest a biochemical mechanism for the effects of ultraviolet irradiation on living systems. The formation of a thymine dimer will change the local structure of a DNA molecule and it might be expected that this change affects enzymatic reactions involved in the degradation and synthesis of DNA. It has been shown, for example, that thymine dimers block the enzymatic degradation of DNA by phosphodiesterases. The block takes place in the immediate neighborhood of the thymine dimer since enzyme-resistant sequences of the form pXpTpT appear as products of enzymatic degradation.[6]

Denatured DNA acts as a primer for DNA synthesis in an enzymatic polymerizing system utilizing a polymerase derived from calf-thymus glands.[3]

$$\text{primer DNA} + \begin{array}{l} \text{dATP} \\ \text{dGTP} \\ \text{dCTP} \\ \text{dTTP} \end{array} \xrightarrow{\text{polymerase}} \text{more DNA.}$$

If ultraviolet-irradiated DNA is used as a primer in this polymerizing system the *rate* at which new DNA is synthesized decreases with incident radiation dose[7] (Fig. 4). DNA synthesis may be followed by using one radioactive

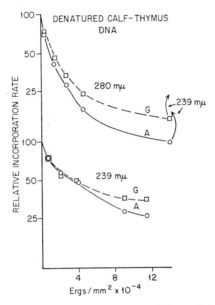

Fig. 4. The effect of ultraviolet-irradiation on the priming activity of DNA. Curves A represent dATP[32] and curves G dGTP[32] incorporation. Primer activity inactivated by 280 mμ is partially restored, as shown by arrows with $1 \cdot 5 \times 10^4$ erg/mm² of 239 mμ.[7]

triphosphate and three nonradioactive triphosphates. It is seen that the rate of incorporation of dATP is affected more than the rate of incorporation of dGTP. Since incorporation of A measures the intact T's in the primer DNA, this is an expected result if thymine dimers are the major cause for the decrease in polymerization rate. This selective effect on the incorporation of A, as well as the decrease in incorporation rate of the other bases, is partially reversible by irradiation with a shorter wavelength (Fig. 4). These biochemical data are similar to those in Figs. 2 and 3 and indicate that thymine dimers affect the process of DNA synthesis *in vitro*. The decrease in priming rate after irradiation depends markedly on the number of TT sequences in the irradiated DNA. DNA's containing large numbers of TT sequences are affected much more than those containing few sequences.[7] One thymine dimer per 200 nucleotides decreases the priming rate to one half its initial value.

A decrease in synthesis rate, with irradiated primer DNA, occurs for all bases tested. Because incorporation of A is affected more than G, the product synthesized using an irradiated primer has a mutant composition compared to the original DNA. It contains relatively more G than the primer

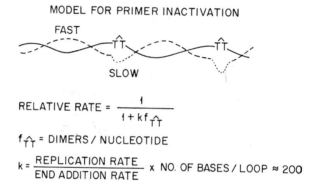

MODEL FOR PRIMER INACTIVATION

FAST

SLOW

$$\text{RELATIVE RATE} = \frac{1}{1 + kf_{\widehat{TT}}}$$

$f_{\widehat{TT}}$ = DIMERS / NUCLEOTIDE

$k = \dfrac{\text{REPLICATION RATE}}{\text{END ADDITION RATE}} \times \text{NO. OF BASES / LOOP} \approx 200$

FIG. 5. A model to explain the action of ultraviolet on primer activity.[7]

DNA. A simple model[7] which can explain these data is shown schematically in Fig. 5. On this model polymerization takes place rapidly along a DNA chain up to the neighborhood of a thymine dimer. At this point the DNA chain has the wrong configuration and synthesis either stops or is drastically decreased. The data indicate that, on the average, DNA synthesis is not completely stopped in the neighborhood of the thymine dimer.[7] It is not yet clear, however, whether there exist dimers or groups of dimers which may act as absolute blocks to DNA synthesis. If such absolute blocks do exist they offer a ready explanation for the cessation of DNA synthesis in irradiated bacterial cultures.[12]

Polymerization in the region labelled *fast* in Fig. 5 represents incorporation of complementary bases into the new chain. In the region of a thymine dimer such fast replication would be replaced by a slow, more-or-less random polymerization — a so-called end-addition reaction.[5] In the region of a TT sequence the end-addition reaction ($\sim 1/100$ as rapid as replicative synthesis) results in the incorporation of bases other than the complementary A.

End-addition might even result in the incorporation of more than two bases in place of two A's. Thus polymerization around a TT dimer is a slow process and accounts for the decrease in incorporation rate observed with irradiated primer DNA. Once the block has been circumvented the replicative reaction proceeds rapidly until the next block, etc.

The type of a model shown in Fig. 5 predicts (a) that incorporation of A will be affected more than that of the other bases, (b) the observed shape of the dose response curve (even after very large doses there is only a limited number of thymine dimers, and hence the synthesis rate cannot fall to zero but levels off at some low value), and (c) that in the newly synthesized DNA the number of AA sequences should be markedly decreased as compared to an unirradiated primer (such a decrease has been observed[26]).

DISCUSSION AND CONCLUSION

Table 5 gives a summary of the experimental evidence that a large fraction of the effects of ultraviolet light on biological systems arises from production of thymine dimers in DNA. The production of thymine dimers accounts for a large fraction of the ultraviolet damage to transforming DNA and their effects on the priming activity of DNA are sufficient to explain the majority of the killing and mutagenic action of ultraviolet light.

TABLE 5. EVIDENCE INDICATING THAT A LARGE FRACTION OF ULTRAVIOLET EFFECTS ON BIOLOGICAL SYSTEMS ARISE FROM THYMINE DIMERS

1. They are produced in sufficient numbers.
2. The action spectrum for mutation production in some intracellular phage is like the thymidine absorption spectrum.
3. Ultraviolet sensitivities of bacterial species increases with the thymine content of their DNA.
4a. Most biological systems are photoreactivable and the photoreactivating enzyme from yeast splits thymine dimers in DNA.
4b. Photoreactivation has been sought for but not found for cross linking, chain breakage and DNA protein binding. Cross linking by 280 mμ is not reversible by subsequent 239 mμ irradiation.
5. Replacement of thymine by 5-bromouracil results in a loss of photoreactivation (but an increase in sensitivity).
6. The sensitivity during the division cycle of E. coli parallels the production of dimers by ultraviolet.
7. The inactivation of transforming DNA by 280 mμ is partially reversed by subsequent 239 mμ. (After enzymatic photoreactivation no 239 mμ reversal is observed.)
8. The inactivation of primer DNA by 280 mμ
   (a) is largest for the DNA with most TT sequences,
   (b) is greater for dATP than for dGTP incorporation,
   (c) is partially reversed by 239 mμ irradiation,
   (d) gives rise to product DNA in which the number of AA sequences is markedly reduced.

Photochemical products involving groups of bases other than thymine dimers have been observed[6] and it is to be hoped that the relation between these as yet unanalyzed products and biological inactivation will be found shortly. It should be clear that in the near future we shall probably understand at least 95 per cent of the biological effects of ultraviolet on DNA and perhaps an equally large per cent of the ultraviolet mutation and killing of a wide variety of cells.

REFERENCES

1. ALEXANDER, P. and MOROSON, H., *Nature*, **194**, 882 (1962).
2. BEUKERS, R. and BERENDS, W., *Biochim. Biophys. Acta*, **49**, 181 (1961).
3. BOLLUM, F. J., *J. Biol. Chem.* **234**, 2733 (1959).
4. BOLLUM, F. J., in *The Cell Nucleus*, p. 163, Academic Press, N. Y. (1960).
5. BOLLUM, F. J., *J. Biol. Chem.* **235**, PC18 (1960).
6. BOLLUM, F. J. and SETLOW, R. B., *Federation Proc.* **21**, 374 (1962).
7. BOLLUM, F. J. and SETLOW, R. B., *Biochim. Biophys. Acta*, **68**, 599 (1963).
8. BOYCE, R. and SETLOW, R., *Biochim. Biophys. Acta*, **68**, 446 (1963).
9. DEERING, R. A. and SETLOW, R. B., *Biochim. Biophys. Acta*, **68**, 526 (1963).
10. DRAKE, D. and SETLOW, R. B., unpublished observations.
11. GLISIN, V. and DOTY, P., *Biochim. Biophys. Acta*, **61**, 458 (1962).
12. HANAWALT, P. C. and SETLOW, R. B., *Biochim. Biophys. Acta*, **41**, 283 (1960).
13. HARM, W., *J. Cellular Comp. Physiol.* **58**, Suppl. 1, 69 (1961).
14. HAYNES, R., Abstracts Biophys. Soc. N. Y. (1963).
15. HOLLAENDER, A. and EMMONS, C. W., *Cold Spring Harbor Symp. Quant. Biol.* **9**, 179 (1941).
16. HOWARD-FLANDERS, P., BOYCE, R. P. and THERIOT, L., *Nature*, **195**, 51 (1962).
17. JOHNS, H. E., RAPAPORT, S. A. and DELBRÜCK, M., *J. Mol. Biol.* **4**, 104 (1962).
18. JOSSE, J., KAISER, A. D. and KORNBERG, A., *J. Biol. Chem.* **236**, 864 (1961).
19. KAPLAN, H. S. and ZAVARINE R., *Biochem. Biophys. Res. Comm.* **8**, 432 (1962).
20. MARMUR, J., ANDERSON, W. F., MATTHEWS, L., BERNS, K., GAJEWSKA E., LANE, D. and DOTY, P., *J. Cellular Comp. Physiol.* **58**, Suppl. 1, 33 (1961).
21. RUPERT, C. S., *J. Gen. Physiol.* **43**, 573 (1960).
22. SETLOW, J. K. and SETLOW, R. B., *Proc. Natl. Acad. Sci. U.S.* **46**, 791 (1960).
23. SETLOW, J. K., *Nature*, **194**, 664 (1962).
24. SETLOW, J. K. and SETLOW, R. B., *Nature*, **197**, 560 (1963).
25. SETLOW, R. B., *Brookhaven Symposia in Biol.* **14**, 1 (1961).
26. SETLOW, R. B., CARRIER, W. L. and BOLLUM, F. J., Abstract Biophys. Soc. N. Y. (1963).
27. SETLOW, R. B. and CARRIER, W. L., *Photochem. Photobiol.* **2**, 49 (1963).
28. SETLOW, R. B. and SETLOW, J. K., *Proc. Natl. Acad. Sci. U.S.* **48**, 1250 (1962).
29. SHUGAR, D., in *The Nucleic Acids*, eds. E. Chargaff and J. N. Davidson. Academic Press, N. Y., 1960, Vol. 3, p. 39.
30. SHUGAR, D. and WIERZCHOWSKI, K. L., *1st. Int. Cong. Photobiol.*, Copenhagen (1960), Elsevier, Amsterdam (1961).
31. SMITH, K. C., *Biochem. Biophys. Res. Comm.* **8**, 157 (1962).
32. STAHL, F. W., CRASEMANN, J. M., OKUN, L., FOX, E. and LAIRD, C., *Virology*, **13**, 98 (1961).
33. WACKER, A., DELLWEG, H. and WEINBLUM, D., *Naturwissenschaften*, **47**, 477 (1960).
34. WACKER, A., DELLWEG H. and JACHERTS D., *J. Mol. Biol.* **4**, 410 (1962).
35. WITKIN, E., *J. Cellular Comp. Physiol.* **58**, Suppl. 1, 135 (1961).
36. WULFF, D. L. and RUPERT, C. S., *Biochem. Biophys. Res. Comm.* **7**, 237 (1962).

DISCUSSION

CHAIRMAN (A. HOLLAENDER): The paper of Dr. Setlow is open for discussion.

F. HERCIK: Dr. Setlow, I would just like to ask you one question: How do you explain the reactivation of the shorter wavelengths from the physical point of view?

R. B. SETLOW: The wavelength dependence of the formation and breakage of dimers has, I think, a very simple physical explanation. If I take the absorption spectra of thymine and thymine dimers, thymine has an absorption maximum at 265 and a minimum at about 235 mμ. The dimer has no double bond and its absorption spectrum has no maximum. If you use a shorter wavelength you absorb energy in the dimer and this breaks it. The quantum yielded for breaking the dimer is about one, so a dimer is a very strange configuration. Every time a quantum is absorbed in it, it goes. Shorter wavelengths are more effective because longer ones are not absorbed. On the other hand, if you go to too short a wavelength, you start getting products that are not dimers. This is the reason why I have not gone below those wavelengths.

C. CHAGAS: Dr. Setlow, I would like to ask you the following question: The equilibrium changes with the radiation, as you have shown on one curve. What would be the reason for this very pronounced change in the equilibrium, and what would be the recombination of dimers?

R. B. SETLOW: I am not sure whether you want a number or not. If one irradiates at a short wavelength, obviously the quanta are absorbed both in thymine and in the dimer... so you both make break and dimers at the same time and at a wavelength of 235 the equilibrium number of dimers that you have made is about 15 per cent of the total possible numbers. Is this the answer to your question?

C. CHAGAS: The question is: When you irradiate the equilibrium constant is lowered. Have you more residual dimers or not?

R. B. SETLOW: No, you do not have more residual dimers. Symbolically, what I am saying is that ultraviolet light produces dimers *plus* other products. When we give a large dose of ultraviolet light, we change both of these. The shorter wavelength only reverses dimers and that is why the inactivation level goes down continuously. There are other products. When you irradiate you get to a maximum survival and if you continue the survival goes down.

H. MARCOVICH: What is the maximum distance which allows a dimer formation? This is related to the second question, which is: Some triplets of the code could be specifically changed by this dimer formation and so you would except to have only some aminoacids?

R. B. SETLOW: Dimers have been observed in the following types of model systems, a dinucleotide, a dinucleotide with a single phosphate. They have been observed with thymine frozen in ice in which case the thymine crystallizes out and gets close together. They have not been observed in the polymer of the type ATATAT or in TppT. I do not know of other possibilities that have been tried. I have the feeling, someone has tried T's separated by another base, and there is no dimer formed there, nor is there one formed in a cyclic diphosphate.

R. HAUSMANN: You would prefer — on esthetic grounds, as you say — that DNA-strands synthesized along a template with thymine dimers were continuous. I think, this esthetic concern comes from the assumption that the DNA replication must begin at the extremities of a DNA molecule. In this case we might admit that after the complementation of a template containing thymine dimers, these, fitting with no complementary base, protrude from the double strand, forming bridges or loops.

Now, in a recent paper (to be published) C. Bresch has elaborated a molecular model for phage-DNA-replication, in order to account for various genetic data. One of his main

Note: This is not the edited discussion.

assumptions is that only the replication of a continuous double strand starts at the ends, while the complementation of a single strand may begin at any point, but proceeds in only one direction. In case this were true, there would be no reason to admit the formation of a continuous complementary strand. The strand could be interrupted when it reaches the dimers and its synthesis could be reassumed at any point beyond the block. Thus, "partial replicas" would be formed along the primer molecule.

R. B. SETLOW: I carefully stated that these are static grounds. I also maintain that models of molecular mechanisms based on genetic evidence are also static models and that the questions you raise are amenable to experimental attack. Even if you say that DNA replication can begin at the center of the chain, one has to explain why the production of a lesion in the middle slows down the rate of DNA synthesis. It does, so you have to say: well, it can start as rapidly then in the middle. The evidence is against starting in the middle in the usual method of DNA synthesis. Dr. Bollum at Oak Ridge, has measured the rate of DNA synthesis using primers of different lengths. As the length of the primer is decreased (by ultrasonics) the rate of DNA synthesis increases. Now, the only thing that increased was the number of free ends. As the number of ends increases, the rate of DNA synthesis increases, even though the total amount of DNA is always the same. It is just in a different configuration.

May I ask Dr. Hamilton if he has any remarks about going from one direction or two directions on strands or not? I have been trying to get Dr. Hamilton to give me the answer to this question for a week and finally I have the opportunity to ask him.

L. D. HAMILTON: I do not know anything about propriety of giving unpublished results from other people and I think this is not for the record — but it is of considerable interest that John Cairns, using radioautography and tritiated thymidine, has been able to show that when the DNA of *E. coli* replicates, the two strands come apart at one end and the new DNA is laid down simultaneously. In other words, the polarity of the ends does not really enter into the synthesis of the new DNA. It appears that the ends which come apart both start synthesizing new DNA. I must say in comment on the previous speaker that, of course, there is very good genetic evidence from the recent work of Brenner Crich *et al.* at Cambridge, that the message is read from a particular fixed point. In other words, the replication or the reading of the message does not take place at random along the DNA but actually begins at a particular point. The effects of interruptions such as Dr. Setlow has achieved obviously open up the possibility of studying in biological systems such as phage recombination, perhaps the genetic effects of such specific deletions. I think clearly this is going to be of considerable interest and Dr. Setlow is to be congratulated on making available a very basic technique.

R. B. SETLOW: If I may say a word, since the second magic word "code" has come up with its subsidiary triplets. There is an analogue of the triplets in the reactions of enzymes with irradiated DNA which is simply this: Suppose that one has a DNA with a thymine pair in it, and we irradiate this DNA and happen to have made a dimer between such adjacent thymines. Now, we attempt to degrade the DNA by enzymatic means with diesterase, derived from snake venom, that splits the DNA, to 5 prime monophosphates. It splits the DNA leading to mononucleotides until it comes to the dimer. The structure of the DNA is not the normal structure in this region, and the enzyme cannot work through this block. Either the enzymes or contaminants in the preparation take over and skip three bases and then continues to give mononucleotides. The products one obtains are trinucleotides, $p X p \overset{\frown}{T p T}$ (where X is either A or G or T or C) containing a dimer. There is the triplet interference, if you like, of the enzymatic reactions on DNA.

E. H. Y. CHU: Dr. Setlow has beautifully demonstrated not only the physical changes accompanying thymine dimerization but also its manifestation on a biological level. It is difficult, however, to extend these findings from the molecular level to the cellular and eventually to organismic level. One example is the ultraviolet induced chromosome aberration. Although we know that DNA is probably the primary site of the ultraviolet injury we don't know how it is damaged, and whether it involves thymine dimerization or other mechanisms are still uncertain.

H. S. KAPLAN: Dr. Setlow referred to the fact that bromouracil sensitizes to ultraviolet and to the fact that there is no photoreactivation. My colleague, Dr. Kendric Smith, has studied the response of bromouracil relative to thymine in DNA *in vivo (Biochem. Biophys. Res. Comm.* **6**, 458, 1961). He finds that the spectral degradation of bromouracil in DNA is greater per unit ultraviolet dose than that of thymine *in vivo*. Secondly, he has studied the ultraviolet photoproducts of bromouracil in frozen solution. He made the very interesting discovery that bromouracil in pure solution, frozen and exposed to ultraviolet, produces absolutely no photoproducts and seems to be totally devoid of sensitivity. But if he added small amounts of cytosine to the bromouracil solutions he then got a striking ultraviolet degradation of the bromouracil. It could be shown by differential labelling that the cytosine did not take part in the photoproducts. It would appear that in frozen solution the bromouracil molecules do not physically relate one to another in a favourable way, unless cytosine is also present, in which case the stacking of bromouracil molecules becomes more favourable. Under these conditions three different photoproducts result, one of which is apparently a bromouracil dimer and the other two are as yet unidentified. The phenomenon is further extended if uracil instead of cytosine is added to the frozen bromouracil solution. Under these conditions 5 photoproducts result, two of which involve interactions between bromouracil and uracil. The other three do not involve the participation of uracil. Thus it would appear that the simplest explanation of the differential ultraviolet radiosensitivity of bromouracil *in vivo* is that more photoproducts can be made by ultraviolet from this base than from natural base, thymine. Now, the striking effect of having cytosine present in frozen solution raises the question that I want to put to Dr. Setlow: Is there any evidence that the nature of the base which occurs adjacent to a TT sequence differentially affects the probability of a thymine dimerization?

R. B. SETLOW: Yes. The experiments are not conclusive. The experiment consists of preparing trinucleotides by ultraviolet light, breaking the dimer bonds and then making dimer bonds. It turns out that compounds of the form C T T are the most sensitive compound for making a dimer, and the least sensitive is GTT. The paradox for bromouracils has not been given to you because the experiments are not completed — the paradox amplified is this: if one irradiates a bromouracil DNA and observes the priming activity, the bromouracil DNA is radioresistant, as compared to the thymine containing DNA. But bromouracil-substituted systems on a biological scale are sensitive, so obviously the priming story is not the whole answer.

H. S. KAPLAN: It is conceivable that one of the photoproducts of bromouracil, as Wacker has claimed, is simply uracil. If you take off the bromine you still code for an adenine at the site of the uracil.

R. B. SETLOW: Yes. But then what has this to do with inactivation?

H. S. KAPLAN: In the primer-polymerase system you would except to get product formation which appears to be normal, but *in vivo* you might expect to kill the organism.

R. B. SETLOW: Why?

H. S. KAPLAN: Because uracil does not belong in the DNA.

R. B. SETLOW: That is what I do not see. . . . It has been proposed that bromouracil is debrominated giving uracil and obviously this does not belong and it is why a cell is killed. But the only evidence is the word "obviously".

H. EAGLE: In the DNA and in the polynucleotides (formed with the irradiated DNA as a primer) with altered base ratios, do you interpret this as a result of a deletion or a substitution?

R. B. SETLOW: I interpret this as a substitution but I have no evidence.

L. R. CALDAS: I would like to ask you a question which is perhaps not directly connected with your work; can you explain the phenomenon of photoprotection described by Jagger?

R. B. SETLOW: The phenomenon to which Dr. Caldas refers is as follows: Cells of *E. coli* are irradiated with wavelength of about 340 mμ in a nonnutrient medium. Subsequent to this irradiation they are irradiated with 253 mμ and the survival curves are compared for two types of cells: cells that have not been exposed to 340, and cells which have. The phenomenon of photoprotection is that cells given 340 survive better than those not given it. This is distinct from photoreactivation in that it is given before the ultraviolet light. I feel that if Dr. Jagger were here, he would say the following (these are Dr. Jagger's experimets, not mine) "340 mμ produces a division delay or actually a growth delay in the bacteria. This growth delay is what is responsible for the higher survival." It is a growth delaying property similar to the various types of holding restorations that one obtains, if you put the cells in nonnutrient medium, after irradiation. It may be similar to the agar healing effect in the lysogenic systems.

P. C. VIGIER: At one point of your talk, you made an allusion to the possibility of dimers being formed between uracils. Was this purely speculative or did you have some evidence for that and what was it?

R. B. SETLOW: There is good experimental evidence for the existence of dimers between urocils. It has been obtained by a number of people. Experiments of the type that have been described by Dr. Kaplan in which uracil in frozen solution is irradiated. Spectrocopically one can detect the formation and breakage of dimers in poly U and in UpU. Now uracils have a complication, in that there are two types of reactions: dimer formations with uracils, of addition of water to uracil. The water addition product takes place at the 5,6 double bond and removes such uracils from the pathway of dimers. The hydration product is a stable compound relatively speaking and so from the irradiation of a polymer containing U one cannot infer whether the damage arises from this product or from dimers. There are two experiments in which the poly U has been irradiated and the resulting product tested for its ability to stimulate the incorporation of phenylalanine into acid-insoluble material. They have been performed by Grossman at Brandeis and by Wacker in Germany. Both experiments agree that the irradiation of poly U depresses its stimulating effect. Unfortunately the doses quoted by the two sets of authors differ by a factor of 10 from one another, and I do not know which is which. Grossman also reports that the irradiation of poly U depresses the stimulation of phenylalanine but increases the stimulation of serine into acid-insoluble material. The interpretation is not obvious.

H. MARCOVICH: I would like to ask Dr. Setlow about Dr. Jagger's explanations. What would Dr. Setlow say about the delay on the dimer formation? When you illuminate bacteria and you have a delay in division, what has this to do with a dimer formation of thymine?

R. B. SETLOW: At various times at this Conference, a magic word has been used and I invoke this magic word. The magic word is "repair" and all things which we do not explain easily, we say are a repair mechanism. One may hypothesize that *E. coli* contains an enzyme that in the dark splits dimers (this concept is subject to experimental verification for if such a repair enzyme exists, you should be able to make an extract of cells, which in the dark can split thymine dimers). The only way to detect such a repair mechanism, I feel, is to have a particular product to work on. There is a photoreactivating enzyme that needs light. Is there one that can work in the dark? If so it obviously needs an energy source.

H. MARCOVICH: Activated before?

R. B. SETLOW: Oh, I am sorry, I misinterpreted. I turned Dr. Jagger's explanations round the other way. He feels that the 340 division delay is a process that is working on the DPN system or something of that sort. This is where the division delay comes about. The division delay or the growth delay gives more time for repair processes, therefore more survival.

H. MARCOVICH: This will give more time for repair mechanism?

R. B. SETLOW: No, it would give just more time for the repair process to go on.

CHAIRMAN: Any more questions regarding these two very stimulating papers we had this morning? I think we had a very successful morning and we would like to thank both speakers for their very excellent presentations.

RADIATION EFFECTS ON ENZYMES
AND ENZYMATIC SYSTEMS, PARTICULARLY
ON CHOLINESTERASES

A. B. HARGREAVES

Instituto de Biofísica, Universidade do Brasil

The interaction of radiant energy and molecular systems may be studied either by the effect of the incident radiation on matter or by the changes produced by the molecules on the efferent radiation.

Absorption spectra of nucleic acids and nucleoproteins, in wavelengths around 2600 Å, of aromatic aminoacids and proteins in the vicinity of 2800 Å and the Soret band of ferroporphyrin compounds are well-known examples of the second aspect of the problem, i.e. the spectrophotometry. However, it is the study of radiation effects on molecules, viruses and cells that constitutes the extensive chapter of radiobiology.

Physico-chemical and biological changes of molecules and biological systems have been the scope of modern radiobiology.

For a radiation beam to provoke a measurable change on a system, it is necessary that the light quanta have enough energy to bring about the expected effect. This effect will depend on the incident intensity, the wavelength and the time of exposition.

The absorbed energy can be degraded as heat or may reappear for instance as fluorescent photons. It can supply the energy for chemical reactions or it can disrupt the molecular organization as in the denaturation of proteins and the inactivation of viruses and bacteria.

Enzymes are protein molecules with catalytic capability, this property being estimated by specific methods. The catalytic power is designed as "enzymatic activity" and it is generally defined as the rate of molecules of a substrate transformed in a period of time per unit of dry weight of the enzyme preparation.

The catalytic property is believed to be located in certain sites of the protein molecules, the so-called "active centers".

Since the enzymatic activity depends on the molecular organization of the protein, enzymes are ideal systems for the radiation action study.

Any effect of radiation on molecules disturbs the enzymatic activity. This can be followed very easily by laboratory methods.

Since the enzyme systems are constituted by molecules, it should be interesting to know the number of absorbed quanta per unit of volume in a period of time. This can be represented by the following expression:

$$\frac{\text{absorbed photons}}{\text{seconds}} = sIN$$

where s is the surface of exposition to radiation, I the intensity of incident light and N the number of units of irradiated substance per unit of surface.

If we assume that not all the incident photons are effective in provoking measurable effect, we may take in account the fraction of absorbed photons that are "effective".

We may then write:

$$\frac{\text{affected molecules}}{\text{time (seconds)}} = \Phi sIN$$

The quantity Φ is known as the *quantum yield* or *quantum efficiency*. We may define the *quantum yield* as the probability that an absorbed photon will be effective.

$$\Phi = \frac{\text{number of molecules affected}}{\text{number of quanta absorbed}}$$

If the initial number N_0 of molecules at the time t_0 is considered in relation to the number N of unaffected molecules, after a time t of exposure under the radiation, we may write:

$$\ln \frac{N}{N_0} = - \Phi sIt \tag{1}$$

and

$$\frac{N}{N_0} = e^{-(\Phi s)\,(It)} \tag{2}$$

From the above expression it can be seen that the relation N/N_0 permits an approximation of the value of Φ for a given value of I and during a period of time t.

Since the same irradiation results may be achieved by using a "high intensity for a short time" or a "low intensity for a long time", according to the "reciprocity law", we define the product of "intensity × time" as "dose":

$$I \times t = D$$

Equation (2) therefore takes the form:

$$\frac{N}{N_0} = e^{-KD}$$ (3)

where $k = \Phi s$.

In the case of irradiation of enzymes the problem is not so simple, because most of them are not yet crystallized. Therefore, their molecular weight is unknown and consequently so is the number of irradiated molecules.

However, if the initial enzymatic activity A_0 is considered as the number of "units" or "active centers" of the enzyme at the time t_0, and A the number of the remaining unaffected "units" at the time t for an intensity I, i.e. with a dose D, then Eq. (3) can be expressed as follows:

$$\frac{A}{A_0} = e^{-KD}$$ (4)

An example of enzyme irradiation is shown in Fig. 1. Acetylcholinesterase was submitted to radiation of 2537 Å wavelength, at the temperature of 275°K. The relative activity A/A_0 expressed in ordinates is plotted against the corresponding dose of irradiation (abcissas). It is seen that within experimental error the logarithm of the relative activity is proportional to the incident energy. The results are the graphical representation of the equation $A/A_0 = e^{-KD}$. The number of unaffected molecules decreases approximately geometrically while the dose increases arithmetically. This means that for each interval of time a similar proportion of the remaining unaffected molecules is inactivated, showing a direct action of the photons.

This expresses the events occurring during the inactivation of the enzyme as the result of the disruption of the active centers molecular configuration. The mechanism of radiation effectiveness may be due to the direct impingement of its photons upon the irradiated enzyme acting as a "target". The notion that the inactivation of the molecules is a result of the hits of the photons upon the irradiated substance is known as the "target theory", devised by Dessauer, Crowther, Terril and Condon and enlarged on by others as Lea and more recently Zirkle and Tobias. This theory introduces a statistical probability in this study.

The "target theory", however, does not explain all the results obtained in radiation experiments. In some other cases the radiation effect is explained through an indirect action: in the surrounding medium, oxidative substances are produced which are toxic to the preparation.

Since the majority of substances are in solution when irradiated, this possibility is particularly interesting. Water irradiation was the object of special attention since Fricke in 1927 suggested that water molecules become "activated" after irradiation. Nowadays, radiation effects on water are described in terms of free radicals, which are secondary products of the first radiation action possible according to the following scheme:

$$H_2O \rightarrow H_2O^+ + e^-$$

From this first reaction, further results follow:

$$H_2O^+ \rightarrow OH + H^+$$

$$e^- + H_2O \rightarrow OH^- + H$$

Many other radicals are possibly formed from the decomposition of water:

H_2O_2	from two radicals OH
H_2	from two hydrogen ions
$H_2O + O$	from two radicals OH
O_2	from two O^- provenient of the above reaction.

All of them are powerful oxidative agents. Water therefore behaves as a true "Red-ox" system.

Ionizing radiations are particularly capable of forming such chemical radicals.

In general more than one substance is dissolved in solution. It may happen that one of them is sensitive to radiation but not the other one, when each is irradiated separately. However, when irradiated together the sensitive substance A may transfer part of the captured activation energy to the substance B which although not sensitive to the photon energy, is sensitive to the energy acquired by the molecule A':

$$A + hv \rightarrow A'$$

$$A' + B \rightarrow A + B'$$

Many substances are capable of producing this effect, the so-called "photodynamic substances".

Proteins as other macromolecules show physical, physico-chemical and chemical changes when submitted to radiations, due to either the "direct" or the "indirect" action.

The response of an enzymatic preparation to radiation is essentially that of its proteic components. However, many enzymes are constituted by a protein moiety and a prosthetic group that may be radiation sensitive too. A great number of enzyme systems work on coupling with coenzymes. which may be affected as well as the enzyme. Therefore, the inactivation of an enzyme system must be carefully analysed.

The protein molecules are constituted by chains of aminoacids. Their properties are dependent on the sequence in which they are disposed and on the free residues of each aminoacid. The catalytic capability of the enzymes is determined by the "active center" which is composed of only a very small number of aminoacids.

Enzyme inactivation is due to the chemical alteration in these aminoacid residues within the active site, or by the disruption of the essential configuration which causes the denaturation of the molecules.

Among the free end groups the sulphydryl groups have been extensively studied. The $-SH$ groups may be classified in three groups:[2] (a) those reacting readily with weak oxidizing agents such as ferricyanate and o-iodosobenzoic acid and alkylating agents; (b) those which react only with powerful mercaptide forming reagents such as iodine and organic arsenical and mercurial compounds such as p-chloromercurybenzoic acid (the so-called "sluggish" $-SH$ groups) and (c) the other groups remaining in the proteic arrangement are so well protected that the reagents cannot attack them until the protein is denatured and may be designated as "masked" sulphydryl groups. A chemical reagent may be able to oxidize two $-SH$ groups which by loosing $-2H$ will take the S–S configuration.

In the case of an enzyme molecule it is possible that the sulphydryl form is the active form of the enzyme and the disulphide the inactive one. The sulphydryl enzymes, i.e. the enzymes in which the $-SH$ group plays an important role in enzymatic activity, are, therefore, particularly sensitive to radiation. Inactivation is due mainly to the indirect effect of radiation, the oxidation effect being possible as follows:

$$2R-SH+2OH \rightarrow R-S-S-R+2H_2O$$
$$SR-SH+H_2O_2 \rightarrow R-S-S-R+2H_2O$$
$$2R-SH+2O_2H \rightarrow R-S-S-R+2H_2O_2$$

In these cases, total or partial reactivation can be obtained if, after irradiation, the preparation is treated by cysteine or glutathione:

$$R-S-S-R+2GSH \rightarrow 2R-SH+GS-SG$$

The sulphydryl enzymes are much more sensitive to irradiation than the enzymes in which the SH groups are unimportant to enzymatic activity. In the latter case inactivation is, as a rule, irreversible.

Efficiency of radiation increases inversely with the concentration of the irradiated preparation. However, "direct" effect follows approximately the kinetics of a monolecular reaction, while "indirect" effect is usually proportional to the dose. The radiation effect of acetylcholinesterase has been studied either by ultraviolet light and ionizing radiations.

With respect to its response to ultraviolet radiation, the results obtained can be reviewed in Fig. 1.

The results follow the equation:

$$A/A_0 = e^{-KD}$$

The number of remaining unaffected molecules decreases in a geometrical ratio while the dose increases arithmetically showing a direct action of the photons rather than an indirect process. Figure 1 also shows that at different concentrations of the enzyme the slope increases greatly when the enzyme concentration decreases. It would appear that the efficiency of radiation increases inversely with the concentration of the irradiated preparation. However, if we observe from Table 1 the number of "inactivated" molecules, we may conclude that with the same dose intensity, the irradiation in absolute figures was 75 per cent less effective in the second case than in the first one and 95 per cent less in the third.

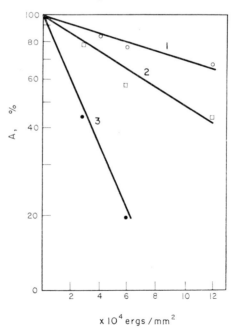

FIG. 1. Ultraviolet light effect upon acetylcholinesterase (Hargreaves[3]).

TABLE 1. EFFECT OF CONCENTRATION OF ACHE UPON THE RATE OF INACTIVATION
BY ULTRAVIOLET LIGHT

Dose: 6×10^4 erg/mm^2		
Total irradiated A_0 units	No. "unaffected" A_x units	No. inactivated $A_0 - A_x$ units
1360	1120	240
136	76	60
23	5	18

This indicates that the inactivation process is random, since the chance that an incident photon will hit the molecule and inactivate the enzyme decreases with dilution.

Acetylcholinesterase, as has been shown, is quite resistant to the action of ultraviolet light although the SH enzymes themselves appear to be very sensitive to irradiation. In fact, besides the radiation effect on acetylcholinesterase, the importance of SH groups on its enzymatic activity

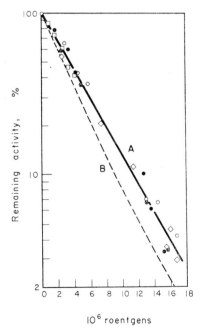

FIG. 2. Co^{60} gamma-radiation inactivation of acetylcholinesterase (Serlin and Cotzias[6]).

was also studied by Hargreaves[3]. In accordance with the works of Mounter and Whittaker[4] and Markwardt[5], Hargreaves found that sulphydryl groups are not important for enzyme activity.

Recently, Serlin and Cotzias[6] (Fig.2) and Hargreaves and Liepin (Table 2) studied the effect of Co^{60} gamma-radiation on acetylcholinesterase. It seems that also in respect of ionizing radiation the enzyme is quite resistant to radiation *in vitro*.

TABLE 2. AChE RESPONSE TO Co^{60} GAMMA-IRRADIATION (γ-IRRADIATION FACILITY, ATOMS AT WORK EXIBIT).

A. B. Hargreaves and L. L. Liepin, Instituto de Biofisica

Material	Total units	Percentage of residual activity
Unexposed:	1700	control
After:		
60,000 r	1560	92
120,000 r	1500	88
200,000 r	1400	82

Besides acetylcholinesterase, pseudocholinesterase has been the object of investigations regarding the effects of radiation. The first communications were not conclusive. Stuttgen[7], for instance, was not able to show any depressive effect of ultraviolet light; in fact he reported an increase of activity proportional to erythema appearance. Kwiatkowski[8] reported similar unsuccessful results with X-rays. Choudhuri[9], using cholinesterase of snake venom, observed irreversible inactivation of the enzyme after exposure to ultraviolet light.

Other authors have published results, especially about the effect of X-rays on serum cholinesterase[10,11] and on cholinesterase of the intestine.[12,13]

Patay[14] and Wilson and Cohen[15] studied the effect of radiation on nerve enzyme by irradiating nerve preparations with ultraviolet light and X-rays. With the enzyme of other organs, Doull and Cummings[16] obtained varying results after X-radiation.

The relationship between the −SH group and the inactivation of the sulphydryl enzymes has been studied more thoroughly by Barron and coworkers mainly by the use of ionizing radiations. Barron, Dickman, Muntz and Singer[17], for instance, have shown that in the case of phosphoglyceraldehyde dehydrogenase, adenosinethiphosphatase and succinoxidase, inactivation by X-rays could be explained at least in part by the oxidation of the SH group. After irradiation, the partially inactivated enzyme can be reactivated by glutathione. Similar results were obtained by Barron and Dickman[18] for phosphoglyceraldehyde dehydrogenase and urease. They irradiated urease previously combined with p-chloromercurybenzoic acid and then treated it with glutathione, obtaining total reactivation. Thus, by protecting the SH group of the molecule it is possible to avoid the destruction which occurs in the unprotected preparations.

Many other authors reported results by using ultraviolet light on both −SH and non-SH enzyme indiscriminately. Among the SH enzymes, urease was studied by Tauber[19] who used photodynamic agents, by Landen[20], by McLauren et al.[21] and by Pillemer et al.[22] Urease is rapidly and irreversibly destroyed by ultraviolet light.

Succinic dehydrogenase was also inactivated with ultraviolet-radiation (Pincussen and Roman[23]). Shugar[24] studied the effect of ultraviolet light on triosephosphate dehydrogenase and observed that cysteine protects the enzyme from inactivation by radiation.

Kauffman and Urbain[25] also studied the ultraviolet-irradiation on enzyme. An interesting aspect of their work lies in the fact that they chanced to use both an SH enzyme papain and a non-SH enzyme trypsin. Under the same experimental conditions, the radiation caused the trypsin solution to loose 90 per cent of its activity in about 12 min, while in the case of papain, the same degree of inactivation was obtained after only 53 sec.

Another enzyme with particular interest in this study is catalase. The main interest in catalase lies in the fact that H_2O_2 is formed by the action of ionizing radiation on water and is highly toxic to most biological systems. Since catalase decomposes hydrogen peroxide according to the reaction $H_2O_2 \rightarrow H_2O + 1/2 \ O_2$, a considerable effort has been made in attempts to demonstrate accumulation of peroxides in vivo and changes of catalase activity both in vivo and in vitro.

Ord and Stocken have revised the studies on this subject[26] and the results are not conclusive enough. Experiments of Forssberg[27] for instance show that crystalline catalase is inactivated in vitro while most of the in vivo experiments do not show any inactivation. On the contrary, in some of them there is activation of the enzyme.

Coenzymes have been also the subject of investigations, since Swallow[28] and Barron[29] directed their interest to the DPN-dependent systems. Most of the enzyme catalysing those systems belong to the SH-enzymes type so that they are very sensitive to radiations in vitro.

Coenzyme A as a coenzyme in which activity the sulphydryl group is of primordial importance was also studied by Barron[29] who verified that in aqueous solutions CoA preparations are easily oxidized.

One of the most striking findings in the study of radiations upon the biological systems is the great difference in the behaviour of these systems when the study is carried out *in vitro* or *in vivo*.

In the case of Coenzyme A, for instance, Du Bois *et al.*[30], Thomson and Mikuta[31] and Romantsev and Zhulanova [32] were not able to obtain evidence of inactivation of any of the Co−A dependent-systems as, for instance, acetylation of sulfanilamide or para-aminobenzoic acid, even after doses of 3320 r.

Adenosinetriphosphatase, an *in vitro* very sensitive enzyme, according to Barron and collaborators, when studied *in vivo* after whole body irradiation of rats and mice, was found by Du Bois and Peterson[33] to have increased activity. The same results were obtained with 5'-nucleotidase.

Regarding the enzymes of blood plasma, pseudocholinesterase, as was stated previously, has been studied thoroughly and it is an example of the few enzymes that show a marked decrease in its activity after radiation. In fact, Luthy[11] and Ord and Stocken[34] found a diminution of ChE in rats and guinea pigs a few hours after irradiation with X-rays in doses of 500–1000 r. The activity returns to normal values 48 hr after irradiation.

On the other hand, Sabine[35] using erythrocytes cholinesterase observed on the contrary an increasing activity 4 days after irradiation. This author also studied acetylcholinesterase of the central nervous system and even using high doses of radiation did not find any depressive effect.

Modern studies in enzymology have been directed to the mechanism of enzyme synthesis, a particular case of protein synthesis. Recent experiments have shown that protein synthesis follows the general pathway indicated in the following scheme:

(a) $A.A. + ATP \xrightarrow{\text{Enzyme 1}} (A.A. - AMP) + PP$

(b) $(A.A. - AMP) + RNA \text{ soluble} \xrightarrow{\text{Enzyme 2}} (A.A. - RNA_s) + AMP$

(c) $(A.A. - RNA_s)_n + n \ RNA_e \xrightarrow{\text{Enzyme 3}} RNA_{\text{soluble}} + RNA + \text{protein}$

$(RNA_e = DNA - \text{information} + RNA)$

Inhibition of DNA synthesis is therefore of primordial importance in the problem of protein synthesis, and consequently of enzyme synthesis. Kornberg and associates[36] obtained DNA synthesis *in vitro* if "primer" DNA was present in the system. In the nuclei of tissue cells the DNA synthesis is accompanied by inorganic phosphate incorporation.

The conclusions in radiation studies in the case of DNA synthesis, as in the previously reported studies on enzymatic systems, are controversial since the the experiments are carried out *in vitro* as well as *in vivo*.

For instance, if the experiments of Hahn and Hevesy[37] show that P^{32} incorporation into DNA is inhibited by ionizing radiation, recent investigations led to the conclusion that radiation does not affect the rate of DNA synthesis in different types of cells.

On the contrary, Painter and Robertson[38] using Hela-cells found that irradiation with 500 r led to considerable increase in DNA synthesis as compared with control cultures. In fibroblasts culture, Harrington[39] did not observe any direct effect of 500 r on DNA synthesis.

Many other observations are also controversial in their conclusions. Kelly *et al.*[40] and Caspersson *et al.*[41] have found that X-irradiation of Erhlich ascites tumors does not inhibit DNA synthesis, but Whitemore *et al.*[42] found that very high doses (4000–5000 r) depressed this mechanism instantaneously. Lajtha and collaborators using radiant energy also inhibited DNA synthesis of bone marrow cells *in vitro*.[43]

The influence of radiation on RNA and protein synthesis has not been studied as extensively as its effect on DNA synthesis. However, a similar situation is seen in both *in vivo* and *in vitro* experiments.

Klein and Forssberg[44], for instance, irradiated Erhlich ascites tumor cells *in vivo* with doses of 1250 r and found no changes of the RNA synthesis. However, Harbers and Heidelberg[45] by *in vitro* irradiation of these same cells inhibited the labelled uracil incorporation into nuclear RNA. Logan *et al.*[46] also showed that irradiation *in vitro*, of isolated liver and calf thymus nuclei, clearly reduced the rate of incorporation of labelled precursors of RNA.

Synthesis of the enzymes themselves has been studied in microorganisms. Using ionizing radiation Pauly[47] obtained a decrease of the lysine decarboxylase induction in *Bacterium cadaveris*. According to this author, every cell possesses one or more "centers of synthesis" each producing a defined number of enzyme molecules, which would be destroyed according to a single-hit kinetic. In contrast to this observation, the induction of catalase by oxygen in diploid mutant of *Saccharomyces cerevisiae* is not only unreduced but stimulated by radiation.

A complete revision of radiation effects on enzymes can be found in several books. For instance, the *Mechanisms in Radiobiology* edited by Maurice Errera and Arne Forssberg, particularly Chapter 3, "The biochemical lesion *in vivo* and *in vitro*", by Ord and Stocken.

The examples presented in this paper, in spite of being in miscellaneous form, have the purpose of showing that *in vitro* irradiation of enzymes can give information about many physico-chemical characteristics and the nature of the studied enzyme molecules. On the contrary, *in vivo* irradiation is still far from a perfect control of the experimental parameters. The observations deal with erratic results which until now do not permit complete conclusions.

Endogenous protective substances play an important role in the *in vivo* effect. It is well known that a variety of chemical substances added to biological systems reduce the effect of radiation. A considerable number of compounds of widely different nature showing protective action have been found. Sulphur-containing compounds as cysteine, cysteamine and glutathione are particularly effective.

Many biological materials like hormones (desoxycorticosterone, estradiol), metabolites (pyruvate, fructose), etc., have protective action.

Little attention has been paid to the endogenous protection substances. Therefore I wish to show a simple but quite demonstrative example of their effect.

Some years ago, Miranda, Faure and Hargreaves[49] obtained from rat liver mitochondria, an extract that protected AChE against inactivation due to denaturation by "ageing", "freezing and thawing", and "purification process". More recently, L. L. Liepin, in our laboratory, was able to protect the enzyme against inactivation by ultraviolet-radiation, using similar preparations. The results are shown in Table 3.

TABLE 3. PROTECTIVE EFFECT OF LIVER "KOCHSAFT" ON INACTIVATION OF AChE BY ULTRAVIOLET IRRADIATION

Percentage variation of enzyme activity in relation to the control		
Group 1. Irradiated enzyme %	Group 2. Irradiated enzyme + Kochsaft (protection) %	Group 3. Irradiated enzyme + Kochsaft (reactivation) %
—57	+ 2	+53
—63	+22	+ 8·5
—55	+37	+ 8·3
—62	+38	+21
—74	+41	+13
—25	+33	+45
—33	+ 3	+37
—31	+58	
—62	+85	
—76	+ 5	
—32	+32	
Av. —57		

Notwithstanding some results that suggest uncontrolled conditions, the data demonstrate a clear difference between the experimental groups, protected and unprotected.

Tissue juices have a high concentration of these substances, which will have an important role in protecting cells against radiation-aggression. On the other hand, there may exist in tissues many other substances possessing, for instance, photodynamic action, which would reinforce the radiation effect. Chemical compounds may exist which after radiation can release the absorbed energy in different ways such as by phosphorescence and vibration. It has been observed that some molecules and macromolecules of biological importance continue to undergo alteration after exposure to radiation has been discontinued — that is, the so-called "after effect". The final *in vivo* effect may result from the balance between the action of the protective and the sensitizing substances existing in tissues.

REFERENCES

1. SETLOW, R. B. and POLLARD, E. C., *Molecular Biophysics*, Addison-Wesley, 1962, pp. 277–351.
2. BARRON, E. S. G., *Adv. in Enzymol.* **11**, 201, 1951.
3. HARGREAVES, A. B., *Arch. Biochem. Biophys.* **57**, 41, 1955.
4. MOUNTER, L. A. and WHITTAKER, V. P., *Biochem. J.* **53**, 167, 1953.
5. MARKWARDT, F., *Naturwiss.* **40**, 341, 1953.
6. SERLIN, I. and COTZIAS, G. C., *Radiation Res.* **6**, 55, 1957.
7. STUTTGEN, G., *Klin. Wochschr.* **24–25**, 758, 1947.
8. KWIATKOWSKI, H., *Fermentforschung*, **15**, 138, 1936.
9. CHOUDHURI, K., *Ann. Biochem. and Exptl. Med. (India)*, **9**, 67, 1949.
10. BARNARD, R. D., *Med. Record*, **162**, 360, 1948.
11. LÜTHY, H., *Radiol. Clin.* **22**, 491, 1953.
12. BURN, J. M., KORDIK, P. and MOLE, R. H., *Brit. J. Pharmacol.* **7**, 58, 1952.
13. CONARD, R. A., *Am. J. Physiol.* **170**, 418, 1952.
14. PATTAY, J., *Arch. Intern. Pharmacodinamie*, **99**, 261, 1954.
15. WILSON, I. B. and COHEN, M., *Biochim. Biophys. Acta*, **11**, 147, 1953.
16. DOULL, J. and CUMMINGS, O. K., *Federation Proc.* **13**, 350, 1954.
17. BARRON, E. S. G., DICKMAN, S., MUNTZ, J. A. and SINGER, T. P, *J. Gen. Physiol.* **32**, 537, 1949.
18. BARRON, E. S. G. and DICKMAN, S. J., *J. Gen. Physiol.* **32**, 595, 1949.
19. TAUBER, H., *J. Biol. Chem.* **87**, 651, 1930.
20. LANDEN, E. W., *J. Am. Chem. Soc.* **62**, 2465, 1940.
21. McLAREN, A. D., SHEPPARD, E. and WAGMAN, J., *Nature*, **162**, 370, 1948.
22. PILLEMER, L., ECKER, E. E., MYERS, W. C. and MUNTWYLER, E. A., *J. Biol. Chem.* **123**, 365, 1938.
23. PINCUSSEN, L. and ROMAN, W., *Biochem. Z.* **2**, 229, 281, 1930.
24. SHUGAR, D., *Biochim. Biophys. Acta*, **6**, 548, 1951.
25. KAUFFMAN, E. L. and URBAIN, W. M., *J. Am. Chem. Soc.* **66**, 1250, 1944.
26. ORD, M. G. and STOCKEN, L. A. in M. ERRERA and A. FORSSBERG, *Mechanisms in Radiobiology* (I), Acad. Press, N. Y. (1961) p. 259.

27. FORSSBERG, A., *Arki. Kemi Mineral. Geol.* **21**, No. 7, 1, 1961.
28. SWALLOW, A. J. in J. S. MITCHELL, B. E. HOLMES and C. L. SMITH, *Progress in Radio-biology*, Oliver and Boyd, Edinburgh (1956), p. 317.
29. BARRON, E. S. G., *Radiation Res.* **1**, 109, 1954.
30. DU BOIS, K. P., COTTER, G. J. and PETERSON, D. F., *Radiation Res.* **2**, 79, 1955.
31. THOMSON, J. F. and MIKUTA, E. T., *Proc. Soc. Exptl. Biol. Med.* **86**, 487, 1954.
32. ROMANTSEV, E. F. and ZHUTANOVA, Z. I., *Biokhimiya*, **21**, 66, 1956.
33. DU BOIS, K. P., and PETERSON, D. F., *Am. J. Physiol.* **176**, 282, 1954.
34. ORD, M. G. and STOCKEN, L. A., *Physiol. Rev.* **33**, 356, 1953.
35. SABINE, J. C., *Am. J. Physiol.* **187**, 275, 1956.
36. JOSSE, J., KAISER, A. B. and KORNBERG, A., *J. Biol. Chem.* **236**, 864, 1961.
37. HAHN, L. and HEVESY, G. DE, *Nature*, **145**, 549, 1940.
38. PAINTER, R. G., and ROBERTSON, J. S., *Radiation Res.* **11**, 206, 1959.
39. HARRINGTON, H., *Biochim. Biophys. Acta*, **41**, 461, 1960.
40. KELLY, L. S., HIRSCH, J. D., BESCH, G. and PETRAKIS, N. L., *Proc. Soc. Exp. Biol. Med.* **94**, 83, 1957.
41. CASPERSON, T., KLEIN, E. and RINGERTZ, N. R., *Cancer Res.* **18**, 857, 1958.
42. WHITMORE, G. F., STANNERS, C. P., TILL, J. E. and GULYAS, S., *Biochim. Biophys. Acta*, **47**, 66, 1961.
43. LAJTHA, L. G., OLIVER, R., BERRY, R. and NOYES, W. D., *Nature*, **182**, 1788, 1958.
44. FORSSBERG, A. and KLEIN, G. *Expt. Cell Res.* **7**, 480, 1954.
45. HARBERS, E. and HEIDELBERGER, C., *J. Biol. Chem.* **234**, 1249, 1959.
46. LOGAN, R., *Biochim. Biophys. Acta*, **35**, 251, 1959.
47. PAULY, H., *Nature*, **184**, 1570, 1959.
48. CHANTRENNE, H. and DECREAUX, S., *Biochim. Biophys. Acta*, **31**, 134, 1959.
49. MIRANDA, M., FAURE, R. and HARGREAVES, A. B., *Ciencia e Cultura*, **7**, 27, 1955.

DISCUSSION

CHAIRMAN (A. HOLLAENDER): The paper is open for discussion.

H. S. KAPLAN: Dr. Hargreaves referred to the discrepancies between the *in vitro* and *in vivo* responses of certain enzyme systems and in this connection he cited the work of Dubois and Peterson. I would like to point out that this work has been criticized by Feinstein in an article in *Radiation Research*, and by myself and others, for the reason that the experiments were done in what I consider to be an invalid way. The rodents were exposed to total body radiation and then the activity per unit tissue weight of certain enzyme systems, notably ATP-ase and 5-nucleotidase, was followed at intervals after radiation in highly radiosensitive tissue, such as spleen. Now, if we imagine the simplest possible model, we may start from the assumption that the spleen consists of at least two different kinds of cells, cell A and cell B. Let us assume further that these two cell classes are not of identical radiosensitivity; let us assume finally that they are not of identical enzymatic activity. If there is a preferential killing of the cell class which normally has a low enzymatic activity, there will remain in the residual spleen, as it undergoes involution after radiation, a predominance of cells which normally have a higher enzymatic activity, and thus what one will observe is an increase in enzymatic activity which has nothing to do with radiation reponse *per se*. I believe that until this kind of difficulty in interpretation can be avoided by proper experimental design, work such as that of Dubois and Peterson should not be considered definitive. The need at the present time in *in vivo* studies is to work with cell systems in which cell death is minimal and to study enzymatic responses under these conditions. Where this has been done, it is my impression that enzymatic responses have not been very striking.

A. B. HARGREAVES: We do not have the same authority as Prof. Kaplan to criticize Dubois' work. Nevertheless, we cannot help being impressed by the great mass of work where we can find this shocking controversy between *in vivo* and *in vitro* effects. In a certain way, Dr. Kaplan's observations are in good agreement with what we said, i.e. that the experiments *in vivo* do not permit as yet, conclusive results, while these experiments cannot be fully controlled. On the other hand, the experiments *in vitro* are much easier controlled and this is why the results are more consistent.

C. CHAGAS: Mr. Chairman, I would like to point out here the following: I think that the problem really is a much more complicated one, because one has to consider that in radiation *in vivo* there is a fact of geometry which is not involved in radiation *in vitro*. There can be no doubt that there is a localization in cells for every enzyme and this creates a very difficult problem regarding the distribution of radiation into the cell. I point out for instance that recent work done in our laboratory by Dr. Almeida and his collaborators showed that there is really a distribution in the cell of the enzyme corresponding to the electron transfer. This would mean, in other words, that unless we know the geometrical space distribution of the enzyme in the cell it is very difficult to correlate the *in vitro* experiment with the *in vivo* one.

L. D. HAMILTON: I would just like to comment on Dr. Chagas's comment and also on the situation in general. When you are irradiating an enzyme *in vitro* it is clear that the target for irradiation is the actual structure of the enzyme itself. When you are irradiating it *in vivo* essentially you are interfering with the synthesis of the enzyme and in this connection, by the way, I would like to say that I do not think it is correct to state that the synthesis of the enzyme must be accompanied by DNA synthesis. DNA synthesis is obligatory for DNA replication, but I do not believe there is any information that would suggest that the transfer of information from the DNA is accompanied by actual DNA synthesis; it is accompanied by a synthesis of a messenger RNA which transfers the information to the ribosomes. So the problem, apart from geometry therefore, is that *in vivo* you are interfering with the other proteins necessary for the synthesis of the enzymes as well as the controlling mechanism, whereas *in vitro* you are actually just dealing with the isolated enzyme itself.

H. MARCOVICH: I did not quite understand how these protective substances are acting inside the cell. Do you mean that they act by a mechanism which is like a radical trapping or lowering oxygen tension in the vicinity of the enzyme side, or by any mechanism of repairing which is particular to the system?

A. B. HARGREAVES: I do not know exactly. Many of the substances like the metabolites fructose, tyrosine, cysteine, etc., may protect the enzymes. I am just showing that the tissue kochsafts, for instance, have substances that are able to protect enzymes against radiation. This is just a simple example. I think any of these substances are capable to show this effect.

C. PAVAN: What I would like to ask here is a question from a biologist to the biochemists. It is the relation of the DNA synthesis with the RNA synthesis. Dr. Eagle told me just now that somebody had shown that during the DNA synthesis there is no RNA synthesis or when the DNA is duplicating is not doing anything in connexion with RNA. I am very much interested in that point just because in our material we do have something that looks like that these things could happen together in the same chromosomal locus. We are studying the physiology of polytene chromosomes of *Rhynchosciara* which are elements formed by bunches of thousands of chromonemata stuck together side by side. They show a series of transversal bands which are formed mainly by DNA. These bands during larval development show specific behavior represented by a more or less intense synthesis of DNA, RNA and proteins. Some of these bands at specific phases of the larval life form very large puffs which increase the diameter of the chromosome at that specific band from four to four times. We have different types of puffs in chromosomes of *Rhynchosciara*. In some of them we have synthesis of DNA followed by synthesis of RNA. In other cases the synthesis of these two nucleic acids occurs simultaneously in the same puff of the polytene chromosome. In all cases the RNA is produced and eliminated from the chromosomes as micronucleoli, while the DNA produced is normally retained in the chromosome at least for a long time. My question here is in the cases where DNA and RNA synthesis are occurring simultaneously, are these syntheses independent or does one depend on the other?

L. R. CALDAS: I think that both situations can be true. If we take the model of replication of the bacteriophage perhaps we can answer this question. In the bacteriophage replication we have independent DNA replicas. We also have separate protein formation that makes the envelope of the phage. So in the first case, DNA is not followed by RNA, but in the case of phage protein formation RNA should give information to make this protein. So I think that both situations might occur.

H. S. KAPLAN: It seems to me that this is an interesting observation but its interpretation has some pitfalls which are important. Thymidine does go into DNA, but there are two ways for the thymidine to get there. The cell can make its own thymidine by what we call the endogenous pathway, or we can give it exagenous thymidine, which is then incorporated via the "salvage" pathway. The mere fact that giving tritiated thymidine is not followed by grain counts in a band does not prove that DNA synthesis is not going on. There are good experiments *in vitro* in which actual cell replication has been proven to occur and in cells which have such an important endogenous pathway that the exogenous thymidine is simply not used. Moreover, there are other cell systems in which it is believed that the cell can go alternately from the endogenous to the exogenous pathway. If your cell system were such a system, one can imagine that in these three cells there could be three different physiological conditions in which DNA is being made in all three, but the endogenous pathway has been used preferentially in one and the exogenous in the other. I would also caution that the incorporation of tritiated uracil and of tritiated cytosine does not prove that the incorporation is exclusively in RNA, because both the uracil and the cytosine can readily and often very quickly be converted to the deoxyribotides and, through the action of thymidilyate synthetase and related enzymes, become converted to thymidylic acid. I think this is an extremely interesting observation, but there are enough pitfalls so it will be necessary to isolate material from these bands and to characterize what the grain counts are actually in.

C. PAVAN: We did an experiment in the following way. If you give one injection of tritiate thymidine to the larvae, normally you will have 70 per cent of cells which show incorporation — and 30 per cent show no incorporation at all. We took three groups of 10 larvae of the same age, the same sex and the same stage of development. To the first group of larvae we gave an injection of tritiated thymidine, and then killed the larvae after 120 min. The second group received two injections at 30 min interval and was killed 120 min after the first injection. The third group received three injections at 30 min intervals and was killed 120 min after the first injection. The first group which had tritiated thymidine available during 30 min, showed about 70 per cent incorporations; the second group which had the precursor for 60 min showed about 90 per cent incorporations; the third which had the precursor for 90 min showed incorporation in over 90 per cent of the cells.

This experiment shows that practically all cells will utilize exogenous thymidine if exposed to it for an interval of about 90 min. Therefore we may conclude that the interval of non incorporation of exogenous thymidine is not greater than about 90 minutes.

H. S. KAPLAN: You have three cells and you say that tritiated thymidine goes into two and not in the third one, but if you give three injections do you find that the three cells show incorporation?

C. PAVAN: We think that the larva at this stage of development show a cycle of DNA synthesis in the salivary gland cells every 90 min and different cells may be different phage of this cycle.

R. B. SETLOW: I thought we should end on a biophysical note. I know absolutely no biochemistry, and I think the point that Dr. Kaplan is making, put in another way, is that the relation between DNA synthesis and incorporation of tritiated thymidine is a proportional one; the amount of DNA synthesis is proportional to the amount of tritiated thymidine incorporated, but we do not know necessarily the proportionality constant. The proportionality constant can vary from time to time with or without radiation and until you can prove that the proportiona ity constant between grain counts and the DNA synthesis is a constant, you cannot say anything quantitatively.

L. D. HAMILTON: I am willing to take Dr. Pavan's experiments entirely at their face value. I do not think that the argument about endogenous and exogenous is really relevant. I think that Dr. Pavan has got an interesting observation that is in no way in conflict with the idea that it is not obligatory to have DNA replication for the transfer of information. But the converse does not hold: in other words, one can have DNA replication, as you have shown, and also the synthesis of the messenger at the same time.

A. B. HARGREAVES: When I was young, I used to go to certain parties, and my father forced me to dance with the hostess' daughter, even when the girl was not pretty, so I could learn to be polite. Perhaps, this is why I was invited to speak in this Symposium. Anyway, I am very happy to have had such a fortunate idea of mentioning the protein DNA and synthesis mechanisms, which does not belong to my field of action, because it gave us a chance to have such a profitable discussion.

RADIOBIOCHEMICAL LESIONS IN DNA AND REPRODUCTIVE DEATH IN IRRADIATED CELLS

H. S. KAPLAN

Department of Radiology, Stanford University School of Medicine, Palo Alto, California, U.S.A.

THE synthesis of a series of analogues of the natural purine and pyrimidine bases has provided us with powerful new tools in molecular biology. Although the analogues were originally introduced as metabolic antagonists, it was subsequently observed that some of them, under favorable conditions, may become incorporated into nucleic acids by substituting for the corresponding natural bases.[1-4] "Fraudulent" nucleic acids are thus produced, which in some instances exhibit distinctly altered properties.[5]

In the series of pyrimidine analogues in which a halogen atom is substituted at the carbon-5 position, one compound, 5-fluorouracil (FU), is extensively incorporated into RNA, but not at all into DNA (2), whereas the other members of the series, 5-chloro-, 5-bromo-, and 5-iodouracil (ClU, BU, IU) and their corresponding deoxyribosides (ClUDR, BUDR, IUDR) are analogues of thymine and thymidine respectively, being incorporated into DNA but not into RNA.[6-9]

Working in Zamenhof's laboratory, Greer[10] first noted that thymine-deficient bacterial mutants grown on 5-BU became sensitized to ultraviolet radiation. Two groups soon undertook further explorations of this phenomenon. Szybalski and his colleagues found that mammalian cells were also sensitized when grown under proper conditions in the presence of BUDR or IUDR.[11] Our studies were carried out with bacterial cells; we found that they were sensitized not only to ultraviolet, but to ionizing radiation as well.[12] In the presence of competitive concentrations of thymine or thymidine, these analogues were much less effective or inert, suggesting that their actual incorporation into DNA was a prerequisite for radio-sensitization; moreover, the degree of sensitization was shown to depend on the extent of incorporation.[12] That the effect was specific for DNA-incorporated analogues was indicated by the failure of FU to alter radiosensitivity.[12] Sensitization has also been observed when BU is incorporated into bacteriophage [13] in which DNA is the sole nucleic acid. Finally, the brominated analogue of deoxycytidine (BCDR), which undergoes metabolic conversion to BUDR inside the cell,[14] is also active as a radiosensitizer in mammalian cells.[15]

Thus, we see that analogues which are exclusively incorporated into DNA cause a striking enhancement in cellular radiosensitivity, that the degree of sensitization is proportional to the degree of incorporation into DNA, and that closely related analogues which are incorporated into RNA, but not into DNA, do not exhibit this effect. It appears justifiable to conclude that DNA must be in the major biochemical pathway leading to cell death through the loss of reproductive integrity after irradiation.

More direct evidence that the initial radiation insult actually occurs within the DNA molecule has been sought in work with bacterial transforming DNA, irradiated either *in vivo* inside the bacterial cell or *in vitro*, after which it is assayed for loss of biological activity. *B. subtilis* transforming DNA into which BU had been incorporated was distinctly more sensitive to ultraviolet irradiation than normal DNA, and the extent of sensitization was approximately the same whether the irradiations were carried out *in vivo* or *in vitro*.[16] Since the *in vitro* irradiations involved highly purified DNA, essentially free from RNA and protein, it would appear that DNA molecules into which BU becomes extensively incorporated are inherently more sensitive to ultraviolet irradiation. Unpublished preliminary investigations suggest that the same conclusion are also true for ionizing radiations.

It has been demonstrated that BU is inherently more sensitive than thymine to degradation by ultraviolet or X-irradiation *in vitro* or in DNA *in vivo*.[17,18] Perhaps the halogen atom enhances susceptibility of the pyrimidine ring to saturation of the double bond between carbons-5 and 6, leading secondarily to hydration and hydroperoxidation. An alternative suggestion put forth by Szybalski[5] is that the phosphate ester backbone of BU–DNA may be more vulnerable to breakage.

In the course of our studies, we turned our attention to the possibility that such effects were not specific for the incorporation of halogenated pyrimidines and might be brought about by other changes in the structural integrity of DNA. Accordingly, we explored the effect of the purine analogues and found that several of these, notably thioguanine, 6-mercaptopurine, and 2-aminopurine, are also powerful radiosensitizers, despite the fact that the maximal extent of their incorporation is almost a hundredfold less than that of BU.[19,20] There is an interesting difference in the mechanism of action of the purine and pyrimidine analogues as radiosensitizers. This was brought out in a study of the interaction of their effects with those of the so-called "oxygen" effect. It was found that the radiosensitization produced by incorporated purine analogues is abolished when irradiation is carried out in nitrogen, whereas the response to the pyrimidine analogues is unaffected.[21]

Another test of the thesis that DNA is the macromolecule within which the initial radiobiochemical lesions leading to cell death occur is the prediction that such parameters as DNA content, ploidy, and base composition should correlate with radiosensitivity of different classes of cells. Base composition seemed a particularly relevant parameter for study, since one can think of adenine as an analogue of guanine and of cytosine as an analogue of thymine. We exploited the known differences in base composition which characterize different species of bacteria[22] and found that the radiosensitivity of eight different bacterial species increased linearly with the ratio of guanine and cytosine (G-C)/adenine and thymine (A-T) in their DNA.[23] It was tentatively concluded that G–C pairs are either inherently more radiosensitive than A–T pairs, or perhaps less readily repaired. Using *B. subtilis* transforming DNA in which several markers of different G–C content have been selected on the basis of differences in melting temperature and density gradient equilibrium (A. Ganesan and J. Lederberg, unpublished), we have observed a reciprocal relationship in response to X-rays vs. ultraviolet. Markers with the highest G–C content were most sensitive to X-rays and most resistant to ultraviolet, and vice versa, when assayed against different auxotrophs, or even against a quadruple mutant strain, suggesting that G–C-rich regions may, in fact, be preferentially attacked by X-rays (H. S. Kaplan and R. Zavarine, unpublished).

Finally, data from the literature have been collated by Terzi[24] and by Kaplan and Moses[25]. Both studies revealed a striking correlation between DNA content and radiosensitivity in the DNA viruses and the haploid micro-organisms. Diploid cells were about tenfold more resistant, but there was again a good correlation between their radiosensitivity and DNA content. Finally, two single-stranded DNA bacteriophages, ΦX174 and S13, were found to be grouped with the RNA viruses on an iso-sensitivity line about tenfold more sensitive than the double-stranded DNA viruses. Thus, it appears that there is indeed a satisfactory correlation between radiosensitivity and DNA content, ploidy, and "strandedness". However, the more complex organisms were distinctly more resistant than the viruses, relative to DNA content. Howard-Flanders[26] and Guild[27] have suggested that repair mechanisms may come into play in the higher organisms to account for their relative insensitivity. We may thus summarize by stating that the lethal effects of ionizing radiation appear to be mediated by lesions induced in DNA (RNA in the plant and certain animal viruses) and that response is governed by the following parameters: DNA (RNA) content, ploidy, base composition (including analogue content), "strandedness", and possibly repair processes.

REFERENCES

1. DUNN, D. B. and SMITH, J. D., Incorporation of halogenated pyrimidines into the deoxyribonucleic acids of *Bacterium coli* and its bacteriophages. *Nature*, **174**, 305–306, 1954.
2. HOROWITZ, J., and CHARGAFF, E., Massive incorporation of 5-fluorouracil into a bacterial ribonucleic acid. *Nature*, **184**, 1213–1215, 1959.
3. WACKER, A., TREBST, A., JACHERTS, D. and WEYGAND, F., Über den Einbau von 5-bromouracil-2¹⁴C in die Desoxyribonucleinsäure verschiedener Bakterien. *Z. Naturforsch.* **98**, 616–617, 1954.
4. ZAMENHOF, S., and GRIBOFF, G., Incorporation of halogenated pyrimidines into the deoxyribonucleic acids of *Bacterium coli* and its bacteriophage. *Nature*, **174**, 306–307, 1954.
5. SZYBALSKI, W., Properties and applications of halogenated deoxyribonucleic acids. In *The Molecular Basis of Neoplasia*, University of Texas Press, Austin, 1962, pp. 147–171.
6. BIEBER, S., DIETRICH, L. S., ELION, G. B., HITCHINGS, G. H. and MARTIN, D. S., The incorporation of 6-mercaptopurine-S³⁵ into the nucleic acids of sensitive and nonsensitive transplantable mouse tumors. *Cancer Res.* **21**, 228–231, 1961.
7. LePAGE, G. A., Incorporation of 6-thioguanine into nucleic acids. *Cancer Res.* **20**, 403–408, 1960.
8. MATTHEWS, R. E. F. and SMITH, J. D., Distribution of 8-azaguanine in the nucleic acid of *Bacillus cereus*. *Nature*, **177**, 271–272, 1956.
9. WACKER, A., KIRSCHFELD, S. and TRÄGER, L., Über den Einbau Purin-analoger Verbindungen in die Bakterien-Nukleinsäure. *J. Mol. Biol.* **2**, 241–242, 1960.
10. GREER, S., Studies on ultraviolet irradiation of *Escherichia coli* containing 5-bromo-uracil in its DNA. *J. Gen. Microbiol.* **22**, 618–634, 1960.
11. DJORDJEVIC, B. and SZYBALSKY, W., Genetics of human cell lines. III. Incorporation of 5-bromo and 5-iododeoxyuridine into the deoxyribonucleic acid of human cells and its effect on radiation sensitivity. *J. Exp. Med.* **112**, 509–531, 1960.
12. KAPLAN, H. S., SMITH, K. C. and TOMLIN, P., Effect of halogenated pyrimidines on radiosensitivity of *E. coli*. *Radiation Res.* **16**, 98–113, 1962.
13. STAHL, F. W., CRASEMANN, J. M., OKUM, L., FOX, E. and LAIRD, C., Radiationsensitivity of bacteriophage containing 5-bromodeoxyuridine. *Virology*, **13**, 98–104, 1961.
14. CRAMER, J. W., PRUSOFF, W. H., CHU, M. Y. and WELCH, A. D., The effect of 5-bromo-2'-deoxycytidine (BCDR) on mammalian cells in culture. *Proc. Am. Assoc. Cancer Res.* **3**, 217, 1961.
15. BAGSHAW, M. A., Modification of the radiosensitivity of hamster cells *in vitro*. *Nature*, **193**, 389–391, 1962.
16. OPARA-KUBINSKA, Z., LORKIEWICZ, Z. and SZYBALSKI, W., Genetic transformation studies. II. Radiation sensitivity of halogen labeled DNA. *Biochem. and Biophys. Res. Comm.* **4**, 288–291, 1961.
17. BARSZCZ, D. and SHUGAR, D., Radiation chemistry of nucleic acids and their derivatives. I. Some pyrimidines, dihydropyrimidines, and hydrated pyrimidines. *Acta Biochimica Polonica*, **8**, 455–470, 1961.

18. Smith, K. C., A chemical basis for the sensitization of bacteria to ultraviolet light by incorporated bromouracil. *Biochem. and Biophys. Res. Comm.* **6**, 458–463, 1962.

19. Kaplan, H. S., Smith, K. C. and Tomlin, P., Radiosensitization of *E. coli* by purine and pyrimidine analogues incorporated in deoxyribonucleic acid. *Nature*, **190**, 794–796, 1961.

20. Gottschling, H. and Freese, E., Incorporation of 2-aminopurine into the deoxyribonucleic acid of bacteria and bacteriophages. *Z. Naturforsch.* **16B**, 515, 1961.

21. Kaplan, H. S., Zavarine, R. and Earle, J., Interaction of the oxygen effect and radiosensitization produced by base analogues incorporated into deoxyribonucleic acid. *Nature*, **194**, 662–664, 1962.

22. Belozersky, A. N. and Spirin, A. S., Chemistry of the nucleic acids of microorganisms. In *The Nucleic Acids*, Vol. III, Chargaff, E., and Davidson, J. N., eds., Academic Press, New York, 1960, pp. 147–185.

23. Kaplan, H. S. and Zayarine, R., Correlation of bacterial radiosensitivity and DNA base composition. *Biochem. and Biophys. Res. Comm.* **8**, 432–436, 1962.

24. Terzi, M., Comparative analysis of inactivating efficiency of radiation on different organisms. *Nature*, **191**, 461–463, 1961.

25. Kaplan, H. S. and Moses, L. E., Manuscript in preparation.

26. Howard-Flanders, P., Factors affecting radiation injury to DNA in bacteria and bacteriophage systems. In *Brookhaven Symposia in Biology*, No. 14: *Fundamental Aspects of Radiosensitivity*, Upton, New York, 1961, pp. 18–31.

27. Guild, W. R., The radiationsensitivity of deoxyribonucleic acid. *Radiation Res. Suppl.* **3**, 257–267, 1963.

DISCUSSION

Chairman (C. Pavan): The discussion is open.

E. H. Y. Chu: I would like to describe some of our recent results on the effect of ultraviolet on mammalian cells *in vitro*, which may have a bearing on Dr. Kaplan's paper. The material we use is a Chinese hamster cell line. The advantage of using the mammalian cell system is that cells are thin and flattened, allowing easy penetration and absorption of ultraviolet energy. The cells are grown directly in quartz dishes and are irradiated from below with monochromatic ultraviolet light.

The ultraviolet-induced chromosome aberrations are not very different from those induced by X-rays in both animal and plant materials. The action spectrum for the production of chromosome aberrations resembles the absorption spectrum of nucleic acids. This is the first indication that perhaps DNA is damaged by ultraviolet, leading to the formation of visible chromosomal aberrations.

Recently, we have attempted to substitute DNA bases with their analogs prior to ultraviolet irradiation. Using 5-bromodeoxyuridine pretreatment, we observed a modified action spectrum. The effect is particularly significant at 2250 Å and 3130 Å. These results support the above conclusion that DNA is the primary site of ultraviolet damage in chromosomes.

A. Hollaender: I would like to take exception of the proof of the conclusion which Dr. Kaplan has made on the basis of his last slide. I believe that the conclusion that sensitivity is proportionate to nucleic DNA content is probably correct but the figures Dr. Kaplan brought on the slide here can be upset very easily when you consider that tetraploid yeast is much more sensitive than haploid yeast, in regard to ultraviolet radiation, I believe also to X-rays. There are many other points on this slide which should be taken with caution, because this crude DNA analysis takes the total DNA and we know from discussions which took place in Sao Paulo and will come out a year again, that the DNA is not only in the chromosomes, it is probably also considerably found in the cytoplasm distributed in different fashion and the concentration of the essential

DNA is in direct proportion to the sensitivity to X-rays and ultraviolet, but the basis of the slide the way it has been shown here, I would personally not be willing to accept.

H. S. KAPLAN: I think Dr. Hollaender has read just a little bit more into what I said than I intended to say. I said, I think, that ploidy was one parameter of radiosensitivity but I did not say, nor did I intend to say, that radiosensitivity would continue to decrease as ploidy increases. The statement that ploidy is a parameter would be true no matter whether the ploidy continues to go up or to go down, as long as the change is a function of ploidy. I think we are all aware of the beautiful work of the group at Berkeley on yeast of different ploidies. The model suggested by Zirkle and Tobias for the interpretation of these results, as later modified by Mortimer, would indicate that the killing of yeast cells goes essentially from a recessive kind of lethal event to a dominant kind of lethal event, as one goes from a ploidy of one (haploid) to the diploid. Because of this change in mechanism, the sensitivity then goes up as ploidy increases beyond two. My statement was not intended to indicate that we would see a continuing series of parallel iso-sensitivity lines shifting toward greater resistance as ploidy went on beyond two, but the fact that there is a difference between ploidies of one and two I consider to be well established from the data in the literature.

A. LIMA DE FARIA: Dr. Kaplan, the table that you have here on the blackboard shows the incorporation of fluorouracil into RNA but not into DNA. This is true for *E. coli*. I would like to know if it is true for mammalian cells.

H. S. KAPLAN: Yes, it is.

R. B. SETLOW: I beg your indulgence in amplifying some of the remarks that Dr. Chu made because I shall not do so tomorrow. They bear on an interesting analytical tool and also on the question of whether bromouracil incorporation produces sensitization because the bromouracil is in DNA. Compare the absorption spectra of bromodeoxyuridine and thymine. Thymine has an absorption maximum at about 265 mμ, and bromouracil is shifted to longer wave lengths and has an absorption maximum close to 280 mμ. Therefore, one expects that a biological system substituted with bromouracil will be extraordinarily sensitive to the longer wavelength, if it is the absorption of quanta in the DNA or in the bromouracil that produces the effect. In actual practice, one finds that at 254 mμ, the region that most people work in, *E. coli* 15 T$^-$ A$^-$ and bacteriophage T-4 are four times more sensitive after bromouracil substitution. If one works at a wavelength such as 313 mμ the bromouracil substituted systems are 100 times more sensitive than the thymine containing systems. The simplest interpretation of these data is that at long wavelengths the thymine containing DNA is not absorbing quanta whereas the bromouracil containing systems are absorbing quanta and are killed. This conclusion is about the same for coli and for T-even phage.

CHAIRMAN: I would like to ask Dr. Kaplan what would be the effect of radiation on the synthesis of DNA? Does the ionizing radiation stimulate or inhibit DNA synthesis?

H. S. KAPLAN: This will involve us in a whole afternoon if we really discuss it in detail. The important point that I would like to make is that there has been a vast amount of confusion on precisely this question. Most of the studies that have been done on DNA synthesis in cells that have been irradiated would indicate a partial inhibition of DNA synthesis. However, more analytical studies would suggest that this "inhibition", which is usually about 50 per cent, is in fact due to the fact that the cells are irradiated with doses which suppress mitosis, and a cell which has already made its DNA for the mitosis in question but which cannot then go through mitosis, has no need to make any more DNA, because it cannot go through the next mitosis until it goes through this one. This is the same as the old problem of the chicken and the egg; which comes first? In this instance, I think the answer is rather unequivocal. The effect of radiation on mitosis comes first, and the apparent inhibition of DNA synthesis comes second. The second point of confusion is that once it was recognized that this apparent inhibition of synthesis is not a true inhibition, some investigators jumped to the opposite conclusion that the effect of radiation could not be on DNA. But I would like to point out that when the cell makes

DNA, it may synthesize, let us say, 10,000 different molecules. If there is a lesion in one molecule which is a lethal lesion, it can still be lethal for the cell even though the replication of the other 9999 molecules is perfectly normal, so that DNA synthesis (referring to the entire complement of DNA molecules) need not be interfered with by radiation, and yet the killing event could be a radiation-induced lesion in a *particular* DNA molecule. I hope I have made this clear.

CHAIRMAN: I would like to make one comment. In the case of polytenic chromosomes DNA synthesis is not related to the mitotic process. It is done independently from cellular division and we have tested DNA synthesis through the incorporation of tritiated thymidine, thus verifying the following: radiations of 1250 r, of 2500 r, of 10,000 r and of 20,000 r show an stimulating effect on the synthesis of DNA. Also, with the 20,000 r dose there is a greater incorporation of tritiated thymidine than that in the control.

H. S. KAPLAN: This is an extremely interesting observation. I would like to call your attention to a similar observation which has recently been made by Das and Alfert, at the University of California, in a quite different biological system, but leading to exactly the same conclusion. I am delighted to hear this.

V. BOND: I wonder if Dr. Kaplan would comment on the fact that in the mammal, very shortly after irradiation the incorporation of tritiated thymidine in the individual cell appears to be reduced which can be interpreted as a reduction in DNA synthesis. This occurs before the cells would go through a division.

H. S. KAPLAN: I am afraid I do not know of any work in which inhibition of incorporation has been shown prior to cell division. The only system in which I think something of the sort may occur would be in the thymocyte, which may perhaps die by a different mechanism closer to that of the spermatogonia, possibly being in the nature of a premitotic cell death. I do not believe any of these conclusions necessarily hold for that kind of cell death, but for ordinary diploid cells all the evidence that I know about would indicate that the "inhibition" of DNA synthesis as measured by impairment of incorporation of tritiated thymidine follows the inhibition of mitosis. If you have other evidence I would be glad to hear it.

V. BOND: We have evidence that at least in the red-cell definitely the grain count is reduced at a level of 600 r irradiation within a couple of hours after irradiation.

M. MIRANDA: Dr. Kaplan, maybe it is too early to ask this question, but I wonder about the sequence of the GC along the molecule. Has it anything to do with the radiosensitivity of the DNA?

H. S. KAPLAN: I really think it is too early to answer that question. There is some indication that ultraviolet may give such information. Dr. Setlow is probably planning to talk about this tomorrow, so I will be brief. I think that some of our rather striking differences in ultraviolet sensitivity in different markers in transforming DNA may reflect sequences along the chain for the reason that thymine dimer formation, as Dr. Setlow will undoubtedly say tomorrow, will be more efficiently accomplished between two thymines that are in the same chain than two thymines in opposite chains. Therefore, if a particular marker had a run of thymines in one chain, even though it might have the same overall AT content as another marker, would make it very much more likely that ultraviolet would produce a lesion in that segment. Thus, one would postulate that some information on sequence along the chain can be provided by differential analysis of marker sensitivity to ultraviolet. I think some of the data I have shown probably will turn out to be explained in this way, but it will be a long time before we can prove it.

CHAIRMAN: We sincerely thank Dr. Kaplan for his excellent paper, and now close the session.

ACTION OF STREPTOMYCIN ON PHAGE DEVELOPMENT IN *STAPHYLOCOCCUS ALBUS*[*][†][‡]

C. A. Elias and M. Miranda

Brazilian National Research Council
(Conselho Nacional de Pesquisas)

M. A. Salgado

Brazilian National Commission of Nuclear Energy
(Comissao Nacional de Energia Nuclear)

and L. R. Caldas

LIST OF SYMBOLS

Staph. albus — Staphylococcus albus.
Sm — Streptomycin.
Sm-sulphate — Streptomycin sulphate.
Dihydro-Sm — Dihydro-streptomycin.
RNA — ribonucleic acid.
DNA — deoxyribonucleic acid.
sr — Streptomycin resistant
ω and (ω) — phage and prophage from lysogenic Staph. albus system.

INTRODUCTION

The present experiments deal with the action of Sm-sulphate on phage infection of Staph. albus, and on phage induction of a lysogenic Sm-resistant Staph. albus, an ultraviolet inducible strain. Sm-sulphate and to a lesser extent the dihydro-Sm are able to:

[*] Instituto de Biofísica da Universidade do Brasil, Av. Pasteur 458, Rio de Janeiro, Brasil.

[†] This investigation was supported by Research Grant Contract Number 68/US from the International Atomic Energy Agency (Vienna).

[‡] After the preparation of this paper, it was reported by Brock[1] that the replication of a RNA phage was inhibited by Streptomycin inside its host strain Sm-resistant in conditions analogous to the inhibition of Staph. albus phage. According to Brock DNA phages, double or single-stranded, did not show the same phenomenon. The only DNA phage which was inhibited this way, was able to infect Streptococcus.

(a) inhibit phage production by the Sm-resistant host strain in the presence of the antibiotic, and

(b) induce phage production in a lysogenic Sm-resistant host strain, but prevent phage maturation; phage mature particles are only released when the Sm-induced cells are transferred to a Sm-free medium.

The effect of ultraviolet induction in the presence of Sm was also investigated. Sm does not interfere with ultraviolet induction and phage maturation.

MATERIALS AND METHODS

(1) Staphylococcus Albus Strains

P (ω) and W5/sr strains were used. The former is a lysogenic strain containing the prophage (ω); the second is the Sm-resistant indicator strain for ω phage. Both strains were kindly supplied by Dr. H. Marcovich (Laboratoire Pasteur de l'Institut du Radium, Paris). A lysogenic Sm-resistant strain P (ω)/sr was isolated in our laboratory by ω lysogenization of W5/sr.

(2) Culture Media

Cells were grown in nutrient tryptone broth:

Difco nutrient broth	3 g
Difco tryptone broth	5 g
Na Cl	5 g
Distilled water	to 1000 ml

1·5% Difco agar was added to the medium for Petri dishes. Cells were plated by Gratia technique; soft agar concentration for platings was 0·75 per cent. Growth conditions were: aerated cells were incubated to full growth at 37°C, corresponding to $\sim 4 \times 10^9$ cells per ml. Before experiments, cells were centrifuged and washed three times in Mg SO_4 7 H_2O 10^{-3} M. In some experiments antiphage serum was used.

(3) Ultraviolet Source

A Philips germicidal lamp in which about 95 per cent of the ultraviolet corresponds to 2537 Å. Dosimetry was carried out with Latarjet dosimeter.

(4) *Streptomycin*

Both Sm-sulphate and dihydro-Sm were used. Sm was added in many experiments to the soft agar tubes for platings; in these conditions Sm concentrations were calculated by assuming homogeneous diffusion of antibiotic in the agar.

Additional information on experimental procedure are given in the text.

RESULTS

(1) *Effect of Sm-sulphate and Dihydro-Sm on the Plaque-forming Ability of ω phage*

Phage plaque formation on the indicator strain is strongly inhibited by Sm-sulphate at a concentration in which dihydro-Sm does not produce any effect (Table 1).

TABLE 1.

	P(ω) colonies/ml	Total phage plaques/ml	Free phage plaques/ml
Control	4.2×10^9	8.8×10^8	7.6×10^7 (supernatant assay)
dihydro-Sm 1000 μg/ml	0	—	7.8×10^7
Sm-sulphate 1000 μg/ml	0	—	0

Full growth lysogenic P(ω) strain is plated on Petri dishes together with the indicator strain W5/sr in the presence of dihydro-Sm and Sm-sulphate. The growth of the indicator strain W5/sr is undisturbed in both cases.

Ultimately it was observed that dihydro-Sm produces the same effect as Sm-sulphate but at higher concentrations. The concentration of Sm-sulphate which is harmless for phage plaque forming ability is 200 μg per Petri dish ($\simeq$ 10 μg/ml).

(2) *Mechanism of Phage Plaque-forming Inhibition by Sm-sulphate*

Such an inhibition could be accounted for by one of three possible mechanisms:

(a) inactivation of free phage by high concentration of the antibiotic;
(b) prevention of adsorption of phage on the host strain;

(c) inhibition of phage reproduction inside the host at some particular step of its replication cycle.

These possibilities were checked as follows:

(a) *Effect of Sm-sulphate on the Free Phage*

A phage stock suspension was diluted in nutrient tryptone broth to a concentration of 5×10^8 infective units per ml and incubated for 15 min at 37°C with or without 2000 μg/ml of Sm-sulphate. Platings with or without Sm gave the same titer of phage indicating that Sm was harmless for free phage.

(b) *Effect of Sm-sulphate on Adsorption of Phage in the Presence of Sm*

A suspension of 5×10^8 phages per ml was mixed to 4×10^9 W5/sr cells per ml and then incubated for 5 min at 37°C in the presence or in the absence of 2000 μg/ml of Sm-sulphate. Phage antiserum was added immediately afterwards to inactivate unadsorbed phage (phage antiserum diluted 10^2 times leaves less than 10^{-3} infective units in 1 min at 37°C). Adsorption was evaluated 1 min after by plaque forming ability in the absence of Sm. In the presence of Sm adsorption is higher. The result of a typical experiment is given in Table 2.

TABLE 2.

Time	Treatment	Phage/ml		Cell/ml
		(+)	(−) Sm	
0		5×10^8	5×10^8	4×10^9
$\updownarrow$	Adsorption			
5'	Antiserum			
	1/100			
6		6×10^5	7×10^3	

Adsorption of ω phage on the indicator strain W5/sr in the presence and in the absence of 2000 µg/ml of Sm. The adsorption of ω phage on the indicator strain is always very low in nutrient tryptone broth.

(c) *Effect of Sm-sulphate on the Phage-Host Complex*

One minute after antiserum addition, the system was diluted in nutrient tryptone broth to stop antiserum action and incubated again at 37°C under aeration with or without 2000 μg/ml of Sm-sulphate. The number of phage plaques from the aliquots of the sample treated with Sm-sulphate decreases rapidly whereas those from the control sample increase gradually. After 3 hr no phage plaques are seen in the sample treated with Sm. Growth of W5/sr strain is similar in the absence and in the presence of 2000 μg/ml of Sm-sulphate. The conclusion is that Sm interferes with phage multiplication at some step of its replication cycle.

(3) *Effect of Sm-sulphate on Ultraviolet Induction of Phage-production of a Sm-resistant Lysogenic Strain*

Since Sm-sulphate inhibits infecting phage replication, one may ask if such an inhibition could be observed in a ultraviolet induced lysogenic cell.

As it was previously shown[2] ultraviolet radiation induces phage development in lysogenic *Staph. albus* P (ω). A dose of 400 erg/mm^2 induces 99 per cent of the cells of a full growth culture and phage release starts after a latent period of 45 min. The burst size is rather small (30–70 infective units per burst). These results also hold for a P(ω)/sr isolated by lysogenization of a W5/sr with ω phage.

Two kinds of experiments were performed with P (ω)/sr strain:

Sm was added to cells immediately before or after irradiation.

It was observed that ultraviolet induction was the same in the absence or in the presence of Sm.

(4) *Effect of Sm-sulphate on the Lysogenic Sm-resistant Strain*

With the lysogenic Sm-resistant P (ω)/sr strain the ratio cell colonies/ infective centers is consistently decreased for high concentrations of the antibiotic as shown by the following experiment: when the concentration of Sm-sulphate is as high as 40,000 μg/ml, no growth of P (ω)/sr cells is observed for at least 7 hr. The cells however remain viable and phage plaques can be detected by plating in the absence of Sm. The number of phage plaques increases exponentially with time after a lag of 2–3 hr as is shown in Fig. 1.

These plaques correspond to infective centers and not to free phages in the medium, since free phages have been eliminated by antiserum. In addition, the number of plaques is the same whether or not antiserum is added to the sample containing Sm.

Therefore, such an increase cannot be attributed to the burst of a small fraction of lysogenic cells which would grow and release phage by spontaneous induction. However, free phages are detected in the medium when the culture starts to grow after 7 hr of lag.

One may conclude that during the first 7 hr, the lysogenic Sm-resistant

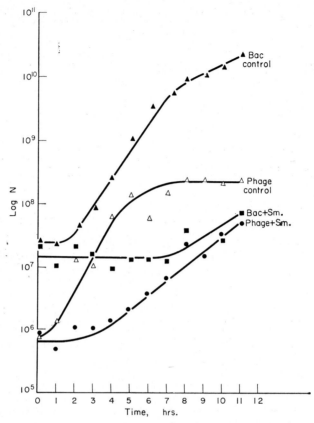

FIG. 1. A full growth culture of P(ω)/sr is washed three times in Mg SO$_4$ 7 H$_2$O 10^{-3} M. Free phage particles are completely eliminated from the cultures by washing and antiserum treatment. Aliquots are diluted in nutrient tryptone broth in the absence and in the presence of 40,000 μg/ml of Sm-sulphate and incubated fully aerated at 37°C. Platings are made in the absence of Sm.

cells are progressively induced, i.e. are being converted into infective centers, but no phage is released as long as these induced cells remain in the presence of Sm. However, if these induced cells are transferred to a medium free of Sm they actually release active phage as Fig. 2 shows.

(5) *Effect of Starvation*

If before an experiment similar to that described in Fig. 1 one starves a fully aerated P (ω)/sr strain for 2 hr at 37° C in Mg SO$_4$ 7 H$_2$O 10^{-13} M the lag of 2–3 hr which occurs before the exponential increase of infective centers disappears. In that situation the process of induction starts immediately (Fig. 3).

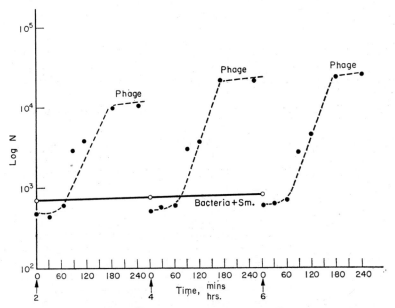

FIG. 2. Aliquots are taken from a P(ω)/sr culture at 37°C under aeration in the presence of Sm-sulphate 40,000 μg/ml, and diluted 1000 times in nutrient tryptone broth without Sm and incubated fully aerated at 37°C. Lysis is observed and the pattern of the curves is very similar to those obtained by ultraviolet induction: same latent period and same burst size.

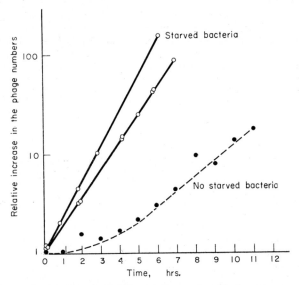

FIG. 3. Effect of Sm-sulphate, 40,000 μg/ml, on the relative increase of phage plaques on starved and non starved P(ω)/sr cells.
It should be noted that starvation *per se* does not induce any phage production.

DISCUSSION

The mechanism of Sm action on bacteria was recently discussed by Spotts and Stanier[3]; they suggested that Sm works by reaction with ribosomes of bacteria. This conclusion was based on observations that Sm was fixed on ribosomes in both sensitive and dependent strains; resistant strains fix the antibiotic depending on degrees of resistance and amount of antibiotic. In indifference no fixation is observed.

These findings were recently supported by the work of Flaks *et al.*[4,5] using the cell free aminoacid incorporating system from *E. coli* described by Niremberg and Matthei. In sensitive strains incorporation of labelled phenyl-alanine into protein, stimulated by polyuridilate, is inhibited if Sm is added to the system before addition of poly-U. With ribosomes of resistant and dependent strains, the same inhibition can be seen but at very high concentrations of antibiotic. The conclusions of Spotts and Stanier on the action of Sm on bacteria do not explain the inhibition of phage development in the Sm-resistant host strain in the presence of Sm.

Spotts and Stanier[3] obtained results analogous to those reported here using a lysogenic Sm dependent *E. coli* induced by ultraviolet that released active phage in the absence of Sm, a condition that makes protein synthesis difficult. For the lysogenic Sm-resistant strain P(ω)/sr an explantation of such findings may be that for lysogenic bacteria to produce phage, the genetic material of the phage must undergo a transition from the prophage to the vegetative state. Based on experimental evidence, Jacob and Monod[7] assume that in lysogenic bacteria the prophage induces the formation of a cytoplasmic repressor that prevents the completion of some reactions necessary for prophage induction. If the repressor is in some way linked to protein synthesis, one may suggest that Sm, blocking protein synthesis at the ribosomal level, stops synthesis of the repressor and hence gives rise to induction. Mature phage particles would not be produced and released because Sm blocking the ribosomes would also block protein synthesis necessary for phage maturation. Phage maturation and lysis of the induced bacteria occur when cells are transferred to a medium without Sm. If this scheme is correct, one could presumably put in evidence Sm induction of lysogenic sensitive bacteria. This experiment is however quite difficult since according to Davis (cited in Spotts, Stanier's paper[3]), in sensitive bacteria Sm not only reacts with ribosomes, but also destroys them. This condition would hardly be compatible with phage replication even when the cells are transferred to a Sm-free medium, as probably Sm-damaged bacteria would lose their capacity for sustaining phage synthesis to its normal conclusion. Experiments are underway to clarify some questions aroused by these observations.

REFERENCES

1. BROCK, T., The inhibition of RNA bacteriophage by streptomycin using hos bacteria resistant to the antibiotic. *Biochem. Biophys. Res. Comm.* **9**, 184–187 1962.
2. CALDAS, L. R. and ELIAS, C. A., Effect of small doses of X-rays on induction of the lysogenic system of *Staphylococcus albus*. *XXI International Congress of Physiological Sciences, Abstracts of Communications*, 49, 1959.
3. SPOTTS, C. R. and STANIER, R. Y., Mechanism of streptomycin action on bacteria: a unitary hypothesis. *Nature*, **192**, 633–637, 1962.
4. FLAKS, J. G. and COX, E. C. and WHITE, J. R., Inhibition of polypeptide synthesis by streptomycin. *Biochem. Biophys. Res. Comm.* **7**, 385–389, 1962.
5. FLAKS, J. G., COX, E. C., WITTING, M. L. and WHITE, J. R., Polypeptide synthesis with ribosomes from streptomycin-resistant and dependent *E. coli*. *Biochem. Biophys. Res. Comm.* **7**, 390–393, 1962.

6. NIREMBERG, M. W., MATTHEI, J. H., The dependence of cell-free protein synthesis in *E. coli* upon naturally occurring or synthetic polyribonucleotides. *Proc. Nat. Acad. Sci.* **47**, 1588–1602, 1961.

7. JACOB, F. and MONOD, J., Genetic regulatory mechanisms in the synthesis of proteins. *J. Mol. Biol.* **3**, 318–356, 1961.

DISCUSSION

CHAIRMAN (F. HERCIK): This paper is open for discussion and comments.

H. MARCOVICH: I would like to ask Dr. Caldas if he has made some experiments of this type with non-inducible strain.

L. R. CALDAS: No, but we have prepared a system for that taking the non-inducible phage from *E. coli* Lisbonne and Carrère and lysogenizing the sensitive strain of *E. coli* K 12.

H. EAGLE: What is the percentage of bacteria that are induced by streptomycin?

L. R. CALDAS: It is very difficult to say with these experiments the percentage of induction. The only thing I can say for the moment is, if the accumulation process would continue for a longer time than 6 hr without any bacterial division, probably all bacteria would be converted into infectious centers.

CHAIRMAN: I would like to ask you what is the role of ribosomes in the case of the sensitive strain?

L. R. CALDAS: The hypothesis of Stanier postulated in a recent article is as follows: There are some structural differences between ribosomes of sensitive, resistant and dependent strains towards streptomycin. In the first case Sm seems to destroy all ribosomes. On the basis of Jacob and Monod repression theory Sm blocking protein synthesis would promote the induction of the prophage by depression if one assumes that the repressor is a protein. However, no mature phage would be released for the reason that ribosomes being destroyed no phage protein would be synthesized. The same scheme applies to resistant strains depending on the degree of resistance.

CHAIRMAN: Any questions or comments? If there are no questions, we will then close for today.

THE RADIOSENSITIVITY OF MATURE GERM CELLS AND FERTILIZED EGGS IN *DROSOPHILA MELANOGASTER*

R. M. VALENCIA* and J. I. VALENCIA†

* Atomic Energy Commission of Argentina
† University of Buenos Aires, Argentina

OUR MAIN interest has been the comparative radiosentitivity of different germ cell stages in *Drosophila melanogaster*, as measured by mutation frequency, mostly by mutations at specific loci, the method explained by Dr. W. Russell earlier in this symposium. We have been especially concerned in recent years with different stages of oogenesis (Valancia and Valencia, 1961). Currently, however, we have been investigating the radiosensitivity of those stages which represent the culmination of germ cell development, the completely mature germ cells, plus those stages which occur immediately after the functioning of the germ cells. Muller has called these stages the "perifertilization" stages. By fertilization we mean the entry of the sperm into the egg.

We are employing two different means of measuring the radiosensitivity of these stages, namely recessive lethal mutations in the X chromosome (considered both quantitatively and qualitatively) and embryonic mortality (dominant lethals).

At this point, I should like to refer briefly to our results (to be published in detail elsewhere) on mutations induced at specific loci in different stages of oogenesis, which will serve as background for interpreting some of the present results. Four-day-old virgin females, carrying one unmarked X chromosome and one marked with a series of 13 recessive mutant alleles (Muller's stock "jynd"), were irradiated with 4000r of X-rays, mated and passed through 4 broods, as follows: brood A, 3 days; brood B, 4 days; brood C, 4 days; brood D, 4 days. Brood A should have yielded progeny from germ cells which were nearly mature or maturing oocytes when irradiated, brood D should have tested oogonia, and broods C and D would have been intermediate stages. Nondisjunctional daughters were examined for mutations induced in the normal X at any of the loci marked in the other X. Table 1 summarizes the mutation frequencies and Table 2 shows

TABLE 1. X-RAY INDUCED MUTATIONS AT 10 X-CHROMOSOME LOCI OF *Drosophila Melanogaster* FEMALES

(See text for explanation)

Brood	No. of Fl females examined	Total mutants (10 loci)	Ave. freq. per locus per r ×10⁸	95% confidence limits
A	11,212	31	6·92	4·68 − 9·80
B	14,774	36	6·10	4·23 − 8·47
C	28,564	56	4·90	3·68 − 6·40
D	42,828	32	1·87	1·28 − 2·63
Total	97,386	155	—	—

TABLE 2. CYTOLOGICAL ANALYSES OF MUTATIONS AT SPECIFIC LOCI IN THE X-CHROMOSOME OF *Drosophila melanogaster* FEMALES

Cytological condition and viability	Brood*				
	A	B	C	D	Total
No aberration (non-lethal)	2	3	4	7	16
No aberration (lethal)	1	3	5	7	16
Deficiency (lethal)	8	1	3	1	13
Inversion (lethal)	3	2	1	0	6
Translocation (lethal)	0	0	0	1	1
Undetermined aberration (lethal)	1	0	0	1	2
Total	15	9	13	17	54
% of total cases per brood which were:					
point mutations	20	67	69	82	
chromosome aberrations	80	33	31	18	

* See text for explanation of germ cell stage tested in each brood.

the cytological nature of the viable mutations. Notice that the most mature oocytes tested (brood A) are about $3^1/_2$ times more radiosensitive (in terms of mutations recovered) than the oogonia. Even more striking is the difference in the cytological nature of the mutations, 80 per cent of the mutations from brood A being associated with chromosome rearrangements (mostly small deficiencies), while even slightly less mature stages (brood B) yielded only 33 per cent aberrations.

Here I would like to point out that the oocytes tested in brood A were *not* fully mature oocytes, but rather should be considered as *almost* mature, since the X-ray dose given (4000r) would have killed all of the fully mature ones. In the present work, on the other hand, we are studying the fully mature oocyte, called "stage 14" by King *et al.* (1956) who have made a detailed study of oocyte development. Stage 14 oocytes are considerably more radiosensitive than these preciously studied oocytes, and probably they are more complex in terms of radiobiological events.

Before proceeding further, it is necessary to review very briefly the nuclear events which occur during the perifertilization period. (See Rabinowitz, 1941, for a detailed account.) The developing oocyte nucleus begins meiosis, but is arrested in a modified prophase stage. Only when the oocyte is fully mature does the nucleus proceed to metaphase I, and it is presumably in this stage at the time of sperm entry. It then proceeds through the two meiotic divisions to yield the female pronucleus and three polar nuclei. The sperm nucleus meanwhile enlarges, becomes rounded and vesicular and migrates to the center of the oocyte where it lies alongside the female pronucleus. The two pronuclei enter mitosis simultaneously, but actual admixture of their chromosome does not occur until telophase. At 24°C this first mitotic division of the paired pronuclei occurs $23\pm1\cdot72$ min after fertilization. There then ensues a series of at least 12 very rapid, synchronous mitoses, without cytoplasmic cleavage, to form the blastoderm. These mitoses (although they are *not* associated with cytoplasmic cleavage) are generally referred to as the "cleavage" mitoses. Only some 2–3 hr after fertilization do cell walls form between the nuclei and then the divisions become asynchronous. Meanwhile, a group of some 55 nuclei (Rabinowitz, 1941; Muller *et al.*, 1954) has become cut off from the syncytium to form the "polar cap". Part of these nuclei eventually give rise to the germ cells.

Ulrich (1956) first reported a very high frequency of recessive lethal mutations (5·8 per cent) induced by 1500r of X-rays in eggs 10–20 min after laying. Later (1958) he reported an even higher frequency (7·2 per cent) with 1000r, obtained, undoubtedly, using improved techniques. This high sensitivity was attributed to either a higher sensitivity of the zygote or the absence of selective elimination of gametes (pronuclei ?) with recessive lethals, as could happen with the gametes of adult males. Oster (1958), irradiating 10–25 min eggs, obtained confirmatory results (6·1 per cent with 800r) and pointed out that the high sensitivity was probably due to the rapid mitotic divisions of the embryo nuclei.

Although zygotic sensitivity, absence of selective elimination of cells with recessive lethals and mitotic activity may all be involved in conferring a high sensitivity to the fertilized egg, it seemed to the writers highly probable that another factor might be the condition of the nuclei before pronuclear union.

The fact that the maternal nucleus is undergoing meiosis could very well make it highly sensitive. St. Amand and von Borstel (1956), testing for dominant lethals induced by X-rays in *Habrobracon* eggs, found the meiotic stages uniformly very sensitive and the female pronucleus even more sensitive than the meiotic stages. In the case of the paternal nucleus, the physiological and structural changes it undergoes could make it vary in sensitivity in a way difficult to predict. If, however, the maternal pronucleus is highly sensitive, then the paternal pronucleus might be expected to be equally so.

The experiments here reported were carried out for the purpose of comparing the frequency of recessive lethal mutations recovered from X-chromosomes irradiated in the paternal nucleus and in the maternal nucleus, in eggs recently laid and presumably recently fertilized, and comparing these frequencies in turn with those obtained after irradiating slightly older embryos, presumably in the stage of cleavage mitoses. These experiments led to further investigations (still underway) of the perifertilization stages, including the mature germ cells and the determination of embryonic mortality as well as of recessive lethals.

MATERIALS AND METHODS

The basic stocks used in all experiments are shown in Figure 1. Basic stock number 1 carries a marked Y chromosome in the males in order to prevent the accidental use of females carrying extra Y chromosomes resulting from nondisjunction, which is frequent in stocks heterozygous for inversions. In all cases, flies whose eggs were to be collected for irradiation

No. 1 $\dfrac{\text{y oc ptg}}{\text{y sc}^{Sl}\text{ B In49 v}}$ females $\times$ $\dfrac{\text{y oc ptg}}{\text{y}^{+}\text{ sc}^{8}}$ males or $\dfrac{\text{y sc}^{Sl}\text{ B In49 v}}{\text{y}^{+}\text{ sc}^{8}}$ males

No. 2 $\dfrac{\text{y oc ptg}}{}$ males $\times$ yf:= females

No. 3 $\dfrac{\text{y sc}^{Sl}\text{ B In49 v}}{}$ males $\times$ yf:= females

FIG. 1. Genetic composition of basic stocks.

and/or counting were mated in a bell jar egg-collecting apparatus resembling
that described by Ulrich (1956). Our modification of his collecting technique has been described (Kirschbaum and Valencia, 1962). Irradiations were
done with a Philips clinical machine, run at 150 kVp and 10 mA with 1 mm
Al filter, at a distance of 10 cm from the edge of the window.

For recessive lethals induced in fertilized eggs, the crossing schemes
(Fig. 2) were planned in such a way that any pre-existing lethals were elimi-

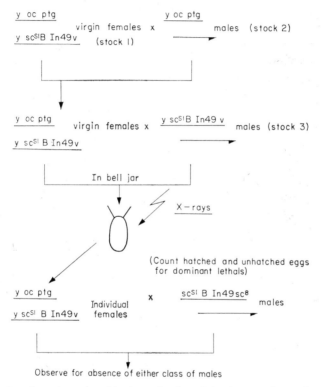

Fig. 2. Crossing schemes used in determination of dominant and recessive lethals
induced in fertilized eggs and embryos *(y oc ptg* of maternal origin, *y sc^{Sl} B In49 v*
of paternal origin).

nated in the immediately preceding parental generations. The genetic
background was made the same in all cases — i.e. the irradiated egg or
embryo in every case was of the same genotype, derived from the same
parental stocks. The only variation was in the origin of the X-chromosomes,
which was alternated in alternate experiments. Females whose eggs were
to be irradiated were collected as virgins and aged 4–6 days. The males
usually aged 2–4 days. About 900 females and 1000 males were mated in

the apparatus, where they were left for two days, with plenty of food. On the third day, they were tested to see if egg-laying was maximum and constant, and if so, irradiations were begun. In order to X-ray recently fertilized eggs, eggs were collected for 10-min intervals and irradiated immediately. For early embryos, eggs were collected for 10- (sometimes 15-) min intervals, held for 30 min and then irradiated. Heterozygous femaes hatching from the eggs were mated individually to sc^{Sl} B $In49$ sc^8 males for the recessive lethal test, as shown in Fig. 2. Apparent lethals in the y oc ptg X-chromosome were confirmed by brother-sister mating, and then made into balanced stocks for later genetic and cytological analyses. Apparent lethals in the y sc^{Sl} B $In49$ v X-chromosome were confirmed by observing one more generation, but balanced stocks were not made, since crossing-over with the sc^{Sl} B $In49$ sc^8 chromosome complicated the procedure.

Recessive lethals induced in stage 14 oocytes are being determined by using the same crossing scheme (Fig. 2), except that the aged Fl females are irradiated without etherizing and then mated in ordinary culture bottles. Females are allowed to lay eggs for no more than 12–15 hr.

Recessive lethals induced in mature sperm were determined using the same stocks, but no pre-cross was made, i.e. males from basic stocks 2 or 3 were irradiated and mated to virgin females of stock 1. In order to have conditions entirely comparable to those for the other perifertilization stages, the males were irradiated and mated (without etherizing) to aged females, which were allowed to lay eggs for 12–15 hr.

Dominant lethals were determined by counting the proportion of eggs hatched and unhatched at approximately 48 hr after laying. (See Kirschbaum and Valencia, 1962). In the case of fertilized eggs, the same egg collections were used for the determination of both dominant lethals and recessive lethals. For stage 14 oocytes and sperm they were determined separately, but similar schemes were used. Eggs for counting were collected for about 10 hr after treatment of the flies.

RESULTS AND DISCUSSION

Recessive Lethals

The recessive lethal frequencies determined in fertilized eggs are shown in Table 3. It can be observed that at all doses and in both the recently fertilized egg and the early embryo, the frequencies are high, as compared with the frequencies obtained irradiating other cell stages with these same X-ray doses. As pointed out by Oster (1958) only the spermatid has shown a comparable sensitivity. If we take into consideration the fact that in the

TABLE 3. FREQUENCIES OF RECESSIVE LETHALS INDUCED BY X-RAYS IN RECENTLY FERTIZILED EGGS AND EARLY EMBRYOS

			Maternal			Paternal		
			No. females tested	No. lethals	% lethals	No. females tested	No. lethals	% lethals
y oc ptg X chromosome	Fertilized egg	400r	228	11	4·82	485	7	1·44
		500r	1405	64	4·56	983	48	4·37
		800r	264	14	5·30	686	18	2·62
	Embryo	500r	566	21	3·72	669	26	3·89
		800r	142	3	2·12	102	3	2·94
	Control		2631	12	0·46	2249	7	0·31
y B v X chromosome	Fertilized egg	500r	689	33	4·79	908	24	2·64
		800r	291	18	6·18	264	8	3·03
	Embryo	500r	669	30	4·49	566	24	4·24
		800r	102	5	4·90	142	4	2·82
	Control		1923	17	0·88	2480	17	0·69

case of the fertilized egg, the recessive lethals are recovered among a smal proportion of surviving eggs, the greater proportion having been eliminated by dominant lethals (Ulrich, 1960; and this paper), then the fertilized egg must be considered by far the most radiosensitive cell stage in *Drosophila*. The stage 14 oocyte, in which case dominant lethality eliminates a comparable proportion of the irradiated cells (Parker, 1960, and this paper), has been shown by Parker (1960) to yield a frequency of recessive lethals of 1·09 after 500r. Our own determinations of recessive lethals in stage 14 oocytes of our stocks (Table 4) are in agreement with this frequency as far as the normal-ordered X *(y oc ptg)* is concerned, and mature sperm in our scheme has yielded frequencies for 500r very much like those for oocytes. It seems that considerably more mutations are recovered from chromosomes irradiated in the fertilized egg than from comparable chromosomes irradiated immediately prior to fertilization, in either the oocyte or the sperm.

TABLE 4. RECESSIVE LETHALS INDUCED BY 500r OF X-RAYS IN MATURE GERM CELLS

	Stage 14 oocytes		Sperm	
	No. X-chromosomes tested	% lethal	No. X-chromosomes tested	% lethal
y oc ptg (500r)	443	1·81	714	1·56
y sc^{Sl} B In49 v (500r)	616	4·22	600	1·86
y oc ptg (control)	755	0·52	125	0
y sc^{Sl} B In49 v (control)	816	1·34	135	0·75

The present results (see Table 3), although not entirely consistent, indicate very strongly that the maternal nucleus is more sensitive than the paternal nucleus in the recently fertilized egg. At all doses and in the case of both types of X-chromosome, with the exception of the y oc ptg X at 500r, the maternal nucleus yielded about 2–3 times the frequency of lethals recovered from the paternal nucleus. No difference is observed in 3 of the 4 groups of irradiated embryos. No difference would be expected, since the maternal and paternal chromosomes are now in the same nuclei.

A lack of proportionality between dose and mutations recovered is obvious, for both recently fertilized eggs and embryos. In some cases, the rise in frequency is very little between the lower and the higher dose, and in other cases there is a considerable drop in frequency at the higher dose. Selective elimination by the death of more sensitive cells, in a population of mixed sensitivities, is strongly suggested. At the higher doses, the elimination is more pronounced. That we are dealing with a population of cells of mixed nature is certain. In the recently fertilized eggs, as pointed out above, both nuclei undergo a series of changes within a very short time (about 20 min). A group of eggs collected during 10 min and irradiated within 5 min more, must include nuclei in various conditions. The possible lack of perfect correlation between fertilization and egg-laying probably introduces an error leading to still further heterogeneity in stage of irradiated eggs. If there is a changing pattern of sensitivity with changing nuclear condition, then any such collection is a population of mixed sensitivities.

Recent results of Würgler (1962) are especially interesting in this connection. He has succeeded in perfecting the egg-collecting techniques of Ulrich to the extent that he is able to make 3-min collections of eggs, with an error of 1·5 min. Testing for dominant lethals in eggs irradiated 9–13, 13–16, 16–19 and 19–22 min after laying, he finds 4 different dose-effect curves. The sum of these curves is equal to that previously obtained by Ulrich irradiating

0–20 min eggs. This is clear evidence for a rapidly and drastically changing radiation sensitivity in recently fertilized eggs, as measured by dominant lethality. It is logical to expect that sensitivity changes should occur with respect to recessive lethals. Just what this sensitivity pattern is, however, and how it varies for the maternal and the paternal nuclei, cannot be determined on the basis of any data presently available. Muller (1958) mentions that data of Oster (unpublished) indicated a severe drop in sensitivity of the paternal nucleus immediately after fertilization, followed by a sharp rise at pronuclear union. Our results have failed to reveal this variation. It is realized, of course, that much shorter collecting periods than ours would have to be used, with a high degree of accuracy as to stage sampling, in order to reveal such a pattern.

In the case of the embryos, there is a population of mixed sensitivities due to variation in the stage of the cell cycle. Since the nuclear divisions are synchronous, any one embryo has all its nuclei in the same stage. It is well known that different division stages vary greatly in sensitivity with regard to dominant lethality. If those stages most sensitive to killing are those most likely to have recessive lethals induced in them, then selective elimination can occur and would be exaggerated at higher radiation doses.

The frequency of lethals recovered from treated embryos was in general lower than that from treated pre-zygotic eggs, though there were some exceptions. Of 8 pairs of frequencies which can be compared (i.e. same chromosome, same dose and same nucleus), 6 show a lower frequency for the embryo. It would, nevertheless, be erroneous to conclude a lower sensitivity for the embryonic stage. At this stage, many induced lethals might not be detected, due to the fact that the nucleus containing the mutation does not give rise to the whole gonad. If the gonad were fractional for a lethal, this would not be detected in the generation observed in the present experiments. Unfortunately, it was not possible at this time to carry out the volume of technical labor necessary to check a further generation and detect fractionals. Since the earlier the embryonic stage irradiated, the less the probability of obtaining fractional gonads, 35–45 min eggs were treated. At this time the embryo should be in the 2–8 nucleate stage. It would seem that if there is not too much moving about and mixing of the nuclei in the syncytium, then there is a good chance that all the nuclei budded off into the polar cap could have originated from the same irradiated nucleus. It is recognized, however, that the egg samples were probably not entirely homogeneous and that the error in stage collected could be considerable. Until further work is done, the question of the proportion of lethals detected and not detected must remain unanswered.

I should like to point out that there was a higher yield of lethals in almost all cases from the y sc^{Sl} B $In49$ v chromosome than from the y oc ptg. I will not enter into discussion of the possible explanations for this difference, but will only point out an obvious conclusion. In order to compare the sensitivity of chromosomes in different kinds of cells or different nuclei, it is necessary to test the same kind of chromosome in the different environments.

The recessive lethals induced in the y oc ptg chromosome are being examined cytologically in salivary gland chromosomes, and the results thus far are shown in Table 5. Although the number of lethals analyzed is still

TABLE 5. CYTOLOGICAL ANALYSES OF RECESSIVE LETHALS

| | Stage 14 oocytes | Fertilized eggs | | | | | | Embryos | Controls | Total |
| | | Maternal X | | | Paternal X | | | | | |
		400r	500r	800r	400r	500r	800r			
Apparent point mutations	19	6	23	11	1	11	9	29	10	119
Chromosome rearrangements	7	1	1	0	0	1	2	0	0	12
Total	26	7	24	11	1	12	11	29	10	131

rather small, it appears that there is a tendency for more rearrangements to be recovered from the paternal X than from the maternal X when recently fertilized eggs are irradiated. Twelve and one-half per cent of the total lethals of paternal origin were associated with rearrangements while only 4·8 per cent of those of maternal origin were rearrangements. If only the higher dose is considered, in which equal numbers of lethals have been analyzed, the comparison is 2/11 (18·2 per cent) for the paternal X and 0/11 for the maternal. Considering only the paternal X, the proportion of chromosome rearrangements among the lethals is quite comparable to the proportion found by Valencia (1954) in a group of lethals induced by 700r in mature sperm. In the latter case 15 per cent were associated with rearrangements. Embryos, on the other hand, yielded no cases of rearrangements. This could be interpreted in either of 3 ways: chromosome breakage is not induced (which seems very unlikely), chromosome breakage tends to result in embryonic death or there is a very efficient restitution mechanism operating in the embryo. Considering the rapid mitotic process which is going on here, it would seem unlikely that restitution would always "win out" over rearrangement. This leaves the second possibility as appearing most likely, but we would not like to venture any opinion very seriously at this time.

The cytological results obtained thus far from the small group of lethals analyzed from stage 14 oocytes indicate a high level of chromosome damage.

Dominant Lethals

The results of our determinations of dominant lethality (i.e. embryonic mortality) induced by 500r of X-rays delivered to each of the 4 perifertilization stages are shown in Table 6. The frequencies obtained for stage 14

TABLE 6. DOMINANT LETHALS INDUCED BY X-RAYS IN THE PERIFERTILIZATION STAGES OF *Drosophila melanogaster*

		500r		800r	
		No. eggs examined	% eggs unhatched	No. eggs examined	% eggs unhatched
Stage 14 oocytes	Treated	6864	67·5	—	—
	Control	6190	7·8	—	—
	Corrected	—	59·7	—	—
Fertilized eggs	Treated	6972	64·7	8555	80·3
	Control	1519	8·0	6251	8·6
	Corrected	—	56·7	—	71·7
Early embryos	Treated	2128	69·8	6641	89·9
	Control	1519	8·0	6251	8·6
	Corrected	—	61·8	—	81·3
Sperm	Treated	6475	18·2	—	—
	Control	5101	8·4	—	—
	Corrected	—	9·8	—	—

oocytes and for fertilized eggs are quite in agreement with those obtained by Parker (1959) and by Ulrich (1960) respectively.

Since the most obvious difference between a sperm cell and a mature oocyte or an egg is the absence of cytoplasm in the one and the relatively enormous quantity in the other, the first thought which comes to mind is that cytoplasmic damage is the cause of the high embryonic mortality resulting from irradiating oocytes or eggs, as compared with that resulting from irradiating sperm. Nevertheless, several excellent experiments (Whiting, 1955; Rogers and von Borstel, 1957; and others) have shown that the nucleus and not the cytoplasm is the sensitive target in cell death. It is necessary, then, to conclude that nuclear damage is somehow different in irradiated sperm and in irradiated oocytes or eggs.

If we consider only the stage 14 oocyte and the sperm, it seems possible that the great difference in sensitivity might be related to the possibility for repair of chromosome damage, combined with certain other factors, as follows. In the case of the oocyte, there is evidently much chromosome breakage. These breaks are probably prohibited from restituting immediately due to radiation damage to repair mechanisms in the cell. In any case, there is very little *time* for repair. Meiosis is already underway, would probably not be delayed by the irradiation at this stage and thus proceeds. Practically all the original chromosome damage would thus be present to interfere with the meiotic process and lead to a high degree of aneuploidy, bridges, etc. In the case of sperm, on the other hand, chromosome breakage might be equal to (or more or less than) that occurring in the oocyte—*but* these chromosomes, upon fertilization, find themselves in the rich, undamaged cytoplasm of the oocyte. There are some twenty minutes time during which repair processes could work before these chromosomes need enter into mitosis. Thus much less damage would be done to the embryo. I think, then, that one can theorize an explanation for the high sensitivity of the mature oocyte as compared to sperm, on the basis of chromosome damage, damaged repair mechanism and lack of time for repair.

The fact that no difference was found between mature oocytes, recently fertilized eggs and early embryos irradiated with 500r is more difficult to explain. If the nucleus is the target in cell death, then increasing the number of nuclei in the cell should influence the probability of death. It may well be, however, that the damages postulated as causing embryonic death after treatment of oocytes are not the major factors involved in embryonic death resulting from treatment of fertilized eggs or embryos. Certainly chromosome breakage and damaged repair mechanisms are involved, but other factors, such as delayed mitosis and disturbed balance between different embryonic processes, do enter into the picture and may assume major importance. Perhaps it is simple coincidence that the frequency of embryonic mortality turned out to be the same at 500r. Further work needs to be done to clarify this question.

SUMMARY

An investigation is being made of the radio-sensitivity of the "perifertilization" stages in *Drosophila melanogaster*.

Recessive lethals were determined in two different X-chromosomes in maternal and paternal nuclei of recently fertilized eggs and early embryos, irradiated with 400r, 500r and 800r of X-rays. These same X-chromosomes were tested in mature sperm and mature (stage 14) oocytes. Both the maternal and the paternal nuclei of the fertilized egg yielded a higher frequency of lethals than did the mature germ cells treated immediately before fertilization. In the recently fertilized egg, the maternal nucleus yielded more lethals than the paternal nucleus, but the lethals revovered from the latter seem to be more likely to be associated with chromosome rearrangements. The early embryos yielded a somewhat lower frequency of lethals than the fertilized eggs, and those analyzed cytologically thus far are apparently point mutations.

Embryonic death is 6 times as frequent after irradiating (500r) mature oocytes as after irradiating mature sperm. It is postulated that this difference might be related to a difference in the possibility of repair of broken chromosomes before they must be involved in a nuclear division process.

REFERENCES

KING, R. C., RUBINSON ANN C. and SMITH, R. F. 1956, Oogenesis in adult *Drosophila melanogaster*. *Growth*, **20**, 121–157.

KIRSCHBAUM, W. F. and VALENCIA, R. M., 1962, Modified egg-collecting technique. *Drosophila Information Service*, **36**, 129.

MULLER, H. J., ALTENBURG, E., MEYER, H., EDMONDSON M. and ALTENBURG, L., 1954, The lack of proportionality between mutation rate and ultraviolet dose in *Drosophila*. *Heredity*, **8**, 158–185.

MULLER, H. J., 1958, Advances in radiation mutagenesis through studies on *Drosophila*. *Proc. Second U.N. Conf. Peaceful Uses of Atomic Energy*, **22**, 313–321.

OSTER, I. I., 1959, The spectrum of sensitivity of *Drosophila* germ cell stages to X-irradiation. *Radiation Biology*, ed. J. H. Martin. Butterworths Scientific, London, pp. 253–267.

PARKER, D. R., 1959, Dominant lethal mutation in irradiated oocytes. Univ. of Texas Publications, 5914, 113–127.

PARKER, D. R., 1960, The induction of recessive lethals in *Drosophila* oocytes. *Genetics*, **45**, 135–142.

RABINOWITZ, M., 1941, Studies on the cytology and early embryology of the egg of *Drosophila melanogaster*. *J. Morph.* **69**, 1–49.

ROGERS, R. W. and VON BORSTEL, R. C., 1957, Alpha-particle bombardment of the *Habrobracon* egg. I. Sensitivity of the nucleus. *Radiation Res.* **7**, 484–490.

ST. AMAND, W. and VON BORSTEL R. C., 1956, Radiosensitivity of the unfertilized *Habrobracon* egg during meiosis and early cleavage. *J. Tenn. Acad. Sci. XXXI*, 138.

ULRICH, HANS, 1956, Effect of oxygen on the mutagenic action of X-rays on uncleaved *Drosophila* eggs. *Drosophila Information Service*, **30**, 155.

ULRICH, HANS, 1956, Die Strahlenempfindlichkeit von Zelkern und Plasma und die indirekte mutagene Wirkung der Strahlen. *Verhand. der Deutschen Zool. Gesell.* in Hamburg. Akad. Verlags. Leipzig, pp. 150–182.

ULRICH, HANS, 1958, Die mutagene Röntgenstrahlenwirkung auf das ungefurchte *Drosophila*-Ei und ihre Sauerstoffabhängigkeit. *Revue Suisse de Zoologie*, **65**, 442–448.

ULRICH, HANS, 1960, Die Beziehung zwischen Strahlendosis und Mutationsrate bei Röntgenbestrahlung von *Drosophila-Zygoten*. *Revue Suisse de Zoologie*, **67**, 287–295.

VALENCIA, J. I., 1954, A cytogenetic analysis of lethals induced by a low and by a high dose of X-rays in *Drosophila melanogaster*. *Caryologia*, VI, Suppl. No. 895. (Proc. IX Intern. Congr. Genetics, Bellagio, Italy, 1953).

VALENCIA, R. M. and VALENCIA, J. I., 1961, Mutations induced in different stages of developing germ cells of *Drosophila* females. *Radiation Res.* **14**, (4), 513.

WHITING, A. R., 1955, Androgenesis as evidence for the nature of X-ray induced injury. *Radiation Res.* **2**, 71–78.

WÜRGLER, F. E., 1962, Experimental analysis of a linear dose effect curve resulting from X-irradiation of *Drosophila* eggs. *Proc. Second Intern. Congr. Radiation Research*, Harrogate, England.

DISCUSSION

CHAIRMAN: The discussion is open.

H. S. KAPLAN: I want to ask what is known about the actual extent of DNA synthesis in these various stages. Is DNA synthesis going on in the mature oocyte or does this not happen until after fertilization? Secondly, you referred to the possibility that damage in the sperm might be repaired by the oocyte. I am not clear on the way in which these mortality experiments are scored, at what time is the mortality actually evaluated and what undergoes mortality?

R. M. VALENCIA: I believe that very little is known concerning DNA synthesis in the oocyte, fertilized egg and early embryo. Somewhat more is known in the case of organisms other than *Drosophila*, such as amphibia, but even there the situation is not at all clear. This question of DNA synthesis in early developmental stages has been treated in some detail by J. Brachet (Symposium on Specificity of Cell Differentiation and Interaction, sponsored by the Biology Division, Oak Ridge National Laboratory, April 1962).

In our experiments, mortality was scored by counting percent of unhatched eggs, and would represent death at any time during the development of the larva.

L. D. HAMILTON: Just a slight comment on DNA synthesis in the fertilized egg. From your diagram and description of the egg of *Drosophila*, it would appear that they behave in the same way as the fertilized sea urchin egg. In the sea urchin it is quite easy to see that the DNA of the egg and the DNA of the sperm undergo one doubling before they actually fuse. This was in fact the basis for my suggestion to Dr. Marcovich that mating in bacteria is after all analogous to fertilization in a way. It was possibly preceded by an independent DNA synthesis of the two mating cells. So at least we do know in the fertilized egg and you suggested in your talk on *Drosophila* that there was actually a cellular division, or rather a chromosomal division of the egg and the sperm independently. Clearly this must be preceded by at least one DNA synthesis, otherwise you would have not a chromosomal division, so that from morphological grounds in *Drosophila* and from the biochemical grounds in sea urchin it does appear that there is in fact at least a doubling of DNA before fusion.

L. B. RUSSELL: I wonder if there is not a result in the mouse, fairly closely correlated with Dr. Valencia's work, which — at least if taken at face value — argues against a very close correlation between sensitivity to killing and amount of DNA. In *Drosophila*, as Dr. Valencia mentioned, the whole interval between sperm entry and the first cleavage is only about 20 min. By contrast, in the mouse, this interval is something like 24 hr, and about 12 hr of this time are spent in the pronuclear stage. The male and female pro-nuclei are separate entities which increase in volume about 10-fold during the first one-third of their existence, after which time they show no appreciable growth (Austin, 1952). We have tested sensitivity to radiation at various times over a $4^1/_2$ hr span of the 12 hr pronuclear period, There is a very marked decrease in sensitivity as time progresses: the early pronuclei, shortly after their formation, are very much more sensitive both to chromosome loss, as measured by frequency of sex chromosome loss, and to mortality, as measured by failure of the zygote to produce a newborn. Nothing is known about DNA content in pronuclear stages, but if there *is* any change during this interval (and there may be none), should one not expect an increase? Yet the change in sensitivity is definitely in the opposite direction. I wonder if Dr. Kaplan would comment on this.

H. S. KAPLAN: Did you say that there was a doubling of DNA during the pro-nucleic stage or not? In the slide I showed DNA content is not the only parameter. Ploidy is also a factor. If DNA doubles it could also double in ploidy and this would mean that although there is twice as much DNA, it is in two separate packages. This makes quite a difference. I think that this should actually be examined in detail before the subject can be analysed.

W. L. RUSSELL: I should just like to comment on a point of great importance for the studies on the oogonia and oocyte stages. I had no chance to mention it this morning, but the mouse is quite different from the human, and probably from several other mammalian species, in the response of the female to radiation effects on fertility. This may not be due to species differences in sensitivity of particular oogonia stages, but to differences in the stage in which the oocytes are arrested in the adult in different mammals. Dr. Oakberg has published some information on this, and there are also some reports from other workers along this line. I think it is vitally important that we fully understand all differences in sensitivity in the female germ cells. This is just the kind of work that we hope the *Drosophila* people will continue to do, and we are very happy to hear of Dr. Valencia's new contributions in this field.

R. M. VALENCIA: There is considerable evidence for a lot of difference in sensitivity not only among widely different stages of oogenesis, as shown by our specific locus data, but also even between slightly different stages of oocytes. Parker (1959; 1960) has found a tremendous difference in both dominant lethals and recessive lethals induced in fully mature oocytes (stage 14, according to King *et al.*, 1956) and in slightly less mature ones (stage 7). Now, we have a little data which suggests that there are also different sensitivity stages within the stage 14 oocytes. This is being investigated further.

C. PAVAN: Dr. Valencia, will you tell us what is the cause of these differences in sensitivity between maternal and paternal X-radiated chromosomes?

R. M. VALENCIA: The maternal and paternal chromosomes are in completely different conditions in the recently fertilized egg. The maternal one is going through meiosis and the paternal one is changing from a condensed, elongated sperm nucleus to a larger, round, vesiculated pronucleus.

H. S. KAPLAN: I want to add to the point that Dr. L. B. Russell made. I think there is recently a little evidence in the literature (and I regret that I cannot cite the exact reference from memory) regarding the sensitivity to killing on our dose response curve based on the mouse egg. There has been some work reported in *Radiation Research* in the past year suggesting that the LD37 of the mouse egg, although the data do not permit great precision, is in the range of 10–20 r. And on the slide that I presented at the end, this fits absolutely perfectly with an extrapolation of the haploid line to the mammalian DNA content. I would like to make a plea for further studies on precisely those points. I do not know how difficult they are, but it is of the greatest importance that we get good quantitative data on haploid mammalian cells.

L. B. RUSSELL: The work to which you are presumably referring was done on mouse primary oocytes, i.e. it involved clearly *diploid* cells. I might also mention that the sensitivity was shown to change radically according to stage of the follicle in which the oocytes are contained, even though the oocyte itself does not undergo cell division.

RADIATION-INDUCED MAMMARY GLAND NEOPLASIA IN THE RAT

V. P. Bond, E. P. Cronkite, C. A. Shellabarger and G. Aponte

Brookhaven National Laboratory, New York, U.S.A.

IN DISCUSSING this subject, data on radiation-induced mammary gland neoplasia in the rat, indicating that direct interaction between the radiation and target tissue is necessary for maximum neoplasia induction, will be presented mainly. Other types of radiation-induced neoplasia, in which little or no information on the mechanisms involved is available, will be discussed briefly. In particular, investigations on radiation-induced mouse lymphoma will be reviewed, in which neoplasia appears to be an abscopal effect. Implications of these data will be discussed, particularly with regard to possible mechanisms involved, and extrapolation to man.

MAMMARY GLAND NEOPLASIA IN THE RAT

It was noted in 1956 at the Brookhaven National Laboratory, that 400 r of total body Co^{60} gamma radiation resulted within 10–12 months in mammary gland neoplasia in a large percentage of exposed Sprague–Dawley rats.[1] Many of the animals had tumors in more than one mammary gland, and as many as ten neoplasms in a single animal was observed. The neoplasms were generally of four types. Adenocarcinomas appeared as early as three months after exposure and comprised some 30 per cent of all tumors. Adenofibromas appeared at about 4 months and constituted about 38 per cent of the total. Approximately 17 per cent were fibroadenomas appearing first at about nine months after exposure. Fibrosarcomas constituted about 4 per cent, appearing approximately 5 months after exposure. Less than 10 per cent of the tumors were of mixed composition, or were not diagnosed. In treating the data, the incidence of all types was combined and only the total incidence was employed. The tumor types were combined not only to improve the statistics, but for other reasons as well. Since over 85 per cent of the tumors were derived at least in part from glandular epithelium, it could be considered that essentially all neoplasms were derived from the same cell type. In addition, each neoplasm independent of its precise origin or histologic type, could be considered as representing a neoplastic change in the target tissue, the mammary gland, initiated by the ionizing radiation.

Experimental Design

The following procedures, given in detail elsewhere, [1-5] were followed, unless otherwise indicated. Female Sprague–Dawley rats were used, and exposure was accomplished at approximately forty days of age. Radiation dose rates were determined by means of Victoreen chambers calibrated by the National Bureau of Standards, and doses quoted represent the dose at the mid-line of the animal, with all exposure apparatus and all other simultaneously exposed animals present. With X-radiation, 250 kVp X-rays were used, filtered with a half millimeter of copper and one millimeter of aluminium.

Following exposure the animals were observed daily and were palpated approximately once each week for the presence of neoplasms. Initially, observations were continued for approximately one year. In later studies, observation was extended to include the entire lifetime of the animal. Neoplasms were removed surgically under ether anesthesia when a diameter of approximately one centimeter was reached, and the animal was returned to the colony for continued observation. Animals were sacrificed when moribund. Histopathology was obtained on all neoplasms removed surgically, and complete autopsies including histopathology were done on all sacrificed animals.

For shielding experiments, $1/8$ in. thick lead was placed over the body region to be protected. Measurements indicated that a dose beneath the shield was reduced to less than 10 per cent of the incident dose.

Hormone Dependency

In studies to determine the possible hormone dependency of neoplasia incidence, the role of the ovary was investigated. Animals were ovariectomized at both 40 days (time of exposure), and 46 days later. In some ovariectomized exposed animals, normal ovaries were later transplanted. The results are shown in Table 1. As will be apparent from the table, 400 r increased the percentage of animals with at least one neoplasm from approximately 2 to 79 per cent (neoplasms scored at approximately one year). Ovariectomy performed either at 40 or 86 days of age reduced the incidence of neoplasms following 400 r from approximately 80 to 20 per cent. Implantation of normal ovaries in the ovariectomized animal restored the

TABLE 1. EFFECT OF OVERIECTOMY ON NEOPLASIA INDUCTION

Procedure	Initial no. of rats	% rats with neoplasms
No irradiation		
1. Intact animals	47	2
Irradiation only		
2. 400r WBR*	29	79
Irradiation ovariectomy		
3. 400r WBR, ovariectomy	17	23
4. 400r WBR, ovariectomy at 46 days after exposure	16	19
5. 400r WBR, ovariectomy implant normal ovaries	11	82
6. As in 5; implant did not take	6	0
Irradiation, shield ovaries only		
7. 400r, exteriorized ovaries shielded	16	69
8. 400r, shield ovarian area	15	40
Irradiate ovaries only		
9. 400r to exteriorized ovaries only	15	0
10. 400r to ovaries *in vivo*, implant non-exposed hosts	17	0
Irradiation, other procedures		
11. 400r, head shielded	16	81

* Whole-body X-irradiation.

incidence to 82 per cent; no neoplasms occurred in those animals in which the ovarian implant did not "take". Shielding of the exteriorized ovaries reduced the incidence by a very small per cent; shielding the ovarian area reduced the incidence to 40 per cent. This reduction could be accounted for in part by the fact that a portion of the target mammary gland tissue was shielded by this procedure (see below under "Partial-body Exposure"). Irradiation of the ovaries alone either *in vivo* or *in vitro* did not increase the incidence of neoplasia. Irradiation of the entire body with the exception of the head yielded the expected high percentage of neoplasms, indicating that exposure of the pituitary probably was not involved in the demonstrated hormone dependence of neoplasia.

Further studies were initiated to determine the effect of added estrogens, pregnancy and hyper- or hypothyroidism on the incidence of neoplasia. Diethylstilbestrol in cholesterol was given subcutaneously to normal and irradiated animals, 1·5 mg per rat. In addition, the effects of pregnancy and lactation were studied in animals in which the ovarian area had been shielded to allow continued fertility. Other groups were given propylthiouracil (PTU), 0·025 per cent in drinking water to determine the influence of hypothyroidism on neoplasia induction. Similarly, other animals were given tri-iodothyronine (T–3), 0·5 μg three times per week for six weeks, to determine the effects of hyperthyrodism.

The results, shown in Table 2, indicate that while DES in the normal animal apparently had no effect in terms of neoplasia induction, the continuous presence of the hormone significantly reduced the incidence of neoplasia in the irradiated animal. This can be interpreted to mean that the normal cycling ovarian function may be required for maximal neoplasia induction. Shielding of the ovarian area reduced the incidence of neoplasia, as expected from shielding part of the target tissue (see below). Pregnancy had no effect on tumor incidence over that in animals in which the ovarian area was shielded. This was true whether or not lactation was allowed to proceed. It perhaps should be noted that termination of pregnancy

TABLE 2. STUDIES ON HORMONE DEPENDENCE OF MAMMARY GLAND NEOPLASIA
INDUCTION

Procedure	Initial no. of rats	Rats with mammary neoplasms, %
None — control	31	13
400r only	31	82
DES[2] only	31	10
400r + DES	31	41
400r — shield ovarian area	31	59
400r — shield ovarian area — pregnancy	30	67
400r + PTU[3]	31	76
400r + T3[4]	31	86

Corrected by the life-table technique.
DES, diethylstilbestrol.
PTU, propylthiouracil.
T3 tri-iodothyronine.

resulted in a reduced rate of a growth of some of the neoplasms. Neither hyperthyroidism nor hypothyroidism changed the incidence of neoplasia over that seen in the groups receiving 400 r alone.

Dose Dependency

In order to investigate the dose dependency of response, animals were exposed to graded doses of X-radiation and were observed for a period of one year. The results are shown in Fig. 1. The data represent the percentage

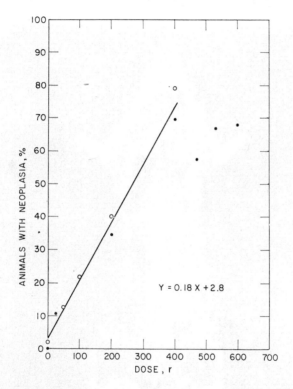

$$Y = 0.18 X + 2.8$$

FIG. 1. Incidence of mammary gland neoplasia vs. dose. Note that curve appears to be straight between limits of 25 and 400 r and that, within limits of error, the curve goes through zero incidence at zero dose.

of animals with one or more neoplasms, scored at approximately twelve months. The curve drawn, a free-hand fit, appears to be linear between the limits of 25 and 400 r. If the small incidence of neoplasia in the control, is subtracted, the curve appears to go through zero incidence at zero dose, within limits of error. Above 400 r, the curve appears either to remain flat or to assume a negative slope. The data are consistent with proportionality between dose and effect between the limits of 25 and 400 r, and a threshold, if it exists must be small.

Partial-body Exposure

In order to investigate the effects of partial-body exposure on the incidence of breast neoplasia, animals were exposed such that approximately one-half of the total breast tumor tissue was included in the beam (see Fig. 2). The one-eighth inch thick lead shields were designed to shield

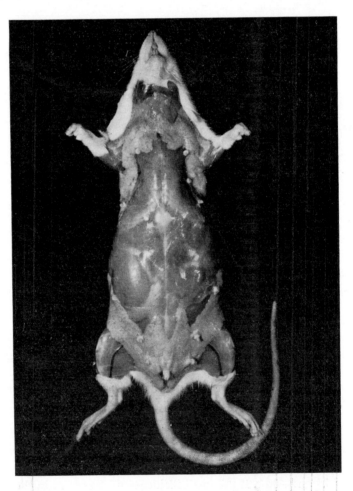

FIG. 2. Skinned lactating female Sprague-Dawley rat, showing location of mammary gland tissue. Note that the distribution makes it relatively easy to expose or shield one-half or one-quarter of the total mammary gland tissue.

either the upper or the lower half of the animal, or the right or left side. The results, again scored at approximately one year, are shown in Table 3. It will be noted that shielding of approximately one-half the breast tissue resulted in approximately one-half the incidence of neoplasia. This result seemed to be independent of the type of shielding employed, i.e. which half of the total target tissue was exposed or shielded. Shielding of the hind leg reduced the incidence of neoplasia somewhat, but no more than would be expected from the protection afforded some mammary gland tissue by the lead shield. It can be noted from Table 3 that from approximately 90 to 100 per cent of all neoplasms in the partially exposed animals occurred in the exposed areas.

TABLE 3. EFFECT OF PARTIAL-BODY RADIATION ON INCIDENCE OF MAMMARY GLAND NEOPLASIA

Procedure	Initial number of rats	% of animals with breast neoplasia	% of neoplasms in exposed area
400 r	28	68	100
400 r, shield right side	31	35	89
400 r, shield chest	29	38	93
400 r, to chest only	29	31	100
400 r, shield right hind leg	30	63	100

Fractionation Studies

Two sets of experiments have been done involving fractionation of dose. In the first experiment, 400 r of X-radiation was given either as a single exposure on the fortieth day of age, in five equal daily doses of 80 r, or in eighteen daily equal doses of 22·2 r. All exposures were given at the same dose rate, approximately 60 r per minute. The percentage of rats with mammary neoplasms in the three groups was 82, 79 and 71 per cent, respectively. A control incidence of 13 per cent was observed in the observational period of one year. It was not possible to demonstrate a significant difference in the groups, and no effect of fractionation was thus evident. A second, larger experiment, in which animals were allowed to live out their lifetime is incomplete, inasmuch as histopathology data are not as yet available. In this experiment, animals were given either 500 r of Co^{60} gamma radiation in a single exposure, 125 r in four semi-weekly exposures, 62 r in eight semi-weekly exposures, 30 r in sixteen semi-weekly exposures or 15 r in thirty-two semi-weekly exposures. One group was given 500 r in a single exposure at the same time that the last increment of fractionated exposure was delivered. Although incomplete, it again appears that there will be no significant difference in tumor incidence as a result of dose fractionation.

Possible Virus Etiology of Neoplasms

Although consideration was given early to possible virus etiology of the tumors, the problem has been investigated definitively only relatively recently by E. Paine, C. Shellabarger, and T. Francis at the University of Michigan. These studies are under way and only a preliminary indication of results can be given. A virus has been isolated from Sprague-Dawley rats used for mammary gland neoplasia induction, both by direct observation with electron microscopy and indirect immunological means. The virus does not produce disease when inoculated into the brain of young mice, but does result in death when introduced similarly into the hamster. The virus is approximately 18–20 mμ in diameter and contains DNA. It is considered definitely not to belong to the polyoma group. No correlation has been found between the presence of the virus in animals and the presence of mammary gland neoplasia following total body irradiation. This virus is thus considered to be present in some of the animals used, but is not now considered to be an etiologic factor in the development of the mammary gland neoplasms. It perhaps should be noted that a preliminary report has appeared,[7] indicating increased tumor incidence in Sprague-Dawley rats given irradiated blood.

Conclusions

A number of conclusions appear reasonable from the data thus far presented. From the shielding experiments, it would appear that the mammary gland tissue must be exposed directly in the beam for induction of neoplasia. Essentially all tumors appeared in the exposed areas; virtually no tumors appeared in the same animals in the shielded areas. If the induction process involved only an indirect or abscopal effect, tumors should have developed in both shielded and unshielded areas since the fact that tumors did appear in the non-shielded areas indicates that the general "internal environment" of the animal was suitable for neoplasia development. This appears to provide clear direct evidence that exposure of the breast tissue itself is a necessary prerequisite for radiation-induced neoplasia under the conditions studied.

From the studies on the effect of the ovary on neoplasia induction, it seems to be clear that intact, probably cyclical ovarian function is required for maximum tumor induction. Thus the development, but not the initia-

tion of tumors appears to be dependent upon secondary hormone stimulation.

Thus the conclusions seem to be inescapable that a two-stage (or more)
mechanism of neoplasia is involved — the radiation acts as the initiating
factor and the ovarian hormones act as a promoting substance.

"Primary" radiation damage in the target organ is necessary, but this
damage generally lies dormant, and may not manifest itself as neoplasia
unless an additional secondary mechanism is operative. A "general metabolic dearrangement" resulting from the exposure could not have initiated
the tumors. The radiation appears to produce a subtle irreversible change
in the tissue, which remains latent until acted upon by other stimulae.

It should be noted that while the results indicate strongly that interaction
between the radiation and target tissue is necessary, it does not necessarily
follow that the irradiation has produced a change within a single cell or
small number of cells that results in a "clone" of malignant cells. The
induction event could still be "indirect" on a local basis, in that neoplasia
could have resulted from radiation-induced disruption of the normal architecture of the target tissue, and perhaps efforts at regeneration. This possibility is considered to be improbable, since histological studies still in progress have indicated minimal if any disruption of architecture after doses
of radiation that result in neoplasia. It is of course also possible that disruption of normal architecture by means other than radiation (e.g. disruption
of blood supply, or transplantation) might result in neoplasia in the irradiated animal, in the absence of exposure of such disrupted "target" tissue.

One might wish to attach further significance to the data as far as mechanisms are concerned. It would appear that a linear dose-effect curve has
been obtained within a limited dose range, and the results are consistent
with the lack of a threshold. The results appear to be independent of the
pattern of dose deposition in time, i.e. no effect of fractionation could be
demonstrated. These results, coupled with the fact that a direct effect upon
the tissue, and perhaps the cells, is involved would appear to provide a
reasonable argument that this neoplastic response is initiated through a
single hit, or "somatic mutation" within the target tissue cells. The data
appear to be consistent with the no threshold, proportionality hypothesis
of radiation-induced neoplasia. Interpretation is hampered by a number
of factors, however, and these are reviewed briefly below. Although the
problems involved are discussed in relation to the mammary gland neoplasia
data, their significance is more general and applies to most experiments of
this nature.

Discussion

Although it apparently is possible to obtain dose-effect curves for genetic effects that are interpretable in terms of primary radiobiological mechanism or mechanisms, a number of problems arise in attempting to obtain and interpret such curves for somatic effects.[8-10] An obvious problem involves the numbers of animals that can be employed, and thus the significance of the results. In general to date, for somatic effects studies, it has been possible to use only a few tens of animals per point, or at best a few hundred animals for an entire dose-effect curve. This is in contrast to the thousands of animals that Dr. Russell has used in the studies of genetic effects. Thus the curves obtained with somatic effects are less reliable than those for genetic effects, and it is not possible to state, specifically with regard to the mammary gland neoplasia data, whether the dose-effect curve obtained is in fact linear or not. As the doses are carried to the lower levels, the number of animals required for significance obviously increases greatly.

It becomes difficult to take into account adequately the increasing incidence of neoplasms in normal animals with increasing age. In the dose-effect curve shown for mammary gland neoplasia, scoring was done at twelve months. At this time the maximum incidence in terms of animals with at least one neoplasm, in the irradiated animals, had been achieved and virtually no neoplasms had appeared in the control animals. With increasing age however, the incidence increased in the controls, and achieved a value of some 40–45 per cent in the life span of the female Sprague–Dawley animal. Accordingly the question arises, whether it is better to score the percentage of animals with one or more neoplasm, or the total number of neoplasms observed (more than one neoplasm per animal). With breast neoplasia, in which it is possible to remove the tumor and return the animal to the experiment, it is possible to score total tumors in addition to the number of animals with one or more tumors. Although the number of animals with one or more neoplasms approaches a maximum at approximately one year, the total number of neoplasms appears to increase indefinitely with time. If one scores early, the control incidence is small but the total number of neoplasms that will be obtained in the irradiated population is relatively small. If scoring is done later, or if animals are observed for the total life span, the number of tumors becomes greater, but the number of survivors becomes rapidly smaller and the statistics accordingly poorer. Methods are available to "correct" for dying animals;[6] however, the degree to which these techniques are satisfactory is open to question.

When neoplasms of the types under study increase in time in control animals, the question arises as to whether the radiation is inducing a process, or merely accelerating a process that would occur normally in time. This question is difficult if not impossible to answer satisfactorily since a meaningful value for the "normal" incidence is difficult to obtain. In general, the likelihood of neoplasia increases with increasing age, and it is not possible to state whether neoplasia of a given type would appear in time in decedents. A much larger incidence might be observed if it were possible to keep animals alive beyond their "normal" life span. It can only be stated that at all times observed, the incidence of mammary gland neoplasia in heavily-exposed rats was well in excess of the incidence among control animals.

The problem of classification of neoplasms becomes real. Mammary gland neoplasms of all types were combined in the reported experiments on the basis that each represents a neoplastic process. Combining neoplasms of different histologic types in clinical human pathology obviously would not be permissible because of the different prognoses involved. Also, it might be argued that the dose-effect response for the different histological types of neoplasms might be different, although it was not possible to demonstrate such a different in the animal experiments described. The general problem appears to be more one of degree, rather than kind. One can justify combining histologically different types of tumors on the basis that each, if it arises within the target tissue, represents a neoplastic change in that organ. If one wishes to treat the histologic types differently, the problem of meaningful classification arises. There is not general agreement on the degree to which neoplasms should be separated on histological grounds, and one can question seriously to what degree histology allows meaningful classification of type as far as mechanisms are concerned. Even histologically similar or identical tumors may be different in type if more refined criteria are employed, e.g. studies of chromosomal number have pointed toward an individuality of tumors.[11]

As can be seen then, the problem of how and when to score neoplasia becomes of considerable importance. The experiments now completed except for histological diagnosis will allow construction of dose-effect curves at varying time intervals throughout the life span of the animals, both as a function of animals with one or more neoplasms and of total neoplasms. In initial analysis, it has not appeared that significant deviation from linearity will be demonstrated even though time intervals other than the 12 months reported in this communication are employed.

The hormone dependency of neoplasia shown in the present experiments also has considerable bearing on the possible interpretation of dose-effect curves. This demonstrated dependency throws doubt on the use of dose-effect curves as arguments for or against a "somatic mutation" hypothesis for the primary event leading to neoplasia. In the present data, it has been shown that both an initiating factor (radiation) and a promoting factor (ovarian hormones) may be necessary for maximal neoplasia induction. Thus, in general, if dose-effect curves obtained are non-linear, nothing would necessarily have been proved about the nature of the primary mechanism involved. Lack of such a response may simply indicate that a secondary promoting factor may not have been operative. On the other hand, if one does in fact obtain a linear dose-effect curve to the lowest doses, and could interpret this in terms of a simple "somatic mutation" mechanism or phenomenon, obviously it would apply only to the particular neoplasms studied and to that strain and species. Extrapolation for purposes of deducing mechanisms, or for prediction of neoplasia incidence under other circumstances, would not be valid.

As noted earlier, the dose-effect curve appears to be linear up to approximately 400 r, above which dose the incidence appears to decrease with increasing dose. A similar "peaking", at perhaps a dose level higher than for whole-body exposure, has been noted in incomplete studies by Dr. Shellabarger, in which only one half of the target tissue was exposed. This phenomenon has been called a paradox and has been observed not only in the data presented, but for both leukemia and ovarian tumor induction in RF mice.[8] With leukemia the curve appears to go through a maximum at approximately 250 r; at approximately 125 r for ovarian tumors. The shape of the curves suggests that the exposure may be killing cells at the same time that neoplasia is being induced. It is now well established that mammalian cells, both in tissue culture and *in vivo*, can be seriously damaged such that they are unable to proliferate, normally, even at relatively low doses of radiation. The fact is reflected in the so-called "survival" curves that have now been obtained for a wide variety of cells. One such a curve was obtained by Till and McCulloch[12] for "stem" cells of the mouse bone marrow, using a technique by which bone marrow was irradiated and then injected into a recipient irradiated animal. These data indicate that the D^{37} for the proliferating cells is of the order of 115 r. While this may well not apply to the breast tissue, it does indicate that an appreciable percentage of proliferating cells can be rendered incapable of proliferating even after relatively low doses. Thus it would appear quite possible that some cells in which damage potentially leading to neoplasia may have been induced, may at the same time be rendered incapable of proliferation as a result of the exposure. The net dose-effect curve would then obviously be the resultant of the dose-effect curve for neoplasia and that for cell killing. At some point, this curve would have to go through a maximum and decrease as the cell killing effects became more prominent with increasing dose. Although at present only a hypothesis, this thesis may have some relevance to the problem of dose-effect curves in general, as will be discussed below.

It has been stated that most curves thus far obtained for dose-effect relationships of neoplasia induction are non-linear in character, and that the curve may increase, remain constant or decrease with increasing dose. Although true to a degree, this statement should be qualified relative to the pertinence of many such curves to mechanisms of neoplasia induction. In the first place, relatively only a very few experiments have been done providing sufficient data to construct a meaningful dose-effect curve. Most experiments have included only a few dose levels and thus a complete curve could not be constructed. The tumor incidence in mice exposed to atomic bomb radiations and followed throughout their lifetime has provided some data in this regard.[13] It should be pointed out, however, that the lowest dose received by any of the groups of mice exposed is in excess of 200 rad, a dose that may well be above any potentially linear portion of a dose-effect curve under circumstances in which a significant cell killing effect occurs. Also, the data of Lindsay and Potter[14,15] have been referred to as a dose-effect curve, in which the incidence decreases with increasing dose. It should be pointed out that the lowest dose on this curve represents 10 μC of iodine to the thyroid of the rat, which results in a radiation dose of thousands of rads. At such high doses, the gland is essentially obliterated, and the incidence of tumors could only be expected to decrease with a further increase of dose. If would thus appear that there are actually very few data on which to base a judgement as to the nature of the dose-effect curves in neoplasia, and what may be the most important part of the curves are frequently missing from the experimental data.

In Sprague–Dawley rats allowed to live out their lifetime at this laboratory, incomplete data (histology not completed) on tumors other than mammary gland neoplasms are available. An appreciable incidence of neoplasms occurred in the adrenals, the kidneys, the pituitary gland, the uterus, the ovary and the thyroid. On the basis of gross tumor incidence, the curves for the thyroid, pituitary, adrenal and kidney appear to be essentially flat over the range of zero to 400 r. The curve for the ovary and uterus appear to show an increase in incidence with increasing dose; however, the curves are only poorly defined as yet.

"ABSCOPAL" NEOPLASIA INDUCTION

Instances have been reported in the literature, in which neoplasia has arisen in irradiated animals in anatomical locations not actually exposed in the beam. Thyrotrophic pituitary tumors have been reported in high incidence in mice thyroidectomize with I^{131}.[16] The "transit" dose to the pituitary with an amount of I^{131} that would obliterate the thyroid is not small, and thus a clear "abscopal" effect remains to be proved. "Indirect" components of ovarian tumor induction by X-radiation in mice have been shown (see Ref. 17 for discussion). Lymphomas arising in irradiated C-57 black mice[18] represent the most completely studied example of "abscopal" induction of neoplasia. Briefly, repeated exposure to X-rays in an optimal pattern produces a large incidence of lymphomas in C–57 mice. Shielding the thymic area, or thymectomy markedly reduces the incidence of neoplasia. If the thymus from a normal animal is transplanted to an animal thymectomized at the time of irradiation, lymphoma apparently develops in the irradiated animal at the site of implantation. Further studies have indicated that the lymphoma can arise from the transplanted "normal" tissue. If the spleen or marrow is shielded, or if isologous marrow is administered, the incidence of lymphoma is markedly reduced. A virus has been isolated from animals with lymphoma and it is considered to play an etiologic role in the development of the disease.[19] Thus one might state that the irradiation has "activated a latent virus infection". It is probable that the host tissue bed is altered by the irradiation, such that it is more suitable for virus growth than are the normal tissues. In any event, the induction of lymphomas by radiation apparently represents a situation in which the target tissue itself need not be irradiated. The irradiation apparently need not interact directly with the target tissue, but modifies the animal's environment in some complex way resulting in the neoplastic process.

SUMMARY

It appears that what might be considered the extremes of possible mechanism of radiation-induced neoplasia have been demonstrated in animals. Some types of radiation neoplasia appear to require a direct interaction between the radiation and the potentially neoplastic tissue; radiation-induced neoplasia in the rat breast appears to represent such a situation. Other types of radiation-induced neoplasia may be completely abscopal in origin and the potentially neoplastic tissue need not be directly exposed. Mouse lymphoma appears to be in this category. With both types, there may be initiating and promoting factors, i.e. a two or more stage process appears to be involved. For many types of radiation-induced neoplasia, it is not clear whether either of the above mechanisms pertain. It appears quite probable that there is not "a" mechanism of radiation-induced neoplasia, and many possible etiologies may be involved. Dose-effect curves appear to be of some value in deducing mechanisms of radiation-induced neoplasia; however many factors must be considered in their interpretation. Because of several different responses shown by various types of radiation-induced neoplasia, it is not warranted to use "a" type of response, or mechanism, as applicable for prediction of all types of radiation-induced neoplasia. It is not warranted to extrapolate from animal data for prediction purpose in man, nor is it permissible to use one dose-effect curve obtained for one type of neoplasia in man, to predict incidence of other types of neoplasia. Certainly it is not permissible to use dose-effect curves obtained from external radiation, for prediction of neoplasia incidence from internal emitters. For accurate radiation neoplasia prediction many dose-effect curves for each type of neoplasia under consideration are required. At present only one such curve appears to be established with a reasonable degree of validity — that for leukemia following single exposure to penetrating external irradiation at doses in excess of 100 r.

REFERENCES

1. SHELLABARGER, C. J., CRONKITE, E. P., BOND, V. P. and LIPPINCOTT, S. W., The occurrence of mammary tumors in the rat after sublethal whole-body irradiation. *Rad. Res.* **6**, 501–512, 1957.
2. CRONKITE, E. P., SHELLABARGER, C. J., BOND, V. P. and LIPPINCOTT, S. W., Studies on radiation-induced mammary gland neoplasia in the rat. I. The role of the ovary in the neoplastic response of breast tissue to total or partial X-irradiation. *Rad. Res.* **12**, 81–93, 1960.
3. SHELLABARGER, C. J., LIPPINCOTT, S. W., CRONKITE, E. P. and BOND, V. P., Studies on radiation-induced mammary gland neoplasia in the rat. II. The response of castrate and intact male rats to 400 r of total-body irradiation. *Ras. Res.* **12**, 94–102, 1960.
4. BOND, V. P., CRONKITE, E. P., LIPPINCOTT, S. W. and SHELLABARGER, C. J., Studies on radiation-induced mammary gland neoplasia in the rat. III. Relation of the neoplastic response to dose of total-body radiation. *Rad. Res.* **12**, 276–285, 1960.
5. SHELLABARGER, C. J., CRONKITE, E. P. and BOND, V. P., Studies on radiation-induced neoplasia in the rat. VI. Response to 400 r given as a single dose, or as divided doses. *Rad. Res.* **17**, 101–109, 1962.
6. SACKS, R., Life table technique in the analysis of response-time data from laboratory experiments on animals. *Toxicol. and Appl. Pharmacol.* **1**, 203–227, 1959.
7. SOUTO, J., Tumour development in the rat induced by blood of irradiated animals. *Nature*, **4848**, 1317–1318, September 1962.
8. UPTON, A. C., The dose-response relation in radiation-induced cancer. *Cancer Res.* **21**, 717–729, 1961.

9. BURCH, P. R. J., A biological principle and its converse; some implications for carcinogenesis. *Nature*, **195**, 241–243, 1962.
10. WOLLMAN, S., Comments on the analysis of dose-response data in experimental carcinogenesis. *J. Nat. Cancer Inst.* **16**, 1095–204, 1955.
11. MOLE, R. H., *CIBA Foundation Symposium on Carcinogenesis*, 247. Edited by G. Wolstenholme and M. O'Connor. Churchill, London, 1959.
12. TILL J. E. and McCULLOCH, E. A., A direct measurement of the radiation sensitivity of normal mouse bone marrow cells. *Rad. Res.* **14**, 213–222, 1961.
13. UPTON, A. C., KIMBALL, A. W., FURTH, J., CHRISTENBERRY, K. W. and BENEDICT, W. H., Some delayed effects of atom bomb radiation in mice. *Cancer Res.* **20**, No. 8 (Part 2): 1–62, 1960.
14. LINDSAY, S., POTTER, G. D. and CHARKOFF, I. L., Thyroid neoplasma in the rat: a comparison of naturally-occurring and I^{131}-induced tumors. *Cancer Res.* **17**, 183–89, 1957.
15. POTTER, G. D., LINDSAY, S. and CHARKOFF, I. L., Induction of neoplasms in rat thyroid glands by low doses of radio-iodine. *Arch. Pathol.* **69**, 257–69, 1960.
16. FURTH, J., HARAN–GHERA, H. and CURTIS, H. J., Studies on the pathogenesis of neoplasms by ionizing radiation. I. Pituitary tumors. *Cancer Res.* **19**, 550–6, 1959.
17. CLIFTON, K. H., Problems in experimental tumorigenesis of the pituitary gland, gonads, adrenal cortices and mammary glands: a review. *Cancer Res.* **19**, 2–22, 1959.
18. KAPLAN, H. S., HIRSCH, B. B. and BROWN, M. B., Indirect induction of lymphoma in irradiated mice. IV. Genetic evidence of the origin of the tumor cells from the thymic graft. *Cancer Res.* **16**, 434–6, 1956.
19. LIEBERMAN, M. and KAPLAN, H. S., Leukemogenic activity of filtrates from radiation-induced lymphoid tumors in mice. *Science*, **130**, 387–8, 1959.

DISCUSSION

CHAIRMAN (H. S. KAPLAN): Dr. Victor Bond's paper is open for general discussion

H. MARCOVICH: I have two questions . First, do you think that the higher sensitivity of children as regards leukemia induction could be explained by the fact that the child body gets more uniform irradiation than the adult?

L. D. HAMILTON: Dr. Bond may want to comment on that, but I really do not feel that in the explosions of Hiroshima and Nagasaki the geometry of the individual bodies would attenuate the dose. I think these people were subjected to a pretty good total body irradiation and the calculation in roentgens I have given you is of a pretty well uniformly absorbed dose for both children and adults. Do you agree with that, Dr. Bond?

V. BOND: Yes, I agree, for the same radiation dose from the nuclear device as it is usually expressed, the dose to tissues of the child would be expected to be somewhat higher than that for the adult. However, the difference would be small, and would not, I believe, account for Dr. Hamilton's findings.

H. MARCOVICH: The second question is: as regards the dose-effect relationship curve you have drawn, you count the tumours that you actually observed as the effect. However, I remember that several years ago a paper appeared by Wollman in which he counted the number of tumours not according to what he actually counted, but he takes into consideration the number of tumours which did not develop, because he assumes that the first tumour could prevent the growth of the latest one. In these circumstances Wollman got a very nice two-hit dose-effect relationship curve that could be explained on the chromosomal basis. Your data could then be an underestimation of the real effect.

V. BOND: I know Dr. Wollman's paper, and we have not attempted his type of analysis. With the system we used, the presence of one tumour has no influence on the subsequent appearence of other tumours. We have had as many as ten neoplasms of the breast in a single animal.

CHAIRMAN: I might mention that Dr. Wollman's analysis led to the conclusion of a two-hit curve for a phenomenon which was later shown to involve a virus in an indirect effect.

P. C. VIGIER: As Dr. Marcovich, I have two questions. The first is: regarding the McMahon data, if I remember well, there is a significant increase of about 1·3 in leukemia incidence for the group age under 8 years old. I was struck by the fact that for 8–9 years old, there was a significant lowering of the incidence that goes somewhere between the 0·3 and 0·7 if I remember well. Could it not be that the increases of leukemia observed in the early years is simply an accelerating effect of a normal event which would occur anyway?

L. D. HAMILTON: We do not know.

P. C. VIGIER: My second question is: if I remember well, you said in the beginning that you had different types of mammalian tumours, and you added them all together. Did you make any separate studies of the various types, because it could very well be that they might originate from different causes?

V. BOND: We did attempt to analyse the data for each histological type of tumor; however, when one breaks down the data in this fashion the statistics become very poor. All I can say is that the incidence of all types appeared to be less in ovariectomized animals and the dose-effect response for any one type could not be shown to be different from the combined response. Again, however, the numbers are small and possible differences in response could have gone undetected.

J. LEJEUNE: I would have one comment about the leukemia process. It is not a question but a comment. Dr. Hamilton told us that it could be something happening in the base pairing of the DNA, exactly as if we know nothing about it. But we know that in some cases there is a specific chromosomal aberration. And I would like to have his comment on that fact: that a partial dilution of the 21 chromosome can be, and is most likely to be the real cause of chronic granulocytic leukemia, whether this should give rise to a one-hit curve and then to a straight line relationship or to a two-hit curve.

L. D. HAMILTON: I am delighted that Dr. Lejeune has mentioned the 21 chromosome, because I wanted it to be discussed this evening. Dr. Lejeune is quite right to say that in chronic granulocytic leukemia there is a specific chromosomal aberration. But it is not yet proved that this in actual fact precedes the leukemia or is responsible for the leukemia, and there is no evidence as far as I know that in radiation-induced granulocytic leukemia the same anomaly occurs. I would like to believe that this is so, and probably it is so, but the proof of which comes first, the leukemia or the anomaly, is still not known. Certainly as far as radiation-induced leukemia is concerned, I am pretty sure it is not known. I do not know whether it is in regard to spontaneous leukemia.

J. LEJEUNE: Well, I must confess that the evidence is small because only two cases of radio-induced, or supposedly radio-induced chronic granulocytic leukemia have been studied; one was negative, and the other was probably an entire loss of one chromosome of this pair.

L. D. HAMILTON: In regard to the specific question about the base pairing, I would just say that this is a pure speculation as far as radiation effect is concerned. We do know that a point mutation can — from Benzer's work — involve just one nucleotide, and that was the base that we say that for the induction of leukemia, somatic point mutation is analogous to genetic mutation. Then it could involve such a small chain as a single nucleotide chain. Clearly, when we are dealing with chromosomal aberration of this sort, we have an entirely different order of magnitude. It is a very much greater chain, and I was not meaning to imply, I hope Dr. Lejeune will not take it that way, that I though there was the same mechanism.

C. PAVAN: When people talk about late effects of radiation, everybody says that we do not know many things about it. I would like to know if there is after all a hypothesis which could explain why a tumour appears only several years after the irradiation, although we know that this discussion might be very speculative.

L. D. HAMILTON: Well, this is speculation. Dr. Pavan asked for it, and he is going to get it. One speculation would be that we know, we hear often about, the linear effect — I think Dr. Bender can correct me — are there chromosomal aberrations in the effect which make chromosomal aberrations linear?

M. A. BENDER: It is true that specific chromosomal deletions which would produce deletions of chromosome number 21 similar to the Ph[1] chromosome would have linear, or "single-hit" kinetics. If a Ph[1] chromosome is really simply a chromosome number 21 which is deficient for a certain segment, however, there are other types of chromosomal aberrations which should produce chromosomes having the same effect. Some of the aberrations have "multi-hit" kinetics. One would thus expect to find a composite curve with yield rising as something greater than the first power of the dose.

L. D. HAMILTON: One could speculate that as a result of radiation, we know that low doses of radiation can produce chromosomal aberrations. And we know that if you irradiate somebody, these chromosomal aberrations would appear in the blood cells and that then they would increase with time. But our speculation is concerned with the delay which involves the manifestation of the malignancy. The reason that it takes a long time to be manifest is that one hypothesizes that it has to arise from a single cell. These malignant cells — remarkably enough — do not divide as frequently as a normal cell, they divide relatively slowly. One of the interesting things about malignant cells is that many types of malignancies have a much longer intermitotic interval. They divide much more slowly than the corresponding normal cells. So this latent period could just represent the gradual accumulation of cells from that single cell that has this malignant transformation.

V. BOND: I should like to ask Dr. Hamilton, the degree to which he believes that the appearance of neoplasia years after radiation exposure can be accounted for on the basis of rate of growth. Do you think the neoplastic process begins shortly after radiation exposure, and that the time a tumour is recognized is a function of the rate of growth?

L. D. HAMILTON: As regards the rate of growth, I do not know, but I do not think it is impossible. I think of a number of tumours where it is distinctly probable. In much of this childhood leukemia it looks quite clear that it is so. The actual change that expresses itself and becomes visible is a result of a slow multiplication of cells. If you look for them very carefully you might even see these cells accumulating and in certain cells in chronic lymphatic leukemia you can gradually see an accumulation of cells of many, many years before the disease becomes clinically overt.

S. OHNO: Whether or not radiation-inducted chronic myeloid leukemia differs from ordinary chronic myeloid leukemia is of great interest. Dr. Keiji Kinugasa of Tokyo University Medical School is studying the chromosomes of the bomb victims of Hiroshima and Nagasaki who developed chronic myeloid leukemia. The Philadelphia chromosome is present in their leukemic cells. Although aneuploid in many instances, the leukemic cells still maintain the Philadelphia chromosome. It appears then that this characteristic chromosomal change was present initially in chronic myeloid leukemia induced by radiation.

CHAIRMAN: I think this is extremely interesting, but I think we should not lose sight of the point raised by Dr. Hamilton, that we have no way of knowing whether the loss of Philadelphia chromosome leads to leukemia or whether the development of leukemia leads to the loss of Philadelphia chromosome. And until there is a conclusive evidence of this point, I think we should not leap to the conclusion that the absence of the chromosome precedes the disease. Dr. Hungerford, you have any evidence on this point?

D. A. HUNGERFORD: We have no evidence.

J. LEJEUNE: Well, possibly we have no evidence that the Philadelphia chromosome does precede the disease. But we have no evidence at all that any disease is able to produce a specific chromosome breakage in the whole kingdom of living people.

CHAIRMAN: Until the Philadelphia chromosome came along, we had no evidence that myeloid leukemia was associated with a chromosome abnormality.

A. LIMA-DE-FARIA: Levan and co-workers found out recently that in measles there is extensive chromosome breakage in human cells.

CHAIRMAN: I have a comment and two questions. I would like to raise some points relative to the pelvimetric cases and particularly the McMahon study which is clearly the most impressive and the most carefully done to date. Even if one accepts at face value the fact that there is a 30 per cent increase in the risk of developing leukemia and other kinds of cancer in children, whose mothers had pelvimetry in later stages of pregnancy, the question of selection has to be very carefully considered: why did these mothers have a pelvimetry and the others not? Were their pregnancies in fact normal? There is little or no evidence on this point that I know of, either in the McMahon study or in any of the others. Now, to be sure some pelvimetries are still done as routine procedures, but a great many pelvimetries are done because the obstetrician fears that the birth canal will be inadequate to permit delivery from below and that a Caesarian section may be necessary. Many of the pregnancies of women who have marginal birth canal measurements are extremely difficult pregnancies, in which prolonged hypoxia is a feature of the delivery. I would not accept it at face value that these children started out equal to the non-pelvimetric children in terms of risk of exposure to all of the hazards. So, I do not believe that the mere fact of pelvimetry proves that X-ray exposure is responsible. I would like to have Dr. Hamilton's comment on this point, before I address myself to Dr. Bond.

L. D. HAMILTON: Well, I think that the Chairman has raised a very valid objection to the MacMahon study, that perhaps the requirement that leads to X-ray pelvimetry and the actual difficulties involved in labour are associated with an increased probability of getting leukemia. This, of course, is an objection which has also been raised against he ankylosing spondilitis data. I really have no answer to this. I think the datum is very suggestive; it is certainly the strongest to date. I would like to have Dr. Russell make a comment about the relative radiosensitivity of foetuses as compared to adult tissue, because I feel this possibility, that the foetus is ten times more sensitive to leukemiogenesis, is within the grounds of probability, bearing in mind the other increases of susceptibilities of the foetus. It is not unreasonable, but I would like to know what Dr. Russell thinks on this point.

L. B. RUSSELL: Well, I think of course it is true, that the foetus is very much more radiosensitive, certainly to lethality and so forth, the lethal effects of X-rays and the criss-cross aberrations, but I am not really quite sure that leukemia induction is the same type of thing, because the cross aberrations, I feel, are in most cases due to cell killing, large chunks of cell killing of specific types, and I am not sure that in the light of the Philadelphia chromosome study and so forth, that leukemia induction has really the same type of effect. But I think it is quite within the realm of possibility that certainly the foetus is more radiosensitive.

CHAIRMAN: Thank you. I would like to offer a comment on Dr Bond's paper. He stated that the mammary carcinoma studies in the rat that he presented and which I think have been very beautifully developed by his group, represented conclusive evidence for the interpretation that this must involve a direct effect of radiation on the target tissue. I would like to say in advance that I do not believe that this has been proved at all. I must cite some analogies to illustrate my point. First of all, let me draw a mouse (on the blackboard). Let me take three different well studied cases of carcinogenesis: two involving radiation, one not involving radiation, all of which have now been proved to be indirect mechanisms. The first is that of the thymus, which you heard about. When exposed to whole-body radiation, animals of suitable strains, after appropriate doses, would get a very high incidence of lymphosarcoma rising in the thymus. In initial studies it was shown that if one places a lead shield over the thymus and irradiates the rest of the animal, the incidence of the leukemia is zero. This appears to prove conclusively that there must be a direct effect of radiation on the thymus. However, it was not quite so simple because, as you heard, if one takes out the thymus, irradiates the animal and then puts back a normal non-irradiated thymus, one still gets leukemia. I think that until Dr. Bond has done something comparable to this for the mammary tissue, that he would not have a crucial test. That is to say: what radiation supplies in this instance may be a kind of non-specific rather than a specifically carcinogenic injury, and it is possible that the radiation can be replaced by a variety of other injuries. All that may be happening in the mammary tumour case is some non-specific tissue injury; until this has been checked with other non-specific kinds of tissue injury, I submit that the case has not been documented. A second case in point comes from the example of ovarian carcinogenesis. If you irradiate the ovaries locally, you get the same incidence of tumors as you get when you irradiate the whole animal. Clearly a case of direct radiation injury. If you irradiate one ovary and take out the other ovary, you get tumours in the irradiated ovary. But if you irradiate one ovary and leave the other ovary in, you get no tumours. Finally, if you take one ovary out and throw it away, and you take the other ovary and do not irradiate it at all, but simply put it to the spleen, it now secretes its hormone by way of the portal circulation into the liver, where the estrogen is inactivated, so that the normal pathway to the pituitary is blocked and this leads to a "feed-back" increase of gonadotropic hormone secretion, which produces exactly the same kind of tumour that the radiation produces, but in far higher yield, with no radiation whatsoever. Here again it is necessary to put the target tissue into a favourable situation to receive the carcinogenic influence, which is not radiation but an induced hormonal in balance. Now the final case might be thought of as being irrelevant, but I submit that it is not. It is a very good case. The final case does not involve radiation at all, it involves the very remarkable carcinogenic system discovered by the Oppenheimers, in which plastic films were inserted under the skin. Originally they were wrapped around the kidneys to cause hypertension, but they did not cause hypertension, they caused sarcomas in rats. When the Oppenheimers placed plastic films under the skin, they again got sarcomas. This proves not to be due to very small amounts of trace carcinogens that are present as impurities in the plastic: you can extract the plastic exhaustively and inject the extract and nothing happens. You can go from one kind of plastic to another and even to metal foil and still get sarcomas. It has even been possible to produce sarcomas with glass coverslips. And if you now take these plastic films and you punch holes in them, you get either no tumours at all, or very few tumours. Yet the plastic film is still in immediate, direct contact with the tissue. Finally, if you take the plastic film and grind it into a powder, where its chemical surface is vastly increased over that of the film, you get absolutely no tumours whatever. Clearly this is not a chemical effect, it is a physical effect and while you might say it is a direct effect, in what sense is it direct? The plastic film never gets inside of the cells that become tumours, yet the plastic film is local at the site of the tumor. What the plastic film has done is to induce a sustained imbalance in local tissue growth equilibrium. I maintain that all the evidence I have ever heard, including what I heard this evening, is consistent with the idea that radiation exerts its carcinogenic effect in all instances by causing a similar sustained disturbance in local tissue growth equilibrium. I would like to hear the contrary argument.

V. BOND: The Chairman has summarized very well some of the key arguments for an "indirect" mechanism of radiation carcinogenesis. I believe I cited the instances he has reviewed in which radiation is involved, and of course agree that the elegant work of the Oppenheimers with plastic films represents a prime example of an indirect mechanism, or one in which the individual cells do not seem to be affected primarily by the injurious agent. In the one case involving radiation, thymona induction, a virus was demonstrated.

This may be considered a type of "indirect" effect, and it is, of course, possible that all tumours may turn out to have this common mechanism of origin. In these discussions, semantics are in part involved; however, a very fundamental question is of course involved as well. I stated that our data demonstrated that tumourogenesis in the system used involves a direct effect of radiation on the target tissue. I believe this statement is true, since only exposed target tissue gave rise to neoplasia while non-exposed target tissue in the same animal did not show this manifestation. The data do not prove, however, as Dr. Kaplan has pointed out, that a direct cellular change induced by the radiation and resulting in the neoplastic process is involved. Also, the "direct" effect on the target tissue could of course be "indirect" in the sense that radiation has destroyed target tissue and disturbed its internal environment, and that this in turn led to the neoplastic process, or made the tissue susceptible to some other indirect process leading to neoplasia. It is possible that other agents producing similar damage to the breast tissue might result in similar neoplasia, and of course mammary gland tumours have been induced in the rat by chemical means.

I conclude that in the system we have used, the radiation to be tumourogenic must act directly on the tissue involved, but that such damage does not manifest itself as neoplasia unless a secondary agent, in this instance, apparently, ovarian hormone, is operative. The data do not prove, however, that the neoplastic process arises from a change produced directly by the radiation within an individual cell (or cells), which causes that cell (or cells) to develop into a neoplasm under favorable circumstances. I do not believe that evidence to date warrants a strong leaning towards a direct cellular, or a more indirect mechanism being involved in radiation-induced neoplasia in general.

CHAIRMAN: Thank you.

The scientific portion of this discussion is over. Now we want to hear from the man whose efforts to organize this symposium here in Rio have proved so fruitful. After the closing remarks of Dr. Chagas, Dr. Hollaender would like to say a few words, and finally I would like to speak again briefly on behalf of the audience.

C. CHAGAS: After days of hard work, both here and in Sao Paulo, I just want to say that really we should be quite glad of the success of the meeting. A meeting like that ends with a sense, I would say, of melancholy. I would like to go on having such brilliant speakers and such lively discussions. But I think that younger people who are here should go to their laboratories and work using up all stimuli they have got in contact with the older people. And those who go back to the laboratory in order to produce more work can meet again with new results and new data. Before giving the floor to Dr. Hollaender, nevertheless, I want to state again my gratitude towards the real organizers of the two Symposia: Dr. Hollaender at first, Dr. Pavan in Sao Paulo and Dr. Caldas here in Rio, and I would like to extend my thanks to those who have helped these meetings to be as successful as they were. I am speaking particularly of the administrative staff and the secretarial work of the Institute of Biophysics here in Rio, as I am sure Dr. Pavan has extended his appreciation to his helpers in Sao Paulo. Our indebtness also goes to our translators, reporters and writers, to my friend Mrs. Lily Salles who recorded the discussions, and to the technical assistance received from the I.B.M. people as one could see that I.B.M. is not only good in producing missiles but also in giving the necessary help to undertake scientific meetings. Finally, I wish to thank all those eminent people who have come to Sao Paulo and to Rio, have taken long trips, have left their laboratories and their homes in a rather conturbed time of our history. I can only say that we are extremely, deeply grateful for the help they have brought to the development of science in Brazil.

Thank you very much.

A. HOLLAENDER: Dr. Chagas, Ladies and Gentlemen: I have the need of repeating our thanks to the organizers of this Symposium, Dr. Chagas and Dr. Caldas here, Dr. Pavan in Sao Paulo. However, a Symposium is not completed when you get through the discussion. The proof of the quality of the Symposium is also its printed publication and here the local people, as well as in São Paulo, need your help urgently. They need your manuscript, if you have not handed it in yet; they need the written discussion and so you have to keep on cooperating with them, in returning proofs and so on, so that we get these Symposia out in a reasonable time. This is a very important point. It is specially important for our friends here in Brazil. I want to express also my personal appreciation for all the hospitality which was shown to us here as well as in Sao Paulo. And we know we are closing this Symposium with a very great feeling of gratitude to all our many friends here in Brazil.

Thank you very much.

CHAIRMAN: Thank you very much, Dr. Hollaender. On behalf of the entire audience, I want to extend our very sincere thanks to Dr. Chagas and Dr. Caldas here, in Rio, to Dr. Pavan and his associates in São Paulo, and to Dr. Hollaender, who has also had quite a bit to do with this meeting. I think that you can rest assured that all of us who have here been most favourable impressed, indeed, almost overwhelmed not only by the hospitality but by the spirit of vitality and dynamism of your country, by its physical beauty, and by the sense of progress and development to which we have been exposed. I am sure that this will not be the last visit for those of us for whom it has been the first.

Thank you once again.

A COMMENTARY ON THE ACTION OF RADIATION ON BIOELECTRIC TISSUES AND ORGANS

C. Chagas

Instituto de Biofisica, Rio de Janeiro

In presenting this commentary, I would like to point out that contrary to the earlier exposés it will deal mostly with the presentation of perspectives of research, stemming from the appraisal of work already published and preliminary work done in our laboratories.

Thus it may be considered only as a thematic introduction presented for the sake of a constructive argument.

Under the term bioelectric organs are includee all organs, and *ipso facto* tissues, whose activity is accompanied by easily measurable electric potentials or action currents, which are either an important part of this activity itself (muscle, heart, nerve cells) or the primordial result of this activity — electric tissues and organs.

Let me emphasize the significance of the electric characteristics of cells and tissues. It should be stressed that this term includes not only the passive electric characteristics of the cells, like the impedance of the membrane, but also its resting potential, to whose maintenance concurs the active transport and thus a metabolic contribution is involved, and its variation during function, the so-called action potential.

The electric activity of a cell, tissue or organ represents its functional state proper, or it may give a picture of functional correlations which either could not have been detected by any other way, or could be understood much more easily by this experimental approach.

The analysis of electric characteristics and activity after irradiation should indicate:

(a) The functional disturbances produced by localized radiation with or without structural modifications;

(b) The perturbation of functional correlations with wide field and TBR radiation;

(c) The relationship between the energy absorbed and the resultant effect (as determined by electric measurements), as observed, for instance, by the irradiation of isolated bioelectric structures.

A detailed analysis of the possible mode of action of radiation on the bioelectric structures can only be developed by taking in consideration the fundamental mechanisms involved in the activity of these structures, and of the tissues and organs in which they participate.

These mechanisms can be outlined taking nerve activity or the discharge of an isolated electroplate as examples.

THE ACTION OF RADIATION ON NERVOUS TISSUES

A comprehensive picture of the nerve activity, based on data described particularly since 1946, is characterized by the successive states of activity, whose modifications by radiation we will try to understand. These steps are: activation of the neurons, conduction and transmission of the neuron's impulse.

(a) The first disturbance connected to the active state of a neuron is a change of the resting potential corresponding to a modification of the state of the polarization of its membrane, and to a change in membrane permeability allowing for the movement of ions across the membrane.

This disturbance may be a localized graded response, not originating a nervous message, or a propagated one, obtained after the polarization attains a certain critical value, in which case the localized disturbance is followed by the conduction of the impulse through the axon.

Radiation may act here either by a change of the molecular structure of the cell membrane, thus protecting a change of the membrane permeability and impairing its reactivity to the trigger mechanism to which it normally reacts, or by disturbing the cell metabolism.

These considerations help to understand the rather heavy ones necessary generally found to produce modifications on CNS activity unless indirect or vascular lesions can be connected to the lesions.

The doses necessary to produce changes in cell permeability in isolated structure are quite massive. Thus the results just mentioned are to be expected. It is nevertheless quite clear that part of the mechanisms involved is remotely influenced by irradiation of the energy transfer *in vitro*. It should be remembered that changes in enzyme systems show also a rather high resistance to irradiation as some of the permeability variations observed. This would again support the concept of a low sensitivity of nerve cells to radiation, so much as one may admit that their activity is linked with their electrogenic capability and this is fundamentally regulated by the permeability of the cell membrane.

Against the concept of low sensitivity of the nerve cell to radiation, a number of data have appeared in the scientific literature. The most impressive ones relate to the abolishment of conditioned reflexes after localized irradiation of the brain, by doses of 5–30 r. The direct action on neurons, in these experiments, is not proved to certainty. As a matter of fact other experimental results are contrary to this hypothesis. Thus, for instance, one has to use a dose rate of 1000 r/min to obtain in monkeys a change in the E.E.G. These data seem to exclude a direct action on the neurons in the aforementioned experiments. Our present knowledge of the cortical functions is nevertheless too scarce to have a complete explanation of these data. It may be that absorption on the brain, of such small doses, may produce transient phenomena, of short duration, triggering some linkage mechanism responsible for the observed effect.

(b) The second phase in nervous activity is conduction along the nerve fiber of the nervous impulse. After the adequate activation of the neuron body the nerve impulse is propagated by a stepwise manner through the axon, thus conducting its message to the following relay.

Strong experimental evidence has been obtained showing the important role played by permeability changes in conduction. They consist of the triggering a sudden change of permeability with an increase of the conductance of sodium, at the beginning, soon followed by that of potassium, the whole cycle of changes lasting for a few miliseconds. Thus at the first part of it, an influx of sodium to the fiber is observed, annulling the value of the resting potential, over passing it, and reversing its sign, followed by an efflux of potassium, up to the point when the primitive value of the resting potential is attained. Metabolic mechanisms will act in the following period — the refractory one, during which no conduction can take place — and restore the intracellular ionic concentrations. This variation of permeability, circularly localized to a small portion of the membrane, will be propagated by successive short-circuits which produce the same ionic movements in the adjacent parts of the membrane.

These changes were well established and carefully studied in amyelinated axons. In the myelinated nerves — which constitute the most common nerves — the ionic changes, due to the presence of the myeline sheath, can take place only when the sheath is discontinuous, the nodes of Ranvier.

Nerve conduction in myelinated axons would be the consequence of a process of electric influence of one depolarized node on the following one, the successive depolarization of the nodes configuring the so-called salutory conduction. A hypothesis receiving general acceptance though strong criticism, has been repeatedly raised against it.

The electric events — and thus the mechanism of depolarization and of recovery — in the nodes of Ranvier are the same as those in the non-myelinated axon.

They may give us a lead to the interpretation of the high resistance of nerves to radiation.

This low-sensitivity is due, probably, to the resistance of membrane permeability to radiation, the overall effect hindered in that case by the small surfaces of membranes where the active phenomena take place. Furthermore, the nerve fiber outside the nodes is protected by the myeline sheath in which the radiant energy absorption is quite unharmful as the *in vivo* yield in peroxide formation by lipids is rather poor.

(c) The third step in nervous activity is the transmission of the nerve impulse through histological discontinuities, the so-called synapses.

Since the pioneer work of Elliott, Dale and Otto Loewi, it has been shown that transmission is the result of the release of a chemical mediator. This concept postulated and experimentally demonstrated by the mentioned authors, for neuro-effector synapses, has been extended more recently to the nervous synapses, such as those found on the central nervous system, where the message passes from a nerve ending (bouton terminal) not to an effector but to a neighbouring neuron body.

The release of this chemical mediator, whose nature is not known, even if suspected in some instances, is the trigger mechanism which initiates the activity of the post-synaptic neuron. In many of the rather more simple synapses, mediating nerve and muscle effectors, the mediator is generally agreed to be acetylcholine.

The evens of chemical transmission may be described in quite a consistent way when all data furnished by electrophysiological, biochemical, pharma-cological, histochemical and electron microscopy experiments are put together.

One may thus admit that the chemical transmitter, possibly in a bound form, is present in the vesicles seen in the nerve presynaptic endings, as visualized by the electron microscope. It is released from them by the nervous influx. The liberated mediator is then able to produce depolar-ization of the post-synaptic membranes, thus bringing about the permeability changes necessary to trigger the ionic movements which correspond to the onset of the active state on the post-synaptic structure.

The mediator after its release has to be destroyed as its continued presence would bring a loss of functionality by the longlasting depolarization it produces. On the other hand, it has to be restored for cholinergic synapses. Two enzymes, one responsible for destruction, by hydrolysis, of acetylcholine and the other for its synthesis, were identified. They are acetylcholinesterase and acetylase respectively. Probably similar systems exist for the other mediators.

This mechanism whose validity for peripherical synapses seems to be rather abundantly proved, is also to be prevalent for synapses in the chord (Eccles *et al.*) and may also be the one responsible for transmission in the brain.

Radiation may act either on the permeability changes involved in transmission or in the enzymatic systems connected to energy transfer mechanism responsible for active ionic transport, necessary to reestablish the concentrations, or on those involved in the resynthesis of the mediator. Both mechanisms are relatively resistant to radiation. It has already been stated that no changes in permeability are observable in isolated structures unless quite heavy doses are used. *In vitro* experiments with acetylcholinesterase also show that 200,000 rad were necessary for an inactivation of the enzyme.

In studying the possible mode of action of radiation on nervous structures and on the C.N.S., it is found that a great disparity exists between certain values obtain for irradiation *in vivo* and the doses employed in *in vitro*, or in isolated structure necessary to obtain changes in the fundamental mechanisms responsible for the nervous function. In most experiments wherein T.B.R. is used, most of the result on the C.N.S. may be related to an indirect action in some of them. Nevertheless, the experimental outlay is such that a direct action on the C.N.S. has to be considered. Among them some indicate a very high sensibility to radiation. At the present time, it is difficult to correlate them with the data obtained from *in vitro* or isolated structures. One may suppose in certain cases that unknown mechanisms are triggered by the absorption of small quantities on the C.N.S. It may also be that the structures involved, rather unsensitive when observed isolated, become highly sensitive when integrated in the complex system which is the C.N.S. These are hypotheses which are far from being proven.

THE ACTION OF RADIATION ON MUSCLES

Activity of muscles is accompanied also by action potentials in which the changes of permeability and ionic transport are quite similar to those observed in nerves. In striated muscles the nerves end in a particular structure, the end-plate, in which cholinergic transmission was first identified.

These considerations explain the high resistance of muscle and heart to radiation. The rather simple nature of these structures may be the reason for the inexistence of any disparity between the results obtained *in vivo* and those seen in isolated structure and *in vitro* experiments.

THE ACTION OF RADIATION ON ELECTRIC TISSUE

The electroplate of electric organs, i.e. the unit responsible for the discharge on the electric tissue, offers possibly the best structure for a closer scrutiny of the mode of action of radiation in some of the mechanisms participating in nervous activity, and in bioelectrogenesis in general.

It may be said that, in a certain way, the electroplate gives a macroscopic picture of many mechanisms involved in nervous activity, mainly if one considers the transmission phase already described.

The electroplates are syncitia, wherein one recognizes the existence of an active, innervated surface, and an inactive one. The active surface, where the numerous nerves end, presents a high concentration of acetyl-cholinesterase, spotly distributed, conforming to the nerve endings present.

An electroplate becomes active by a process of depolarization which can be achieved in a dual way. It can be activated either by nerve excitation which presumably liberates a mediator, supposed to be acetylcholine, or it can be triggered by the passage of electric current in the direction able to produce the necessary critical initial depolaritazion.

This structure offers, probably, the possibility of a direct relationship determination between the energy absorbed and the various effects it produces, as determined by histochemical, biochemical and electrobiological methods. In this sense, it seems that the electroplate offers an interesting field for close analysis of the action of radiation in some fundamental cellular mechanism.

Some preliminary work has been done on the subject by Frota-Moreira, Carvalho, Marcovich, Elias, Salgado. A rather low sensitivity was observed. They have shown, by irradiating small pieces of tissues with X-rays, that radiation will depress the electric discharge. The onset of the observed phenomena, whose initial phase is reversible, occurs after exposure to doses of about 40,000 r. It is followed by a continuous depression of the discharge even after the irradiation has been stopped. This after-effect may be connected to enzyme inactivation, or maybe permeability changes due to macromolecular depolymerization. The inactivation of cholinesterase, as observed, is more sensitive than the *in vitro* experiments would indicate.

Much work has to be done in order to establish the mechanism involved in the effect of radiation in bioelectric tissues. These are in general rather resistant to radiation, and this fact can be explained by analysing the fundamental events pertinent to their function. However, some few experiments undertaken *in vivo* point to a high sensitivity of some mechanism to radiation. The interpretation of these facts is a challenge to the team work of electro-biologist and radiobiologist. Their clarification may help the brain physiologist to advance in his knowledge and the radiobiologist to understand better the ratio between the dose effect relationships obtained *in vivo* and *in vitro* or *in vivo* and in isolated structures.

THE EFFECTS OF X-RAYS ON EXCITABLE TISSUES

J. G. Nicholls*

University Laboratory of Physiology, Oxford

UNTIL recently the nervous system and nerve cells were generally considered to be highly resistant to ionizing radiation. This view depended on evidence obtained from several different types of experiment. For example, animals or patients did not appear to develop neurological signs or behavioural changes after they were subjected to doses of X-rays considerably in excess of the LD50, delivered either to the head or to the whole body.[1] Peripheral nerve and skeletal muscle cells irradiated *in vitro* were also found to be highly resistant to X-rays. Large doses of the order of 100 kr were required before any changes could be found in their electrical properties and these were not specific; conduction would fail and the resting potential fall over a period of several hours after irradiation.[2,3]

Since the last war, however, many workers have concluded that the central nervous system and excitable membranes are in fact affected by small doses of X-rays, often of the order of roentgens or hundreds of r; during the past year alone two volumes were published on the effects of ionizing radiation on the nervous system.[4,5] Most of the effects of small doses of X-rays on the nervous system have been demonstrated on complex functions, whose physiology is little understood at the present time. For example a dose of the order of 10 r can alter conditioned reflexes[6] or can act as a conditioned or unconditioned stimulus affecting the behaviour of the animal;[7] larger doses of about 100–300 r can affect the electrical activity of the cerebral cortex or the hippocampus.[8] In some cases even the peripheral nervous system appears to be sensitive to small doses of X-rays. Thus, the small intestine of the rabbit contracts during irradiation with 20 r. This effect is blocked by atropine and enhanced by eserine and can therefore be attributed to an increase in the activity of cholinergic autonomic nerve fibres.[9,10]

All these responses arise during or shortly after the period of radiation, and in some cases are reversible and repeatable; in these complex systems,

* Work done during tenure of a Beit Memorial Fellowship. Present address: Laboratory of Neurophysiology, Department of Pharmacology, Harvard Medical School, Boston.

non-neural elements as well as nerve cells must have been irradiated. Using larger doses (of the order of 10 kr or more) immediate and reversible changes of this type have also been reported in other more simple preparation previously thought to be highly resistant. For example, the excitability of the sciatic nerve of the frog increases,[11,12] the resting potential and sodium conductance of Purkinje fibres fall,[13] and in rat nerve the size of maximal action potentials, the electrical excitability and the conduction velocity may all increase before conduction becomes blocked[14] (see below).

The mechanism by which small doses of X-rays could affect synapses or excitable membranes has not yet been described. It has, however, been suggested that these effects of X-rays are the result of changes in the permeability of cell membranes to potassium and sodium ions.[15,16,17] According to this hypothesis the change in permeability would occur during irradiation, last a short while and then be reversed. The failure of earlier workers to demonstrate effects on the central nervous system, peripheral nerve or skeletal muscle, might then be due to the fact that their observations were made only some time after the irradiation was over. Another suggestion is that small doses of X-rays can rupture synaptic vesicles with the concomitant liberation of transmitter substances, and in this way influence synaptic transmission.[18]

It was of interest to study the immediate and delayed effects of X-rays on an isolated mammalian nerve muscle preparation; here direct measurements could be made of the properties of the membrane and of the processes involved in transmission through a simple synapse under controlled conditions. The experiments to be summarized in this paper were mostly performed in collaboration with N. Allen, and have been reported elsewhere in detail.[19]

PROCEDURE

Recordings were made from the isolated phrenic-diaphragm preparation of the rat by conventional electrophysiological techniques[19] during and after irradiation with X-rays. Control preparations can normally survive for over 24 hr in oxygenated Krebs's fluid at room temperature. The dose-rates ranged from 1 to 100 kr/min and were delivered by a Philips "Contact Therapy" machine (45 kV, h.v.l. 6 mm in water) or by a Siemens "Dermopan" (50 kV, h.v.l. 2·5 mm in water). Using intracellular microelectrodes or external electrodes, the following measurements were made on the muscle and the nerve: (a) the electrical resistance of the muscle membrane, which is inversely related to its conductivity and its permeability to ions; (b) resting potentials of muscle membrane (normally 65–70 mV), excitability and action potential size in nerve and muscle; (c) miniature end-plate potentials (henceforth "miniature potentials").[20] These potentials, recorded at the motor end-plate, occur randomly and are caused by the spontaneous release of "quanta" of the transmitter, acetylcholine, from the nerve endings. Their frequency and amplitude provide an index of the state of the nerve endings, of the chemoreceptors of the motor end-plate and of the membrane resistance of the muscle fibre. The mean frequency is 1–5/sec under resting conditions, and varies with the resting potential in the nerve endings; thus, applied currents or potassium ions, which reduce the resting potential, can cause the frequency to rise to several hundred per second.[21] The mean amplitude is 0·5–1·0 mV, but it falls to zero when curare (10^{-7} g/ml) is used to reduce the sensitivity of the receptors in the motor end-plate.

IMMEDIATE EFFECTS OF X-RAYS

In order to detect rapid or transient effects of X-rays continuous recordings were made during irradiation at 1–7 kr/min. No changes were observed in action potentials or excitability in the nerve or the muscle, in the membrane resistance or resting potential of muscle, in neuromuscular transmission or in miniature potentials. For example, Fig. 1 illustrates a graph of miniature potentials recorded continuously from the motor end-plate of a muscle fibre during irradiation at 7 kr/min. The slight decrease

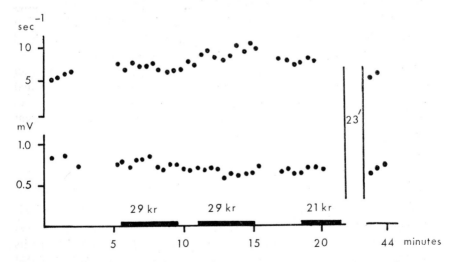

FIG. 1. The frequency (sec⁻¹) and amplitude (mV) of miniature potentials recorded during irradiation at 7 kr/min. The microelectrode remained in the fibre throughout the period of observation; note the break of 23 min in the abscissa.

in amplitude and increase in frequency can be attributed to damage caused by the recording microelectrode rather than the radiation, since similar changes are observed in control fibres impaled over long periods. It was concluded that up to 100 kr of X-rays, applied at 7 kr/min, had little immediate effect either on the amount of acetylcholine spontaneously liberated from the nerve endings, or on the sensitivity of the chemoreceptors in the motor end-plate which react with acetylcholine.

Using higher dose-rates (of 70–100 kr/min), the frequency of miniature potentials increased to about 7 per sec during the irradiation period. The increase occurred after approximately 50 kr had been given, and persisted subsequently for some hours. The finding that the dose-rate was an important factor suggested that some process of recovery or restoration was occurring during the period of irradiation. It was therefore of interest to determine the effect of even higher dose-rates.

OBSERVATIONS WITH A PULSED RADIATION SOURCE DELIVERING 60 krad/2 μsec PULSE

Some experiments have recently been undertaken in collaboration with Dr. J.W. Boag, using the electron pulse generator at the British Empire Cancer Campaign Unit in Radiobiology at the Mount Vernon Hospital. Preliminary experiments showed that after 2 or sometimes 3 pulses of 60 krad (2 μsec duration) were delivered in a total of 40 msec, the frequency of miniature potentials rose abruptly to approximately 15/sec. The effect was apparent as soon as the electron beam was switched off, and persisted for at least 30 min. Over the same period there was no change in the mean amplitude of miniature potentials. These results were not strikingly different from those obtained by the use of X-rays at 70 kr/min. The effect of a single 60 krad pulse delivered in 2 μsec was equivocal.

DELAYED EFFECTS OF X-RAYS

The increase in frequency of miniature potentials was not accompanied by changes in the action potentials of nerve and muscle, with large doses applied at 7–70 kr/min. It therefore seemed likely that the nerve terminals were relatively sensitive to X-rays. It was not possible to make direct measurements on this part of the nerve during or after irradiation, as its branches are surrounded by muscle fibres and are too small to be impaled by microelectrodes.

Other experiments, nevertheless, confirmed that a region near the nerve terminals is more vulnerable than the synapse, the nerve trunk or muscle fibres. When phrenic-diaphragm preparations were irradiated with 70 kr at 70–100 kr/min, the transmission of impulses from nerve to muscle became irreversibly blocked after a latent period of about 15 min. In these blocked preparations stimulating the nerve still gave rise to action potentials of normal size and shape but failed to liberate acetylcholine from the nerve endings. At the same time the muscle still responded to direct stimulation and its membrane resistance was unchanged. No deterioration of the nerve or the muscle was observed for at least 24 hr after the block had occurred unless doses of more than 160 kr were used. We were not able to confirm that the action potentials in nerve or muscle increased in size either during or after irradiation.[14]

The block in neuromuscular transmission, like the increase in frequency of miniature potentials, depended on dose-rate as well as dose. A 10-fold reduction of the dose-rate to 7 kr/min necessitated an increase of about 25 per cent (to 90 kr) in the dose required for block, while the latent period increased to 1–10 hr. Preparations irradiated with smaller doses remained similar to controls throughout their life *in vitro*.

The nature of the block was investigated by recording miniature potentials. Their amplitude was normal which showed that the block could not be attributed to a change in sensitivity of the receptors (see above). Their frequency was normal or increased (after irradiation at high dose-rates, see above), hence the nerve endings were still able to liberate acetylcholine spontaneously at rest. Furthermore, depolarizing the nerve endings by increasing the potassium concentration still caused a large increase in the frequency of miniature potentials. It follows that if nerve impulses were able to reach the nerve endings they too would have caused the liberation of acetylcholine, by reducing the membrane potential. Since this was not the case it was concluded that the block caused by X-rays was due to a "presynaptic" failure of impulse propagation somewhere near the fine nerve endings. One mechanism by which the failure to conduct might have been produced is by a persistent depolarization. A depolarization would in turn be expected to increase the frequency of miniature potentials. This was in fact the case after irradiation after high dose-rates. However, in the absence of direct evidence, the conclusion that X-rays cause a depolarization must remain speculative.

Presynaptic failure is also caused by anoxia,[22] and at first sight it might seem possible that X-rays cause block by removing molecular oxygen from the solution. It is clear, however, that this factor was not important in the mechanism of the block since the maximal removal of oxygen occurs during irradiation and must have been rapidly reversed in our experiments by the gas (95 % O_2, 5 % CO_2) which constantly stirred the solution; furthermore, the effect of X-rays became maximal only after a latent period and was irreversible, whereas the effect of anoxia is rapid and reversible.[22]

CONCLUSIONS

Our results suggest that small doses of X-rays have little immediate or delayed effect on the properties of the membrane in mammalian peripheral nerve or skeletal muscle. It is unlikely that extensive alterations in permeability occurred during irradiation.

It should be emphasized that even if it were convincingly shown that the resting potential fell, that sodium ions entered and that potassium ions leaked out of the cell, this in itself would not necessarily mean that the initial effect of X-rays was on the permeability of the membrane. Changes in metabolism or alterations in intracellular binding of ions could produce the same result, without altering the permeability of the membrane.

There was no evidence in our experiments of any increase in the size of maximal action potentials, such as Bachofer observed;[14] the reason for our failure to observe enhancement remains unexplained, except possibly by differences in the electrical recording techniques used (see Ref. 19 for full discussion).

Massive doses of X-rays applied at high dose-rates blocked the conduction of impulses in the intramuscular part of the phrenic nerve and increased the frequency of miniature potentials. It is tempting to speculate on the factors that might make the terminal branches of the nerve more sensitive than the main nerve trunk, the synapse or the muscle; the decrease in fibre diameter and loss of myelin that occur near the terminals might contribute to the increase in vulnerability, but the evidence that exists on this point is inconclusive and contradictory.[19]

It may be that polysynaptic reflexes or synapses in the higher nervous system are far more vulnerable than neuromuscular transmission, peripheral nerve, skeletal muscle, or monosynaptic reflexes.[23] On the other hand there is some evidence that the effects of small doses of X-rays on conditioned reflexes and on the electrical activity of the brain are mediated indirectly; in experiments of this type local irradiation of the head is often less effective than X-rays applied to the stomach or diffusely to the whole body.[7,8] If the initial effects occurred in tissues, such as the gastric mucosa, which are known to be sensitive, afferent impulses could arise by the stimulation of pressure receptors or **C** fibres. Alterations of the central nervous system in response to ionizing radiation would then be non-specific and only of secondary interest.

REFERENCES

1. PROSSER, C. L., PAINTER, E. E., LISCO, H., BRUES, A. M., JACOBSON, L. O. and SWIFT, M. N., 1947, The clinical sequence of physiological effects of ionizing radiation in animals. *Radiology*, **49**, 299–313.
2. GERSTNER, H. B., 1956, Effect of high-intensity X-radiation on the A group fibres of the frog's sciatic nerve. *Amer. J. Physiol.* **184**, 333–337.
3. WOODBURY, J. W., 1958, Studies on membrane resting potentials of muscle. *Exp. Cell. Res.* Suppl. **5**, 547–559.
4. *Effects of Ionizing Radiation on the Nervous System*, IAEA, Vienna, 1962.
5. HALEY, E. T. and SNIDER, R., *Response of the Nervous System to Ionizing Radiation*, Academic Press, New York, 1962
6. LIVSHITS, N. N., 1960, Physiological effects of nuclear radiations on the central nervous system. *Adv. Biol. Med. Physiol.* **7**, 173–248.
7. GARCIA, J., BUCHWALD, N. A., FEDER, B. H. and WAKEFIELD, C., 1962, Habituation as a factor in radiation-conditioned behavior. In *Effects of Ionizing Radiation on the Nervous System*, IAEA, Vienna.
8. HALEY, T. J., 1962, Changes induced in brain activity by low doses of X-irradiation. In *Effects of Ionizing Radiation on the Nervous System*, IAEA, Vienna.
9. CONARD, R., 1951, Effect of X-irradiation on intestinal motility of the rat. *Amer. J. Physiol.* **165**, 375–385.
10. HUG, O., 1960, Reflex-like responses of lower animals and mammalian organs to ionizing radiation. *Int. J. Radiat. Biol.* Suppl., pp. 217–226.
11. ROSEN, D. and DAWSON, K. B., 1962, Fall in threshold to electrical excitation of X-irradiated isolated frog nerve. *Int. J. Radiat. Biol.* **5**, 535–541.
12. REDFIELD, E. S., REDFIELD, A. C., and FORBES, A., 1922, The action of beta rays of radium on excitability and conduction in the nerve trunk. *Amer. J. Physiol.* **59**, 203–221.
13. PILLAT, B., HEISTRACHER, P., and KRAUPP, O., 1962, Effects of X-irradiation on Purkinje fibres. In *Effects of Ionizing Radiation on the Nervous System*, IAEA, Vienna.
14. BACHOFER, C. S., 1957, Enhancement of activity of nerves by X-rays. *Science*, **125**, 1140–1141.
15. HUG, O., 1962, Hypotheses on the action mechanisms of the effect of ionizing radiation on the nervous system. In *Effects of Ionizing Radiation on the Nervous System*, IAEA, Vienna.
16. BERGEDER, H. D., 1962, On the action mechanism of ionizing radiation to irritation processes. In *Effects of Ionizing Radiation on the Nervous System*, IAEA, Vienna.
17. BACQ, Z. M. and ALEXANDER, P., 1961, *Fundamentals of Radiobiology*. 2nd Edition. Pergamon Press, Oxford.
18. BRINKMAN, R., 1962, Radiobiology of nervous receptors. In *Effects of Ionizing Radiation on the Nervous System*, IAEA, Vienna.
19. ALLEN, N. and NICHOLLS, J. G., 1963, A study of the effects of X-rays on the electrical properties of mammalian nerve and muscle. *Proc. Roy. Soc. B* **157**, 536–561.
20. FATT, P. and KATZ, B., 1952, Spontaneous subthreshold activity at motor nerve endings. *J. Physiol.* **117**, 109–128.
21. LILEY, A. W., 1956, The effects of presynaptic polarization on the spontaneous activity at the mammalian neuromuscular junction. *J. Physiol.* **134**, 427–443.

22. KRNJEVÍC, K. and MILEDI, R., 1958, Failure of neuromuscular propagation in rats. *J. Physiol.* **140**, 440–461.
23. SATO, M., AUSTIN, G. M. and STAHL, W. R., 1962. Delayed radiation effects on neuronal activity in the spinal cord of the cat. In *Effects of Ionizing Radiation on the Nervous System*, IAEA, Vienna.

DISCUSSION

CHAIRMAN (C. CHAGAS): The paper is now open for discussion.

H. MARCOVICH: I would like to know what conditional reflexes were studied with small doses.

J. NICHOLLS: By Garcia?

H. MARCOVICH: Yes.

J. NICHOLLS: Garcia and his collaborators used ionizing radiation to produce avoidance reactions in rats. They paired a distinctive stimulus with radiation exposure and obtained a significant effect (avoidance of saccharinated water) with doses of about 10 r. There are many experiments of this nature in the Russian and in the American literature. I quoted Garcia's work because it was done particularly carefully, and with collimated beams. I am sure Dr. Zeleny could give many other examples.

V. ZELENY: I think, if this is correct, there is another American researcher, Kinedorf, who worked on conditional avoidance reflex, and he found that rats avoid the irradiation chamber if they are, I think, three times exposed to a total dose of some 50 r.

H. MARCOVICH: My question was about accidental radiation in people, with small doses, doses which are supposed to be harmless, — was there any change in the behaviour of the people?

J. NICHOLLS: As far as I know there are no reports of behavioural changes in people exposed to small doses of radiation.

V. ZELENY: I would like to make one more comment on this, namely: in behavioral studies on primates it was found that a sub-lethal total body irradiation increases the degree of concentration of attention. The exposure facilitates the ability of learning which to some extent seems curious; but if one accepts the explanation that the pathological influence of stimuli from the damaged periphery decreases the distraction from other environmental stimuli, one could perhaps understand it better. But there again it would seem that it is not the direct effect on the central nervous system, but it is the pathological signalization from the damaged periphery.

H. S. KAPLAN: I do not know if you gentlemen would accept the retina as being a nervous tissue. If the retina is acceptable as a nervous tissue, this is perhaps one of the best documented instances of sensitivity to ionizing radiation, because one can see X-rays and this is one of the best ways to determine whether an individual who has cataracts still has a functioning eye behind the cataract.

CHAIRMAN: I am going to answer Dr. Kaplan, if you allow me. The problem of the retina is a very specific one because you have special features in the retina which you do not have in any other tissues. My presentation, which I think was well covered on experimental grounds by Dr. Nicholls, is the fact that we cannot explain some small dose effects, which are observed on the central nervous system by taking in consideration the mechanism we know of nerve activity in general, with exception for instance naturally of photoabsorption in retina, which is a very special situation. Either we have to consider that other indirect factors act, or we have to take in consideration phenomena which may be disturbed by very small doses but are not known at the present moment. Of those phenomena which represent a new approach to the central system physiology, I think the most important is the one extremely well exploited in this sense of studying conditional reflexes by a colleague of Dr. Hercik and Dr. Slizynski — Dr. Bureš — who has shown that here really you have an abolishment of the cortical activity and in that case you have a complete disappearance of conditional reflexes. But at the present moment, I would say that by what we know on activation of neurons, conduction of impulses and transmission on synapses, we are unable to explain the facts as they are related in action of radiation on the central nervous system, and I must say that most probably there are very few fields in biology in which the experiments have been driven to a detail, an exact detail, as they have been done in modern electro-physiology. The sole example of the miniature potential by which Katz is able to assume the number of molecules which are yielded, shows that this is a technique in which we may have a good limit of confidence. This is what I wanted to present. With the present knowledge it is difficult to understand.

J. NICHOLLS: I would like to make one more answer to Dr. Kaplan's question.... You are quite right about the eye, but then the effect of irradiation is to bleach visual purple, as Lipetz and others have shown, and I don't think that visual purple is present anywhere else.

B. M. ZELENY: To the question of retina. There it is the role of the extreme physiological amplification factor which makes the difference. Lipetz has made some calculations of the absorbed energy and compared the action of X-rays with visual light and his conclusion is that in terms of absolute energy the visual light is about 500 times more effective than X-rays. This proves that it is the physiological factor that is responsible for the sensitivity, since the response is most sensitive to the physiologically adequate stimulus i.e. light.

CHAIRMAN: If there are no more questions, I want to thank Dr. Nicholls for his communication and I want to invite you to see how an isolated electroplate works.

NAME INDEX

SUBJECT INDEX